THE COMPLETE ENCYCLOPEDIA OF CACTI

LIBOR KUNTE
RUDOLF ŠUBÍK

THE COMPLETE ENCYCLOPEDIA OF CACTI

Informative text with hundreds of photographs

Key to symbols:
wintering:

□	- very cold
▣	- cold
■	- warm

requirements for light:

○	- full sun
⊙	- moderate shade
◐	- half-shade

Text: Libor Kunte
Photographs: Rudolf Šubík 542, Libor Kunte 58 and Studio Granit 1
Drawings: Libor Kunte
Graphic editing: Studio Granit
Editing and production: Granit, s.r.o., Prague
Typesetting: Artedit, s. r. o., Prague
Translation: Dylan Edwards and Charlie Stanford in association with First Edition Translations Ltd, Cambridge UK
Proofreading: Alfredo Franco, Jarmila Pešková Škraňáková, Ivo Pešek, Robert Romeri
Editing: Andrew Mikolajski in association with First Edition Translations Ltd, Cambridge UK

ISBN: 90 366 1494 5

Contents

Introduction 7

Cacti and their habitats 7

Cacti in close up 8

Cactus-growing in brief 11

Pests and diseases 12

Cacti and conservation 12

Cacti in the service of mankind 12

1. Mexico 15
2. USA 125
3. Peru 139
4. Bolivia 175
5. Argentina 199
6. Brazil 219
7. Chile 235
8. Minor areas 251
9. Cultivated hybrids and specialist varieties 267

Selected bibliography 283

Index 284

Introduction

This book is devoted entirely to a single family of plants –*Cactaceae*. From a strictly botanical point of view, this may seem a very narrow, limited field, but in terms of how these plants live, and their distinctive forms, and also in terms of their sheer popularity, *Cactaceae* is a unique and fascinating plant family. Under present botanical classification, *Cactaceae* contains roughly 300 genera with about 2,500 species of cacti. It would be unrealistic to give an exact number of genera and species. Partly because much depends on how this family is defined botanically, but also because new species and even entirely new genera of cacti are constantly being described – including, recently, *Geohintonia*, *Cintia*, and *Yavia*. The first references to cacti date from the sixteenth century, when reports of discoveries reached Europe from the New World. Old chronicles contain references to "melon-like flowers" which were unlike any other plants known at the time. One of the first reports of cacti to appear after the conquest is a reference in chapter XXVI of the "Historia general y natural de las Indias" (1535), whose author, Hernández de Oviedo y Valdés, describes the cactus as a plant remarkable for its "spines" and also for its unusual fruit, which the natives eat every day. Cacti naturally aroused great interest among Europeans, because they were completely different in shape from any known plants. Judging by the descriptions, explorers first brought cacti of the genus *Melocactus* to Europe, and later, other genera and species began to be imported. Cacti first found a place in the gardens of the aristocracy. Only the wealthiest could afford to have cacti in their collections, and the desire to own exotic plants turned into a kind of mania which drove prices up to dizzy heights. By the second half of the nineteenth century, there were several large firms engaged in cactus-growing as well as the import of cacti from the wild. This made cacti more affordable, and by the beginning of the twentieth century there were large numbers of specialized collections with hundreds and thousands of specimens. Today there is hardly a household that has not had a cactus or two growing at some time or other. These undemanding, beautiful plants have found a permanent place on our windowsills and balconies and in our greenhouses. It is to all such admirers of this "prickly beauty" that this book is addressed.

Left: *Eulychnia spinibarbis*

Cacti and their habitats

Cacti come from North, South, and Central America. Only a few "renegades" of the genus *Rhipsalis* have their origins outside the New World. It remains a mystery why a few species are found as an indigenous part of the flora in Madagascar and Sri Lanka. Of course, thanks to human activity, cacti are now found throughout the world. They are to be seen in practically every country with a tropical or subtropical climate, especially in parks and gardens, but are also to be found in the wild as introduced species, for example on long stretches of the Mediterranean coast. It is interesting to see that a wild cactus growing in Europe (apparently *Opuntia ficus-indica*) features in the painting "The Land of Cockayne," which Pieter Brueghel painted in 1565 while traveling in Italy. This is evidence that cacti became established in Southern Europe very soon after they were imported into the Old World. We believe, however, that experimental planting of cacti in the wild is risky, as people know in Australia, where opuntias got completely out of human control and, under conditions that suited them, entirely displaced the original plant population. A similar situation now threatens southwestern Madagascar, where imported opuntias and cerei have found ideal conditions in which to live.

A closer look at the original habitats of cacti reveals that they are by no means confined to deserts as most people imagine – on the contrary, only about a quarter of the total number of species live in deserts. The rest have preferred the less forbidding conditions of semi-desert, dry steppe, deciduous forest, or grassland. But cacti (roughly 5 % of the species) may be encountered even at the tops of the tallest jungle trees, in tropical rainforests. Further details of the environmental conditions in cactus habitats are given at the beginning of individual chapters of this book.

Cacti in close up

The stem

Anatomically and morphologically, the cactus stem reflects the conditions in which these plants grow. Cacti are succulent plants, a category which encompasses a huge number of species and genera belonging to many families. Any plant capable of storing water in its stem is a succulent. Succulents are divided into the following categories according to where they store their water: leaf succulents (e.g. *Aloe, Agave, Crassula, Haworthia, Kalanchoe, Lithops*), root succulents (e.g. Ibervillea, Kedrostis, and some members of the genus Euphorbia), and stem succulents, of which the most typical and best-known are cacti. However, a number of other families and genera belong to this category, e.g. *Pachypodium, Stapelia, Trichocaulon,* and some members of the genus *Euphorbia*. In other words, all cacti are succulents, but not all succulents are cacti. Succulence (from succus, "juice") arose as one of the reactions of plants to unfavorable climatic conditions in regions where water – or rather the lack of it – is a limiting factor. The forerunners of cacti were probably deciduous or semi-deciduous broadleaved species, assumed to be similar to the so-called "primitive" cacti now existing in the sub-family *Pereskioideae*, e.g. the genera *Pereskia* and *Maihuenia*.

The most interesting feature of the cactus is the characteristic shape of its stem, which cactus growers generally refer to as the "body," a term which has no botanical significance. This succulent stem evolved gradually, mainly as a result of adverse climatic conditions in which water was scarce. The plant was obliged to store water so that it could easily survive even the harshest drought. For this purpose, cacti developed a succulent stem with tissues capable of holding a large volume of water. However, it should be noted that the water is bound up in the form of cell juices. Anyone who thinks a delicious drink of water will flow from a cactus when it is cut open is seriously mistaken. A cactus can no doubt save the life of a thirsty wanderer in desert conditions, but what flows out of a cactus can hardly be called a refreshing drink.

So, over time, cacti developed stems which are extremely varied in shape (see the shapes referred to in the headings for individual species) but have a basic feature in common – a large volume of tissue capable of holding a store of water. To survive in arid conditions, cacti also developed a special metabolism enabling them to open their stomates at night when it is cooler, rather than during the hot, sunny daytime. A cactus takes in the necessary carbon dioxide at night and is able to store it in its vacuoles, using it only in the daytime for photosynthesis.

Armature

The most striking feature of any cactus is its spines. Technically, these are thorns. A thorn is a modified organ – in the case of the cactus, it is a modified leaf – while, strictly speaking, a spine is an outcrop of the epidermal or sub-epidermal layers. (For example, a rose has spines, although its stems are usually described as thorny!). Armature evolved in cacti partly as a mechanical defense against herbivores, and partly as protection against excessive solar radiation. Cactus spines may be very hard, woody, and spiky, or extremely fine, even downy. Those that are most feared are the fine glochids which grow on members of the subfamily *Opuntioideae*. These are equipped with barbs which make them very difficult to remove if they pierce the skin. There have even been cases where glochids carried on storm winds have caused unpleasant, very painful eye inflammations. The barbs on the large thorns of Opuntia also have another function. The easily detachable thorns, e.g. on *Opuntia tunicata*, break off when they pierce the skin of a large mammal, and are then carried to a different place where they take root and form a new plant. The thorns of some cacti (e.g. *Discocactus horstii*) are even capable, to a limited extent, of taking in the water that settles on them in the form of dew.

Some cacti have also adapted to the most unfavorable conditions with a layer of crystalline hairs on the surface of the epidermis, which give the typically grayish coloring seen, for example, in some species of the *Copiapoa*. A number of species solve the problem of water shortage with a large modified root (*Peniocereus greggii*, *Gymnocactus subterraneus*), which serves partly as a water reservoir, but also as a spare organ which can renew

Development of mammilla and areole: A) The areole begins to grow from the axillary bud (1); in some species, the mammilla grows from the base of the leaf-stalk (2). B) The leaf decreases in size, the base enlarges. C) On the mammilla (3), the areole (4) grows, from which the spines and, in some cases, the flowers grow. D) In other cases, flowers grow from the axil (5), which develops in the angle of the mammilla – *Mammillaria*.

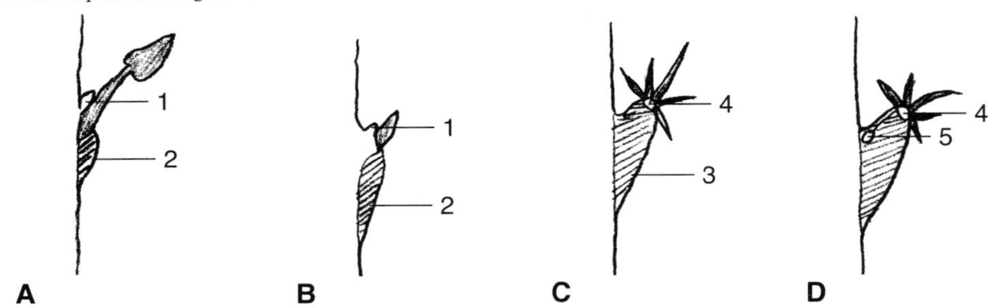

Examples of extreme forms of spines: A) very woody, with transverse grooves – *Echinocactus texensis* – upper radial (1), lower radial (2), central (3); B) fine radial spines growing from an elongated hatchet-shaped areole – *Mammillaria pectinifera*

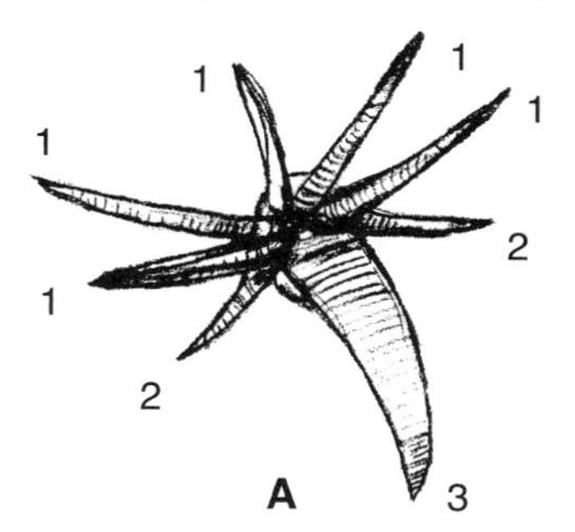

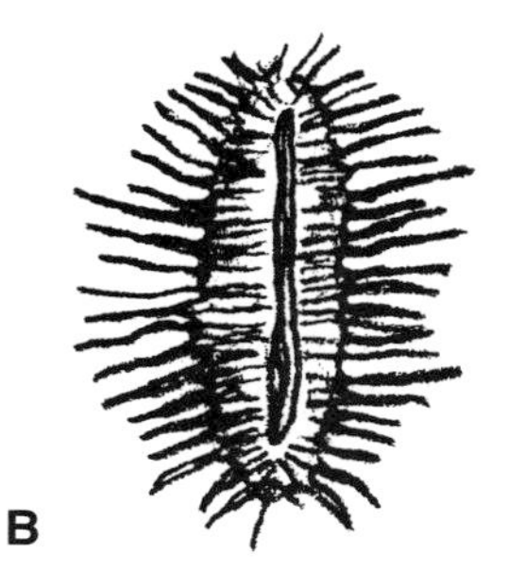

the stem if the above-ground part of the plant is lost (dried up, eaten by an animal, broken off, etc.).
Closer examination of a cactus stem reveals that the spines grow in clusters. The points from which they grow are called areoles, and these are essentially axillary buds. In cacti, these axillary buds have shifted to the tip of the part known as the podarium, which was formed by dwarfing and abnormal enlargement of the lower part of the leaf. In some cacti the areole has divided into two parts: the lower partbears the flowers and fruit and is called the axil.
The podarium arising from modification of the leaf became further enlarged until it formed the typical mammillae, sometimes known as tubercles. In the case of the genus *Mammillaria*, the author who described this genus chose its name precisely because of the mammillae. In many genera, e.g. cylindrical cacti or the genus *Astrophytum*, the podaria do not form mammillae, but extend upward and downward, thus forming another typical cactus feature, the ribs.

The flowers – beauty with a purpose

The flowers, essential for the plant's reproduction, are also an object of fascination to laymen and specialists alike. Descriptions hardly do justice to their beauty and variety of color, and a cactus in flower cannot fail to raise the spirits of even the most confirmed pessimist. The flowers grow, as mentioned above, from the areole or axil; they are sessile and do not form a flower stalk. Some cactus names, e.g. *Gymnocalycium* ("with a bare calyx"), are rather misleading, because in cacti the flower is not divided into calyx and corolla: they form an undifferentiated perianth. However, the cactus flower has greenish or scaly outer sepals resembling a calyx, and colored inner petals reminiscent of a corolla. According to their shape, three basic types of flower can be distinguished – funnel-shaped, tubular, and bell-shaped. The great majority of cacti have diecious flowers, i.e. with male and female reproductive organs. The female reproductive organs (stigma, style, ovary) are situated in the middle of the flower, and the male organs (filaments, anther) are arranged in several circles around them. Most cactus species have regular or actinomorphic flowers (the flower can be divided at several planes of symmetry). A smaller number of species have symmetrical or zygomorphic flowers (the flower can be divided at only one plane of symmetry, into two matching halves). Typical examples are some species of *Matucana, Oreocereus, Schlumbergera,* etc. These zygomorphic, often narrow-necked flowers are usually visited by hummingbirds which pollinatethem.
Cactus flowers open mainly in the daytime, but the flowers of some genera have nocturnal pollinators *(Discocactus, Echinopsis, Neobinghamia,* etc.): these flowers begin to open at dusk, and are mostly white, and often have a pleasant scent, which helps hawk-moths or other moths or bats to find them. Cactus flowers bloom relatively briefly – a sign that cacti are economical with water. The open flower releases a large amount of water vapor, and a few hours after opening, or the next day, it fades. It is interesting that an unpolli-

Eriosyce villosa

Shapes of cactus flowers: A) tubular – *Echinopsis kermesina*, B) funnel-shaped – *Gymnocalycium calochlorum*, C) broadly funnel-shaped (bell-shaped) – *Pediocactus peeblesianus*

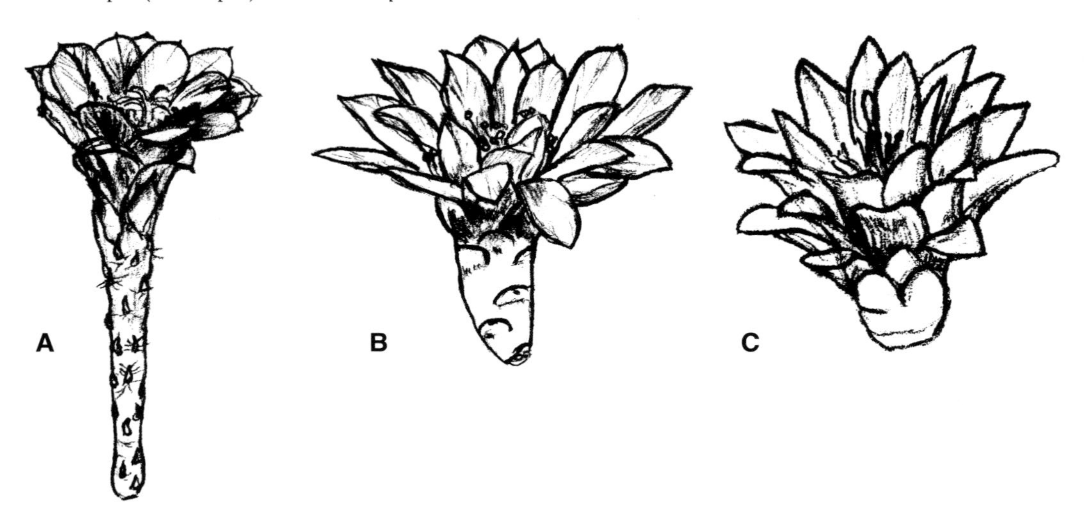

nated flower remains open and fresh longer than a pollinated flower. The unpollinated flower of *Leuchtenbergia principis* remains in bloom for four or five days, while the pollinated flower may not open again after the first day. It has fulfilled its mission and function, and there is no further need for it to use up the plant's reserves.

For most cacti, two individuals of the same species are needed for fertilization, i.e. a large percentage of cacti are allogamous. In the wild, pollen is carried mainly by insects, and to a lesser extent by hummingbirds or bats. In the case of cultivated cacti, the cactus grower transfers pollen from one plant to another with a brush or cotton-wool swab. There are also some species which are self-pollinating, e.g. some members of the genus *Rebutia* or *Notocactus.* The plant's own pollen is sufficient for pollination and fertilization. There is a special type of self-pollination known as cleistogamy, where pollination and fertilization take place in the bud, so that the flower does not emerge, but the fruit develops straight away. The cactus grower is deprived of beautiful color, but can be sure that the species has not cross-pollinated with another to produce some kind of hybrid. This characteristic is found mainly in members of the genus *Frailea*.

The fertilized flower or ovary turns into a fruit, and the fertilized eggs turn into seeds, which are actually the next generation of plants. The cactus

Cross-section of cactus flower: A) broadly funnel-shaped, B) tubular – ovary (1), style with stigma (2), stamens (3), petals (4)

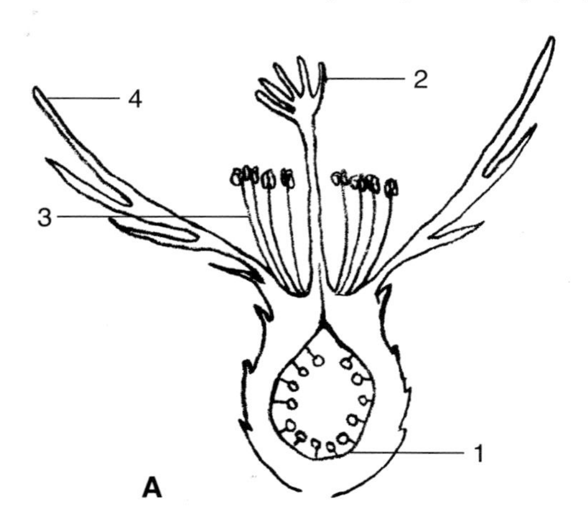

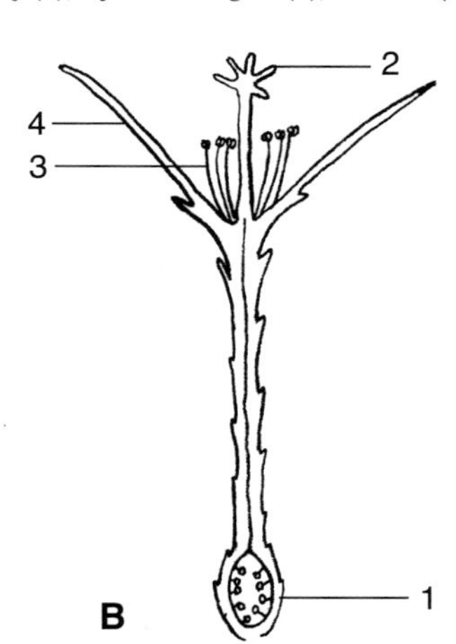

fruit is a berry, and may be either fleshy or dry. The fruit is edible in many cases, and some Opuntia are even cultivated for their fruit. The fruit from small plots of land planted with *Opuntia ficus-indica* is often the only source of income for the indigenous people in the dry regions of Mexico.

Cactus-growing in brief

Cacti are basically very undemanding plants which require a minimum of water, enough sun, and certain temperatures during the growing season and when dormant. The main instructions are therefore given in the form of symbols for each species. This book does not aim to give detailed descriptions of cactus growing methods; for this, it is advisable to choose a handbook devoted exclusively to the subject. Here, it is only necessary to explain a few terms used in the text of the book, which relate mainly to cactus propagation.

Vegetative propagation of cacti is a relatively simple method in which a particular part of the parent plant is used – the root, sucker, or part of the cluster. A special method of indirect vegetative propagation is cactus grafting, which is used mainly for species which are difficult to grow, or species which do not produce chlorophyll. Rootstocks are used for this purpose: reliably growing species of cacti, on which grafts take well and grow well. The main rootstock cacti include *Myrtillocactus geometrizans, Trichocereus pasacana, Eriocereus jusbertii, and Echinopsis eyriesii,* and for the grafting of seedlings, annual shoots of Pereskiopsis species give good results.

There are specific requirements for cactus propagation: emerging seedlings must be given the right conditions for growth and, above all, an environment free of pathogenic fungi and mold. The *Fleischer method* is ideal for this purpose. Sprinkle about 1in of soil mix into a preserving jar, and sterilize with water in an oven or pot. After cooling, seeds impregnated with a suitable fungicide should be scattered over the surface. Close the jar immediately, and place it either under a growing lamp or at a window out of direct sunlight. This is a very important factor, because in an enclosed space, excess sun can soon cause overheating and scorch the seedlings. Once the seedlings have grown large enough and are putting out their first spines, begin carefully ventilating, reducing the atmospheric humidity, and later, when the seedlings start to become cramped, they can be pricked out.

Pests and diseases

In cultivation, cacti – especially under glass – are prone to a number of pests and diseases. Fungal diseases and bacterial infections spread very quickly and the only effective remedy is to remove the affected part of the stem and try to protect the plant by grafting.

Amateur collection of cacti

The pests found on cacti are suckers, and the most frequent uninvited guest in the cactus collection is definitely the spider mite (*Tetranychus urticae*). It is capable of causing enormous damage, and tissues damaged by sucking regenerate very slowly. First, a gray surface forms on the plants, which later turns brown and, in the final phase, begins to suberize. Spider mites are particularly troublesome because they are practically invisible and go unnoticed until the first signs of damage appear. Prompt action should be taken: the sooner action is taken, the better the chance of saving the plant. If you are using chemical controls, follow the manufacturer's instructions closely and spray several times in succession until all the development stages of the pest are destroyed. Biological controls are available.

Scale insects are also unwelcome visitors, but the damage they cause is not usually as extensive as spider mite damage. They are usually detected and identified in time, because the scarcely moving little bodies of these pests, enclosed in a waxy coat, are visible on the stems or roots. Scale insects may weaken the plants considerably, especially during the dormant phase. As soon as they are discovered on the roots or stem of a cactus, the affected plant must be isolated.

It is advisable to make one or two preventive applications of an insecticide through the entire cactus collection, and keep a close look-out for pests, while cacti are wintering.

Cacti and conservation

The conservation of cacti in their natural habitats is a much-discussed subject which in recent years has gained in topicality.

Cacti were imported in bulk into the USA, Europe, Australia, and also Japan, where they were a relatively profitable commodity, but this uncontrolled collection and export virtually ended before the Second World War.

In most countries where cacti grow, export is strictly prohibited by special laws governing conservation in the country concerned. A further protection against uncontrolled trade in cacti is the fact that all the species are included in Appendix I and II to CITES – the Convention on International Trade in Endangered Species.

Unfortunately, the situation today is so bad that cactus colonies are threatened not only by amateur growers and enthusiasts who collect them from the wild, but also, and especially, by the growing pressure on the habitats where cacti grow. The increasing population and its demands, highway construction, heavy industry – these are the real risks which are the greatest threat to cacti in the wild.

The ban on collection of cactus seeds, e.g. in Mexico, is the hysterical culmination of the efforts of certain nature conservationists. The harvest of fruit from a few plants in one locality represents a small, insignificant fraction of the seed output of the species in that area. But as experience from past decades has shown, there is no doubt that exported seeds have provided the basis for many generations of new plants, and this has naturally reduced the demand for imported plants. The seeds obtained from plants with a specified location are the basis for botanically valuable material.

At present, obtaining permission to export cacti from any American country is, one might say, an insoluble problem; for this reason, many cactus-growers try to keep plants in collections with an indication of the locality from which the original material came. Apparently this method of keeping botanically valuable material works well for many genera, but it depends on the cactus grower's scrupulousness in keeping strains pure and not, for instance, crossing *Thelocactus bicolor* from Parras de la Fuente, Coahuila with *Thecocactus bicolor* grown from seeds which, according to the catalog, are from Huizache, San Luis Potosí.

We think this situation will have to end in a reasonable compromise, where, for study and collection purposes at least, it will be possible to obtain permission to import seeds, provided their collection cannot under any circumstances threaten the stability of the population in situ.

Cacti in the service of mankind

In areas where cacti grow, the local people are able to use these plants as a natural resource, in otherwise relatively poor terrain. The fruits of some species are a welcome variation in the diet, compensating for the scarcity of other fruit. The sour berries of some (e.g. *Myrtillocactus geometrizans)* or mammillae are collected by the local people when they come across them in the wild, just as elsewhere people gather berries or fungi in the woods. Opuntia, on the other hand, are deliberately cultivated on plots of land, and their fruit are not only used by the family, but serve as a source of income for many of the villagers, who sell them in the markets. The fruit of Opuntia, known as tuna, is made into a very tasty jam called "queso de tuna". Young pads, known as nopalitos, are also used in cooking. After peeling, they are prepared in a great variety of ways: they are fried, stewed, or pickled in a sweet-sour vinegar.

Opuntia have even been trialed as a basic feed for livestock. But because of the unsuitable biochemical composition of their stems, further experiments were abandoned, and for farmers today, Opuntia serve only as a supplementary type of feed, not the basic resource that agriculturalists had imagined.

Opuntia served as a food plant for the nopal

worm *(Dactylopius coccus)*, which was raised mainly on *Opuntia ficus-indica* and *O. tomentosa.* This worm was the source of the natural red dye, cochineal, used in many branches of the chemical, cosmetic, and food industries. With the introduction of synthetic dyes, interest in cochineal waned, but now that people are returning to natural products, the demand for this type of dye is rising again.

The time when cactus seed, e.g. from *Carnegiea gigantea*, was used for making flour for boiling and baking has gone forever, because it has been replaced by the corn or wheat flours that are available everywhere. But cacti in the form of candied fruit can still be found quite often in markets in the central states of Mexico. The local people cut off the soft parts of the stem of *Echinocactus platyacanthus*, sweeten them with a saturated sugar solution, and sell them under the name of "acitrón" or "dulce de visnaga."

The woody stems of cacti, or their lignified vascular bundles, serve as building material or, in many places, as the only source of fuel. In the past, the hooked spines of cacti were used for fishing, and straight ones were used as needles. But that's already long gone, like the trick formerly used by fishermen in Baja California: crushed stems of *Machaerocereus gummosus* were thrown into the water, where they released large quantities of substances that stunned the fish – then, according to witnesses, the immobile fish were simply collected from the surface.

A chapter on hallucinogenic and medicinal cacti could turn into a book in itself, so I shall confine myself to mentioning that in Mexico and the USA, the best-known cactus used in the past for ritual ceremonies was *Lophophora williamsii*, also known as peyote or peyotl. Thanks to its high content of hallucinogenic alkaloids, *Trichocereus pachanoi* is used in a similar way in South America, where it is known by the nickname San Pedro.

Opuntia ficus-indica with fruit serving as feed for livestock

1. Mexico

Mexico is a Mecca for all cactus lovers. Within its territory, the greatest number of species can be found, including many miniatures, endemic genera, and, from the grower's point of view, some of the most attractive cacti.
Mexico is bounded to east and west by the great mountain massifs which extend from north to south. Between them lies a central plain which, for the cactus enthusiast, is equally intriguing. The Sierra Madre Oriental, stretching from the US border to the east of Mexico, has many interesting localities, and perhaps the most noteworthy places are to be found in the regions of Galeana, Rayones, and Aramberri. The Sierra Madre Occidental has not been explored so thoroughly, but its eastern foothills, in particular, are the habitat of many interesting genera. The plateau, divided into a number of small mountain ranges, offers extensive areas where hardly any botanical investigation has been carried out, but now, as new roads and highways are built, these formerly isolated regions are becoming more accessible. A quite separate and distinct part of the country comprises the regions south of the capital, which differ sharply from northern Mexico. Cactus genera unknown in the north are found here, e.g. in the federal state of Oaxaca there are some very interesting representatives of the genus *Mammillaria*. The Baja California peninsula is another entirely unique territory, which might not seem like part of Mexico at all. The magnificent scenery of reddish brown mountains and azure sea, complemented by mighty cacti and other succulent plants, creates another paradise for cactus growers. The most interesting representatives of the genus *Ferocactus*, and splendid examples of *Echinocereus*, grow on this peninsula and the nearby islands.
Cacti in Mexico have spread mainly in the semidesert regions, in plant communities where a great variety of succulents and other xerophytes predominate. These specialized habitats are called "matorral," and are divided, according to location and proportions of plant species, into "matorral micrófilo," "matorral rosetófilo," and "matorral crasicaule." But cacti in Mexico grow in other habitats, such as grassland ("pastizal") or semideciduous dry forest ("bosque subcaudicifolio").
Mexican cacti are now strictly protected, both under the national legislation and under very strict international protection. Unfortunately they have been quite seriously damaged, so that many of the protective measures are ineffective, because the natural space in which the cacti used to grow is gradually disappearing.

Left: *Cephalocereus hoppenstedtii*

Ancistrocactus megarhizus

Ancistrocactus megarhizus ▣ ○

GLOBOSE

Its classification as an independent species has constantly been questioned. But due to its study and observations in the wild, it is now justified. The Czech cactus grower Alberto Vojtěch Frič even created and named a separate genus for it, which is not yet validated:
Roseia castanedai. It produces a globose stem 2–3in wide, often with offsets. The fleshy root forms a bulky storage organ underground. The spirally arranged ribs are divided into conical mammillae about 1/4in high. The areoles bear more than 20 peripheral and 4 central spines, with one longer than the others, pointing-upward and often ending in a hook. The flower is greenish yellow and about 3/4in wide.
In the wild, it grows in the state of Tamaulipas, but specific centers of distribution are the flatlands in the vicinity of Ciudad Victoria, and a well-known locality near Estación Calles, where it grows in association with *Astrophytum asterias*. Due to its large fleshy root, it is quite sensitive to watering at the wrong time. It tends to rot, and withers away within a few days. Excessive watering is inadvisable on cold days and during summer heat, when cacti usually remain dormant and do not grow. Less experienced cactus growers are well advised to grow grafted specimens; more experienced growers are undoubtedly able to grow plants on their own roots in a well-drained, slightly alkaline soil mix.

Ancistrocactus uncinatus

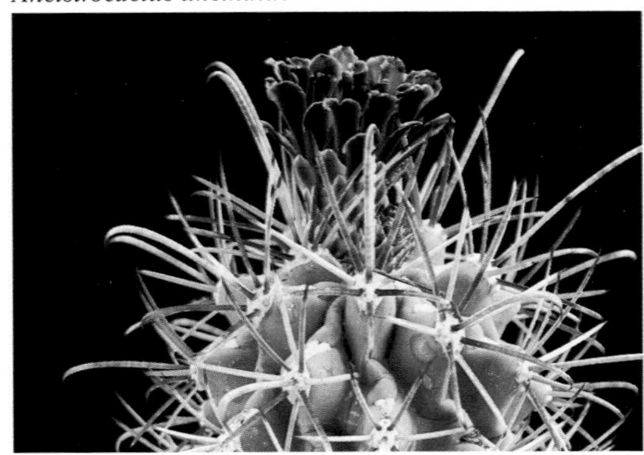

Ancistrocactus uncinatus 

CYLINDRICAL

The stem of this cactus is usually cylindrical and may reach a height of up to 6in; its width does not exceed 3in. It is interesting for its striking, dark flowers, which, in some locally occuring variants are almost brown.

It grows in the central regions of Mexico, mainly on hilly terrain, but can also be found on the plains of the state of San Luis Potosí. In collections, *A. uncinatus* var. *wrightii* is grown far more often that the type species. It is distinguished by its very long central spines, which may be as much as 6in long in some individuals. It is more popular not only because of its splendid spines, but also because it is easier to grow. For grafting, either *Myrtillocactus geometrizans* or forms of *Echinopsis* can be used. If plants on their own roots are preferred, a suitable well-drained soil mix should be chosen, and water should be given early in the morning or at sunset, and only during warm weather.

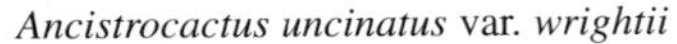

Ancistrocactus uncinatus var. *wrightii*

Ariocarpus agavoides ▣ ○

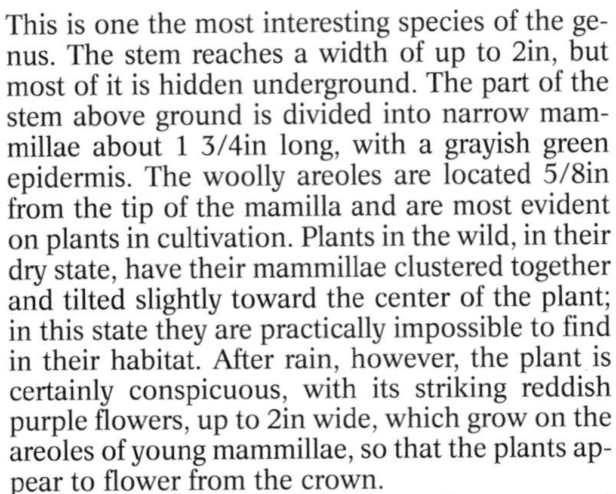

GLOBOSE

This is one the most interesting species of the genus. The stem reaches a width of up to 2in, but most of it is hidden underground. The part of the stem above ground is divided into narrow mammillae about 1 3/4in long, with a grayish green epidermis. The woolly areoles are located 5/8in from the tip of the mamilla and are most evident on plants in cultivation. Plants in the wild, in their dry state, have their mammillae clustered together and tilted slightly toward the center of the plant; in this state they are practically impossible to find in their habitat. After rain, however, the plant is certainly conspicuous, with its striking reddish purple flowers, up to 2in wide, which grow on the areoles of young mammillae, so that the plants appear to flower from the crown.

A. agavoides grows in the Mexican state of Tamaulipas not far from the little town of Tula, where the last remnants of the habitats are seriously threatened by human activity (garbage dumping, livestock grazing). A new habitat of this species was recently discovered in the state of San Luis Potosí, but it is kept top secret because of the risk of destruction. It is relatively difficult to grow, and in collections, growers usually maintain stocks by grafting on a suitable rootstock, e.g. *Myrtillocactus geometrizans*. Of course it can be grown on its own roots, on a perfectly drained soil mix with added crushed brick, keramzit, perlite, or gravel. It is propagated almost exclusively by seed, but sometimes by grafting offsets.

Ariocarpus bravoanus 

GLOBOSE

The botanical classification of this species within the genus is problematic: sometimes it is classed as a subspecies of *A. fissuratus*, while others see it as a connecting link to *A. kotschoubeyanus*. In terms of its stem, it is probably most similar to *A. fissuratus* ssp. *hintonii*, but its mammillae are more upright. The large purple-red flower appears toward the fall, and the seeds ripen the following year in early spring.

The habitat of this rare species is an extremely small area in the Mexican state of San Luis Potosí; surprisingly, this locality is about half a mile from the main highway linking México D.F. and San Luis Potosí. It grows in flat, elevated places in a coarse, stony substrate of limestone soil. The stems are very well camouflaged in the soil, and finding this microlocality without precise knowledge is a hopeless task. It is very likely that there are other places where it grows, but unfortunately it has not yet been possible to discover them. At present they are grown only to a very limited ex-

Ariocarpus agavoides

Ariocarpus confusus

tent, because of the serious shortage of material for propogation. Very strict protective regulations and CITES legislation prevent the export of plants from the country, which is a sensible measure in this case. However, it would be a good idea to find legal means of satisfying the market demand; this would be a very significant defense against plunder of the natural habitats.

Aliocarpus confusus ▣ ○

GLOBOSE

An aptly named but problematic taxon: The describers suggested the name *confusus* (confused) because this is a distinct, variable, and yet, unevaluated plant population. They are large plants that reach over 8in across, and their aboveground part has a characteristic gray-green color.
The shape and distribution of the mammillae on the stem are extremely variable, differing from one plant and locality to another. The pink color of the flowers is one of the main visible features distinguishing them from the species.

A. retusus and A. trigonus.
Their occurrence in the wild has been long known, and the colonies observed are numerous and stable, not showing any dramatic decline in the past ten years. This cactus grows in the localities of the small town of Aramberri in the state of Nuevo León, where it colonizes the plains and gently sloping terrain. The surface of the ground is often covered with limestones and the individual plants grow mainly in the open rather than under the cover of the taller vegetation. Cactus growers have been cultivating this species for many years; but the dispute over its systematic classification might lead to a more thorough exploration of the terrain. As far as it is known, this appears to be a plant closely related to *A. retusus*, therefore often grown.

Ariocarpus bravoanus

Ariocarpus fissuratus

Ariocarpus fissuratus var. *hintonii*

Ariocarpus fissuratus 

GLOBOSE

The stem is divided, as in other *Ariocarpus*, into an above-ground part, which in this case is formed with mammillae arranged like tiles, and an underground part, which merges into a bulky beet-like root. *A. fissuratus* reaches a height of up to 6in and, when mature, blooms in fall with a wide, pink-purple flower up to 2in across.
It grows in the northern regions of Mexico, and also in Texas. It is very popular there; the Americans call it the "living rock" because of its unusual appearance. Two other varieties grow in Mexico, *A. fissuratus* var. *lloydii* and *A. fissuratus* var. *hintonii*. The former has a large semi-globose stem up to 8in across, and grows in the Sierra de Parras mountain range; the latter has a small flattened stem, which does not grow taller than 2 1/2in, and is very well camouflaged on stony terrain with a sparse covering of grass. The same cultivation principles apply to all three taxa. When growing plants on their own roots, great care should be taken with watering at the beginning and end of the growing periods. The soil mix must be well-drained and have good drying properties. Grafting is possible on all the currently used rootstocks. In the case of *Ariocarpus*, excellent results have also been obtained with walnut-

Ariocarpus fissuratus var. *lloydii*

Ariocarpus kotschoubeyanus

sized seedlings of *Echinopsis* sp., when seedlings with their first mammillae are grafted onto them.

Ariocarpus kotschoubeyanus 

FLATTENED-GLOBOSE

The Mexicans call it "pezufa de venado" (deer's hoof), but it is more reminiscent of a multi-pointed star. The greater part of the stem is hidden underground, so that in the wild, only the upper surfaces of the mammillae are visible. This species is very well camouflaged. Its stem does not reach large dimensions, and specimens 2 1/2in wide are real giants. It does not have any spines when matured. The beautiful purple-red flowers grow up to 1 1/2in wide on the youngest mammillae near the crown, which often cover the whole plant.
A. kotschoubeyanus is a variable species covering a wide area. It is found in the north of Mexico and distributed as far as the states of San Luis Potosí, Queretaro, and Zacatecas. A place near the town of Matehuala (San Luis Potosí) has been established as the type locality. A white-flowered variety also grows in the wild close to the town of Tula in the state of Tamaulipas: this is treated as a varietas, *A. k.* var. *albiflorus*, but some authorities consider it a separate species. Growing either of these taxa is quite a difficult task, and flowering plants on their own roots are always a glorious achievement for the cactus grower.

Ariocarpus kotschoubeyanus var. *albiflorus*

Ariocarpus retusus, wild

Ariocarpus retusus ▣ ○

GLOBOSE

The best-known and most widely grown member of the genus. The species name *retusus* means "blunt" in the sense of "non-prickly," because it has no spines. Its stem grows to a height of up to 10in, and its upper part consists of three-sided mammillae with a grayish green epidermis. In the fall, white flowers, with a yellow stigma and dark yellow anthers, are produced from the center of the plant. The flowers, when fully open, may be up to 1 3/4in across. *A. retusus* is distributed over a wide area in northern Mexico, where it grows on gentle slopes or on limestone hillocks, always in full sunlight. The local people use its extracted juice as medicine, and also as a fairly powerful hallucinogenic drug. In cactus collections, grafted plants are the rule, but with special care, plants can be grown on their own roots. The species is propagated by seed. After germination, it is recommended that the seedlings should be grafted onto the tips of plants of the genus *Pereskiopsis* and then, after one or two seasons, the rootstock should be cut off, and it should be inserted into the soil mix.

Ariocarpus retusus cultivated

Ariocarpus scaphorostrus ▣ ○

GLOBOSE

Few cacti manage to hide themselves in their surroundings as well as *A. scaphorostrus* does. It is no dwarf, because it can grow to 3 1/2in across, but finding it on slate hills is not at all easy, because it is a real master of camouflage. Its spineless, blunt-ended mammillae have a gray-green epidermis, and it protrudes only partly above the surface of the slate fragments covering its habitat. At first glance, you can miss these plants altogether. But the 1 3/4in-wide, reddish purple flowers, with their numerous fiery yellow anthers, are unmissable.

The species is found in a very limited area in the immediate vicinity of the small town of Rayones in the Mexican state of Nuevo León. Unfortuna-

Ariocarpus scapharostrus, wild

tely the prospects for its survival in the wild are relatively poor. It is also quite rare in collections, and collected plants bear little resemblance to the plants in the wild. Grafted specimens, however, grow without serious problems.

Ariocarpus trigonus 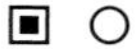

GLOBOSE

Unlike other *Ariocarpus*, this cactus blooms with a whole garland of white flowers on the older areoles around the crown. The name *trigonus* clearly refers to the three-sided spiky mammillae standing out from the stem, reaching a diameter of up to 10in.

Ariocarpus scapharostrus, cultivated

The species is distributed over a large area in North-eastern Mexico. It colonizes low-altitude locations, up to 1,500ft above sea level. Cultivation methods are analogous to those used for the species. *A. retusus.* The mature stage, when these plants can be relied on to flower, is reached in ten years by plants on their own roots, while grafts may flower as early as the third year after germination.

Ariocarpus trigonus

Astrophytum asterias

Astrophytum asterias ▣ ○

FLATTENED-GLOBOSE

At first glance, this spineless cactus is immediately captivating. Its flat stem grows to a height of about 3in, and it has very elegant, regular articulation given by the flat ribs, and also by the densely woolly areoles. The regularly spaced white tufts are also an important element of its beauty. The Czech cactus specialist Alberto Vojtěch Frič intervened in the fate of this species, when he rediscovered it in Mexico and, in 1925, took it back to Europe. *A. asterias* grows in lowland areas in the eastern part of the State of Tamaulipas. Several localities still exist in Texas. Unfortunately, it occupies localities which, in terms of their soil and geographical position, are also suitable for cultivation of farm crops. It is therefore one of the cacti which are under serious threat. Cactus growers are propagating this species in quite significant quantities, but it is a relatively sensitive cactus with low tolerance of errors in cultivation.

Astrophytum capricorne

Astrophytum capricorne ▣ ○

CYLINDRICAL

The species epithet *capricorne* means goats' horns, referring to the twisted spines which, for the author of the description, were clearly reminiscent of the horns of a goat. The stem of this species in the wild is in the form of a short cylinder (height 2ft, width 6in), although in collections it is more globose in shape. The epidermis is flecked and in the youngest growth area of the plant, the flakes have a brownish color, which gradually changes to white. The long spines, up to 2 3/4in long, may drop off the oldest areoles, or break. The beautiful, glossy, brilliant yellow flowers are up to 2 3/4in across, with a dark red mouth.
In the wild, the species is distributed in the southern part of the State of Coahuila, and also occurs

Astrophytum capricorne var. crassispinum

in the neighboring state of Nuevo León. It is a great favorite with growers, and is likely to be found in every collection. Provided the basic rules are followed – well-drained soil mix, watering when completely dry, and completely dry wintering – there are no problems with cultivation.

Astrophytum capricorne var. *crassispinum* ▣ ○

GLOBOSE

An almost legendary plant. The description referred to a coarse-spined *A. capricorne* without flecksand with a pure yellow flower, without a red mouth. For a long time this cactus was not discovered in the wild, and we now know that this is probably another case of the selection of distinct forms of plants with a habit described in this way. It is, however, quite possible that the plants on which the description was based did indeed come from the mentioned locality, which none of the cactus explorers discovered in subsequent years.
Occurrence is reported in two places, both of them in the Mexican state of Coahuila. One report mentions the area around the town of Parras de la Fuente, and the other mentions the Sierra de Ovejas range near the town of Cuatro Cienegas. The colonies in both places are well known to us, but we did not find any plants resembling this species in either location. Most of the specimens in collections do not correspond to the description at all, and many cactus growers mistakenly think they have the true *A. capricorne* var. *crassispinum*. In this case, it is clear that the plants of greatest value corresponding to the description come from a verified source, where the origin of the seed from which the plants were grown is known. Even in the case of the plant in the picture, it is doubtful whether the origin of the seed can be proven.

Astrophytum myriostigma ▣ ○

GLOBOSE–CYLINDRICAL

The epidermis is covered with a huge quantity of white, woolly scales, therefore named *myriostigma* (many-pointed). This large, spineless cactus is globose in shape when young, and forms a cylindrical stem when mature, 6in diameter and over 20in tall.
The beautiful yellow flowers are up to 1/2in across when fully open. All *Astrophytum* produce interesting 1/8in long, brown seeds with a distinctive saucer shape.
This species lives throughout the central Mexican plateau, and often in the shade of bushes or grasses. It requires, however, a site in full sunshine cultivation. It is readily raised from seed, which, when fresh, germinates very well. Seedlings in the initial stage of development should be kept in a shady place. Almost all *Astrophytum* species will hybridize with each other; the progeny vary in shape. But, precise records of experiments should be kept, to avoid undesirable confusion of a hybrid with a botanical species. Cactus growers also cultivate a completely fleck-free *A. myriostigma*; prolonged attempts to isolate these bare plants succeeded in stabilizing this deviation, and it is known as *A. myriostigma* f. *nudum*.

Astrophytum myriostigma

Astrophytum myriostigma f. *nudum*

Astrophytum myriostigma f. quadricostatum

Astrophytum myriostigma f. *quadricostatum* ▣ ○

GLOBOSE

The botanical name indicates that this is a four-ribbed form. Many authors regard it as a variant or as an entirely separate species. In the wild, however, four-ribbed plants grow in a locality in association with the typical five-ribbed plants, and only long-term efforts by man have led to selection of lines which have almost exclusively four-ribbed descendants. As a result, these plants now appear quite routinely in collections. Growers are now going even further in their efforts, and now three-ribbed plants are also beginning to appear: *A. myriostigma* f. *tricostatum*. These have never been found in the wild, so this is a case of capture of a deviation found in cultivated plants.

Astrophytum myriostigma f. *tricostatum*

Astrophytum myriostigma var. *strongylogonum* ▣ ○

GLOBOSE

The division into varieties and forms may be overdone in the case of *Astrophytum*, but *A. myriostigma* var. *strongylogonum* fully deserves its status as a varietas. This is a plant from the region around the town of Guadalcazar in the Mexican state of San Luis Potosí, which is clearly differentiated by its flatter growth, rounded ribs, and relatively large flowers. In collections this varietas is, unfortunately, quite often crossed with other ecotypes of *A. myriostigma*, so that many plants in cultivation bearing this name are of dubious botanical value.

Astrophytum ornatum ▣ ○

CYLINDRICAL

This is unquestionably the largest representative of the genus, and may grow 3ft high, with a stem diameter of about 1ft (the largest giants in the wild measure around 6ft!). On the sharp edges of the ribs, there are densely woolly areoles, from which grow spines 2–2 3/4in long, yellow to brown in color. According to the form of the ribs, the color of the epidermis, the length of the spines, the size of the flowers, and the number of flecks, many forms have been described, but these are losing their significance. *A. ornatum* is a very variable species, and in a single locality, it is quite possible to find all the variants that have been described so far. Specialists therefore distinguish all *Astrophytum* (and others besides) mainly on the basis of the place of occurrence. Several typical localities of this species are now known, and perhaps the best-known is in the vicinity of the small town of Metztitlan in the state of Hidalgo. *A. ornatum* is very widespread in collections, and a group of flowering plants is a real feast for the eyes, not only because of the beauty of the flowers, but also be-

Astrophytum myriostigma var. *strongylogonum*

Astrophytum ornatum

cause of the variable arrangements of the spines, flecks, and other features. Unfortunately, the first flowers of this cactus do not appear for more than 15 years after germination.

Aztekium hintonii 

GLOBOSE

Its important discovery was not validated for many years, and was described as an entirely distinct genus, *Geohintonia*. Grown in the state of Nuevo León in the Sierra Tapias range, *A. Hintonii* is an enlarged version of the miniature A. *ritteri,* which has been known for many decades. In the wild, it reaches 1ft height with a stem diameter of roughly 8in. Its transversely grooved ribs are quite interesting. The spines retain only on the crown, topped with a delicate gray-yellow tomentum. Red-purple flowers, up to 1 1/2in wide, grow from the tip. The habitat is very restricted, but its density is so great that it is not a risk. It favors vertical surfaces with a gypsum base, where it grows in association with *Geohintonia mexicana*. Seedlings appear now in collections. Its growing is not yet mastered, but the same rules as in *A. ritteri* might be applied.

Aztekium hintonii, cultivated

Aztekium hintonii, wild

Aztekium ritteri, cultivated

Aztekium ritteri ▣ ○

FLATTENED-GLOBOSE

Because this cactus, until recently the only representative of the genus, was reminiscent of Mexican Aztec art, the author of the description named this particular genus *Aztekium*. It is one of the smallest Mexican cacti, and its flattened-globose stem barely reaches a diameter of 2in and a height of 1 1/4in. The spines are retained only on the youngest parts near the crown of the cactus, and grow to a maximum of 1/4in. The pinkish white flowers appear at the beginning of summer, and when fully open, their diameter does not exceed 1/2in.

Aztekium ritteri, wild

A. ritteri occupies an extreme type of habitat on the vertical slate walls in the deep canyons of the Sierra Madre Oriental massif. Unfortunately, its habitats are very restricted, and are known, to date, only in the vicinity of Rayones in the Mexican state of Nuevo León. Luckily, however, it grows in places inaccessible to man, and so there is unlikely to be any threat of destruction of this beautiful cactus in the wild. It is extremely popular among cactus growers. In the great majority of cases, grafted plants are grown, because this miniature, with its powdery seeds, grows very slowly. The best method is temporary grafting onto *Pereskiopsis*, and subsequent re-grafting onto a permanent rootstock. Plants can, of course, be grown on their own roots, but this requires a lot of experience. Apart from seeding by the Fleischer method (see "Cactus-growing in brief"), the species can be propagated vegetatively – by grafting an offshoot.

Backebergia militaris

CYLINDRICAL

The whole genus was named after one of the greatest cactus specialists, the German professor

Backebergia militaris

Kurt Backeberg. The genus is monotypic (containing only one species). The tree-like *B. militaris* grows as high as 20ft, and has golden-yellow terminal cephalia at the ends of the branches.
In the wild, the plant grows on a very restricted territory in the Mexican state of Michoacán. Because of its size, it is one of the less sought-after cacti, although its habit and splendid cephalium certainly deserve the attention of cactus enthusiasts. It hardly ever appears in collections; another sign of its rarity is the fact that it is included in the first supplement to the CITES law (but this does not always correspond to the actual classification of the plant among such threatened species).

Cephalocereus hoppenstedtii ▣ ○

CYLINDRICAL

A very beautiful species, growing as high as 30ft with a stem diameter of up to 1ft. It is not as spiny as its most popular relatives (see below), but the seedlings are equally pretty. In advanced old age it produces a lateral cephalium, from which grow white flowers, up to 3in wide.
The species is distributed in southern Mexico, in the state of Puebla, where it inhabits the slopes of

Cephalocereus hoppenstedtii

Cephalocereus senilis

the Tehuacán valley. Cultivation is the same as for *C. senilis*, which is represented in collections more often than *C. hoppenstedtii*.

Cephalocereus senilis 

CYLINDRICAL

A very popular "oldie" which attracts everyone's attention with its long white hairy spines. It looks especially elegant as a seedlingust a few years old, but full-grown specimens, too, are highlights of any collection. It grows to a height of up to 30ft, and in places such as Barranca Venados and Barranca de Metztitlan (Hidalgo, Mexico), it creates beautiful scenery. Because of this cactus, the region is also poetically known as "old men's valley."
Cultivation is not at all complicated, provided winter temperatures do not drop below 50 °F for prolonged periods. Despite its thick covering of hair, the species is relatively sensitive to the first rays of sun which can scorch its skin after the winter.

Coryphantha borwigii

Coryphantha borwigii ▣ ○

GLOBOSE - CYLINDRICAL

In old age it becomes slightly cylindrical in shape, about 4in high and 2 3/4in in diameter. The striking mamillae have a green-gray skin, and the central spine is slightly bent toward the base of the plant. The flower is relatively large, up to 2 1/4in across, deep yellow in color, with a red mouth. The species belongs to the taxonomically complex range of plants related to *C. difficilis.*
C. borwigii is found in the northern Mexican state of Coahuila, on rocky limestone hillocks. The type locality is not precisely known. This species is widely grown, usually on its own roots. It dose not tolerate prolonged overwatering, to which older plants, in particular, react by shedding their roots. The roots then re-grow with some difficulty.

Coryphantha bumamma

Coryphantha bumamma ▣ ○

FLATTENED-GLOBOSE

Flat or globose stem (mainly in cultivated plants), up to 8in in diameter. The flat tubercles into which it is divided have only peripheral spines, and in the axil of the mammillae, quite a large quantity of white down forms. Also characteristic of the plant are its strong, almost beet-like roots, found even on small seedlings. The flower emerges from the white down on the crown of the plant; it is yellow and, when fully open, may be up to 2in across. The fruit is a fleshy, green, pellet-like berry, containing brown seeds up to 5/8in long.
It is distributed over a wide area, and can be found in many localities in several states (Morelos, Michoacán, Guerrero, and Oaxaca). It is closely related to *C. elephantidens*, from which it is distinguished by the color and smaller size of its flowers. It is widely grown, but its seeds have

Coryphantha elephantidens

been less widely available lately. Growing from seed is not difficult, but a better approach is to start with young plants grown in a deeper pot, to allow better development of the root system. Like most *Coryphantha*, it is often attacked by spider mite, which is capable of doing serious damage to the plant. Wintering in the cold, and preferably in good light, is a guarantee of good flowering in the next season.

Coryphantha elephantidens 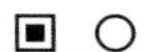

FLATTENED-GLOBOSE

This cactus usually has a single stem which is flattened, or flattened-globose in shape. Only rarely, in old age, does the cactus begin to produce offsets. The largest specimens may be up to 10in in diameter. The distinctive mammillae bear an areole from which, as a rule, 5–9 peripheral, yellow-brown spines grow. In the axil of the mammilla, a large quantity of white down forms. But the glory of this species is its flowers, which are usually pink-purple with a lighter-colored mouth.
The species originates in central Mexico, where it colonizes mainly grassland on humus-rich soils. Thanks to its flowers, it is one of the most attractive cacti, although it takes many years to flower (usually 10 years or more). Cultivation is not difficult; the secret of success is ripe seeds with good germinating ability. As with all *Coryphantha*, beware of attacks by spider mite, which causes damage which is not easy to remedy.

Coryphantha erecta 

CYLINDRICAL

The cylindrical stems reach a height of about 1ft and a diameter of 2 1/4–3in. They are divided into conical mammillae, and on the tip of each there is an areole with 8–14 peripheral spines and 2–4 central spines growing from it. The spines are yellow-brown in color and almost completely cover the plant. The light yellow flowers appear in late spring

Coryphantha erecta

and early summer, and are up to 2 1/4in wide.
One of the sites where this plant grows is the Metztitlan valley in the Mexican state of Hidalgo, where it forms part of a rich community of cactus flora. It grows not only in open spaces, but also in the shade under shrubs. Cultivation is the same as for other members of the genus. They should be placed in full sunlight and potted in a well-drained, slightly alkaline soil mix. Keep cool and dry overwinter.

Coryphantha georgii 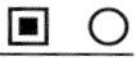

GLOBOSE

It is a flattered globose or slightly cylindrical plant whose stem is divided into narrow mammillae ending in an ellipsoidal areole with 1 needle-like and 8 or 9 peripheral spines. The flower is light yellow to cream with central red-brown streak outer petals.
Found in the wild in the state of San Luis Potosí at altitudes of about 6,500ft above the sea level. In collections, it is an uncommonly grown species although its cultivation is not at all demanding.

Coryphantha georgii

Coryphantha longicornis

Coryphantha pallida

Coryphantha longicornis ▣ ○

GLOBOSE

This beautiful representative of the genus grows a single stem which, in cool climates, tends to be globose in shape, while the oldest specimens in the wild may be slightly cylindrical, 8in tall and 4in in diameter. The conical mammillae have circular areoles at their tips. Growing from these areoles, there are usually 12 short peripheral spines and 3 thick, dark central spines, the lowest of which are up to 1in long. The flower, 1 1/2in wide, grows from a fleecy crown, and every part of it is yellow, including the stamens, style, and stigma.
Although we have looked for this species in the wild, our searches have never been successful. According to the literature, it can found in the Mexican state of Durango in the region of the Rio Nazas, but we have no further details of its whereabouts. The principles of cultivation are the same as for other *Coryphantha*. Spider mites can be a problem. This cactus is rarely seen in collections, probably because of the limited availability of the seeds, the only means of propagation.

Coryphantha neglecta

Coryphantha neglecta ▣ ○

GLOBOSE

This cactus usually grows a single stem, but at an advanced age it may produce a few offsets from the base. The stem is globose; in cultivation it sometimes becomes slightly cylindrical, but does not exceed a diameter of 2 1/4–2 3/4in. The ribs are divided into mammillae which are slightly less than 1/2in in height and width. The oval or circular areoles have a white tomentum, and from this grow 15–17 peripheral spines, and a central spine which grows to a length of about 5/8in. In mature specimens, the flowers are up to 1 1/2in wide. The outer petals have a brown central streak, and the inner ones are pure yellow. The flowers appear in late summer and, when fertilized, develop an olive-green fruit containing light brown seeds about 1/16in long.
The home of this species is the northern region of Mexico, but the area over which it is distributed is not continuous, and it occurs in several places which are a few hundred miles apart. It grows in the vicinity of the town of Monclova in the state of Coahuila, but also not far from Monterrey near the small town of Higueras, where we have observed it. However, the type locality is Cuesta de la Muralla in Coahuila, approximately at the 94th mile of the Mex. 57 highway between Monclova and Piedras Negras. In collections this is a relatively uncommon species, and not very widespread. For a long time it escaped the attention of cactus growers, and in the past it was not very often observed in the wild. But it is extremely elegant, easy to grow, and undemanding. In terms of its needs, it is comparable to other members of the genus, but it must be protected from spider mite, which is prone to attack it.

Coryphantha pallida ▣ ○

GLOBOSE

This cactus usually grows as a single stem, but in old age it may produce offsets, and in the wild it often forms groups numbering dozens of individuals. The epidermis is green-gray, and the spiral ribs are divided into prominent mammillae. There are usually 20 radial spines, and in most cases 3 central ones, which are always thick and, as a rule, brown-black. The large flower is about 2 3/4in wide, and the petals are yellow, as are the stigma and style. The red filaments and orange stamens make a beautiful contrast. The fruit is a green berry which takes almost a year to ripen.
The species originates in the central states of Puebla and Oaxaca, where it grows in many localities, always on a limestone substrate. The associated vegetation varies, but the places where it occurs are usually among the xerophytic plant communities with the richest variety of species. We saw it on such terrain many times, but perhaps the most beautiful colonies, in terms of their habit and spination, are to be found in the vicinity of the town of Tehuacán. A well-drained, slightly alkaline soil mix is the main requirement for cultivation. By planting several individuals in a bowl, it is possible to obtain a fine group of plants which can then be given enough space to form a large root system. Seed propagation is the same as for other members of the genus, but it must be borne in mind that this species grows slowly, and that the first flowers may take roughly ten years to appear.

Coryphantha palmeri ▣ ○

GLOBOSE-COLUMNAR

A solitary cactus which forms a globose or slightly columnar stem, 2 1/4in in diameter and slightly more in height. It is divided into spirally arranged conical tubercles; on the tip of each is an areole, from which grow 11–14 radial spines, and usually 1 central spine, which is thicker, and dark in color. Yellow flowers grow from the woolly center of the plant; these are about 11/4in wide when fully open. The plant keeps the green fruit in its stem for almost 10 months, and then puts out a green, conical berry full of brown seeds.
It has an extremely wide area of distribution, and is correspondingly variable. It is found in the Mexican states of Durango, Zacatecas, Coahuila, Nuevo León, and Tamaulipas, where it grows both in higher uplands, and also in lower, flatter areas. Because of its variability, it is possible to build up a very interesting collection of this species from various localities. Growing from seed is not difficult, and the plants flower, as a group, 5–7 years later. They tolerate full sunshine as well as cold wintering, but it is important to look out for spider mite, which attacks the plant all too readily.

Coryphantha palmeri

Coryphantha pseudoechinus

Coryphantha pseudoechinus ▣ ○

GLOBOSE-COLUMNAR

A distinctive and intriguing species, which has recently started to grow widely. Single formed, 3 1/2in high and 2in in diameter semi-cylindrical stems. Filled with white down axils of the mammillae in the upper half of the body. There are usually 18–25 radial 1/2–5/8in long spines and 1 central chestnut brown one over 3/4in long grown from the areole. The 1 1/4in wide flowers grown near the apex are light or dark pinkish purple. The fruit is a green, fleshy berry, full of small, light brown seeds.
The area of distribution is relatively wide but not continuous. Found among quite dense shrub vegetation in isolated localities, and the Sierra de la La Paila range. However, it colonizes the less shady places. Found in the states of Coahuila and Zacatecas. Germination and growing on the seedlings is not at all demanding; all they need is enough sunlight and quite a large amount of water during the summer. The cactus flowers from late summer until the end of the growing season.

Coryphantha retusa

Echinocactus grusonii f. albispinus

Coryphantha retusa ▣ ○

GLOBOSE-COLUMNAR

This species is closely related to *C. bummama*, and has a characteristic globose or slightly columnar stem, 1 1/2–4in in diameter. The stem is divided into mammillae arranged in 8 to 13 spiral rows. The axil of the mammilla, on the side facing the crown, is full of white down. From the elliptical areole grow 6–12 radial spines. Some authorities distinguish a more spiny variant, which they call *C. retusa* var. *melleospina*, with 17–19 radial spines on each areole. The flower is yellow and about 1 1/2in wide. The fruit is a greenish, club-shaped berry containing brown, elongated seeds.
In the wild, this species is encountered over a relatively wide area in the Mexican states of Puebla and Oaxaca, where it grows on the grassland known as pastizal. Cultivation is the same as for other members of the genus. This species, too, is prone to spider mite. Especially during a warm end to the season, its destructive presence is revealed by unsightly patches on the epidermis, which grow out with difficulty. The species is propagated by seed, and seedlings take 5–7 years to flower.

Echinocactus grusonii ▣ ○

GLOBOSE

This golden-spined globe is undoubtedly one of the best-known cacti. It can be found in practically every cactus collection, and is one of the highlights of every botanical garden among the *xerophytes*. It grows to more than 3ft, with a stem divided into more than 30 ribs bearing golden-yellow spines up to 2 3/4in long. The relatively small flowers (only 2in across) take many decades to appear.
E. grusonii is relatively rare in the wild, although it is one of the most widespread species in collections and nurseries. Huge "plantations" can be seen in the Canary Islands, where the conditions are very favorable to cacti: not only the soil composition and temperature range, but also the clean air, and adequate irrigation by gardeners, and occasional applications of fertilizer. In addition to the yellow-spined form, this cactus exists in a white-spined form (*E. grusonii* f. *albispinus*), and also a completely spineless form. There are no problems in the cultivation of this cactus. It propagates exclusively from seeds, which very readily

Echinocactus grusonii

Echinocactus grusonii, spineless form

germinate, even after several years. Plenty of water should be given during the summer, but not a drop during winter. Flowering specimens are available in the trade. Its characteristic shape has earned it the common name of Mother-in-law's cushion.

Echinocactus horizonthalonius ▣ ○

GLOBOSE

This is the smallest member of the genus – its stem grows to a maximum diameter of 8in. Although some ecotypes may be up to 16in tall, this cactus is usually globose or flattened-globose. The spination is enormously varied, and there are short-spined forms and plants with impenetrably dense spines. The cactus blooms with beautiful reddish purple flowers, up to 2in across, which may be lighter or darker in color.

In the wild, this species is distributed over a huge area. The northern limit of its distribution extends into some states of the USA (Arizona, New Mexico, Texas). In Mexico, it can be found practically throughout the north, where it is very abundant in places, and as far as the states of central Mexico. Although this is one of the commonest cacti in the wild, its cultivation in collections presents a number of problems. The seeds germinate poorly, and the seedlings grow slowly and have low tolerance for growers' mistakes. Grafting onto *Pereskiopsis*, at least during the first year of life, is recommended, but plants on their own roots are much more beautiful and resemble wild specimens more closely.

Echinocactus horizonthalonius

Echinocactus platyacanthus

Echinocactus platyacanthus ▣ ○

GLOBOSE-BARREL-SHAPED

This is one of the largest of the "barrel" cacti. It grows to a height of about 6 1/2ft, with a stem diameter of up to 3ft. These huge specimens may weigh more than a ton. The number of spines on the areole varies between 1 and 7, but they are always straight and very firm. Yellow flowers up to 3in across grow from the thick down on the crown of the plant. *E. platyacanthus* exists in several forms, which many specialists now regard as the same.

In Mexico it grows over a relatively wide area from the state of Coahuila as far as Puebla. In the wild, it is one of the conspicuous dominant plants. The local people call it "visnaga," and to this day they use the soft part of the stem to make the candy which can be bought in Mexico under the name of "dulce de visnaga" or "acitrón." In collections, it is one of the commonly grown species. Initially it grows very well, but later becomes less tolerant of frequent replanting. Take care, the cactus scorches easily in the first spring sun. Seeding presents no problems; the seeds retain their viability for a long time.

Echinocactus texensis

Echinocactus texensis ▣ ○

FLATTENED-GLOBOSE

This species was formerly regarded as the only representative of the separate genus *Homalocephala*, but it is now classified within *Echinocactus*. It is flat in habit, and the diameter of its stem may exceed 1ft. Because of its thick central spines, which are certainly very firm, farmers used to regard it as a weed which could cripple their livestock. It blooms with a beautiful flower, usually light pinkish mauve in color, with a darker center, and with fringed outer petals (but the color of the flower may vary between cream and deep pink).

In the wild, this cactus occurs over a huge area from the southern USA to central Mexico. Cultivation depends to some extent on where the particular ecotype comes from. One type of cultivation is suitable for plants from Oklahoma, and another for plants from Tamaulipas. In either case, there should be a very well-drained soil mix, completely dry wintering preferably in the light, and adequate sun in summer. Seed is practically the only method of propagation; the seeds germinate freely, even after 10 years.

Echinocereus ferreirianus ssp. *lindsayi* ▣ ■ ○

COLUMNAR

One of the most beautiful spiny *Echinocereus*, and a rarity, only seen in the wild by a few fortunate people. The columnar stem may grow to a height of 10in and a diameter of about 3in. There are 8–13 ribs bearing large woolly areoles, and the spines growing from them are dense and wildly twisting. The central spines may grow more than 2in long. The flowers appear on the upper third of the stem and are funnel-shaped, up to 2in long, pinkish mauve with a darker mouth and a light green stigma.
As mentioned before, it is very difficult to find the species in the wild, and the precise locality is known only to a very small circle of cactus specialists. It grows in the relatively harsh conditions of the Mexican peninsula of Baja California, where it grows on gentle hillocks in sparse outcrops. Ten years ago it was still very highly prized because of its rarity, and was practically non-existent in amateur collections. With the availability of seeds, its numbers have greatly increased, and the species is now produced in thousands commercially. However, it is definitely not easy to grow; grafting on a slower-growing rootstock is advisable. More experienced growers may try plants on their own roots, but these must have full sunshine, a slightly alkaline soil mix, and fairly warm wintering between 54 and 60 °F.

Echinocereus ferreirianus ssp. *lindsayi*

Echinocereus grandis

Echinocereus grandis 

COLUMNAR

Its erect stems, over 20in high, make it one of the largest columnar representatives of all *Echinocereus*. Individual shoots reach a diameter of 3–5in, and are divided into 21–25 ribs. In the large, densely crowded areoles grow 15–25 short radial spines and about 8–12 central spines, very similar to the radial spines. A pinkish white flower, with outer petals that are often greenish in color, appears on the upper part of the stem; it is roughly 2in across. When ripe, the ovary turns into a fleshy berry with a thick covering of spines.This fascinating cactus grows on a few islands in the Gulf of California. The island of San Esteban is regarded as the type locality. The American botanist George Lindsay, an expert on the cacti of the Baja California peninsula, also found this cactus on San Lorenzo Island – but here, the plants were blooming with flowers of the most varied colors, from white through pink to (according to his findings) yellowish. As yet there are not many collections where this cactus can be found. Because of the limited supply of seeds and relatively labor-intensive cultivation, it remains a rarity for cactus growers. It is usually grown as a graft; self-rooted plants require a very well-drained soil mix, and careful, only occasional watering, as much sun as possible, and wintering preferably at temperatures around 60 °F.

Echinocereus knippelianus ssp. reyesii

Echinocereus knippelianus ssp. *reyesii* ▣ ○

GLOBOSE

Originally, about 20 years ago, the plant was described as a varietas of the typical species, but under the new taxonomic definition of the genus, it has been granted the status of a subspecies. The plant forms offsets, and the individual stems are 3/4–2 1/4in in diameter, and their height is roughly equal to their diameter. The stem is divided into 5–7 prominent ribs, which have small areoles on their edges. From these grow 1–4 spines, to 1in long. The flower of this subspecies grows very near the crown and is roughly 2in across. The color varies from light to dark pink.
The habitat of this subspecies is high in the mountains, and the journey there is quite an adventure. The type locality is the region between Siberia and Encantada in the Mexican state of Nuevo León. It grows in the forest, in open glades, and is often covered with leaves and needles from the trees. In view of its beet-like root, it should be remembered that it can easily rot after badly timed watering. It is therefore advisable to water often, but sparingly. Grafting should certainly be considered, but plants on rootstocks grow unnaturally large.

Echinocereus leucanthus ▣ ○

CLUSTERING

Until now this cactus has been included by some specialists in the genus *Wilcoxia*, but in terms of affinity and the new conception of the genus, it is obviously more appropriate to assign it to *Echinocereus*. This is a bushy cactus, and the stem turns woody upward from the base. It branches laterally from the base, and the individual shoots do not grow taller than 1ft, with a stem diameter of up to 1/2in. The very fine spination consists of about 15 radial and 3 central spines, all of which are only 1/16–1/8in long. The beautiful white flowers are up to 1 1/2in across when fully open; there are also plants with a slight pink tinge on the inner petals.
The few known locations where this species occurs are all in the north Mexican states of Sonora (Guayamas) and Sinaloa (Los Mochis). The species favors slight elevations above sea level in coastal zones (about 165ft), where it grows in meadows of tangled shrubs, among which it can very often be found. In the wild, it is very inconspicuous, and it is easiest to find in the flowering season. Because of the roots, which form a kind of underground tuber, cultivation is rather difficult, since it does not tolerate prolonged waterlogging. When grafted, the plants grow very luxuriantly and lose their natural habit. Propagation from seed is not difficult, but in the juvenile phase the seedlings grow relatively slowly, because the plant builds up the bulky root system first, and "neglects" the formation of the above-ground part.

Echinocereus morricalii ▣ ○

TRAILING

This species was described in 1975 by the Czech cactus expert Jan Říha. On the basis of taxonomic studies made by N. P. Taylor, it is classed as *E. viereckii* ssp. *morricalii*, but it is distinct enough to be considered a separate species. The plant, trailing from the base, forms procumbent stems, up to 20in long and about 1 1/2in in diameter. There are 5–8 wavy-edged, wrinkled ribs with small, woolly areoles; these may have inconspicuous spines about 1/16in long, or may be completely spineless. The funnel-shaped flowers grow on the up-

Echinocereus leucanthus

per third of the stem; they are 2 3/4–3 1/2in in diameter, and deep pinkish-mauve in color. The green and red berries, with deciduous spines, are full of small black seeds (1/16in in diameter).
The original habitat is in the Mexican state of Nuevo León, near the La Boca dam, south-east of the capital, Monterrey. The species grows in the moderate shade of the sparse oak forest on rocky limestone terrain at altitudes of 1,000–1,200ft. Apart from the Morricals, who discovered it, this species has been seen in the wild by a number of other cactus specialists. It was added to European collections in the 1980s, as seed under collection number L 1221. In cool climates, propagation and growing do not present any problems. The species is very tolerant of overwatering, but reacts to it by growing disproportionately. It is therefore advisable to grow it in quite a large pot with a well-drained soil mix, possibly with added humus, in full sunshine, or possibly in light shade; cold wintering at about 41 °F is essential in all cases.

Echinocereus pectinatus ▣ ○

COLUMNAR

For growers, this is definitely one of the best-known cacti, but the high degree of variability of the plants according to locality, and the huge area in which they occur, make this one of the most difficult problems for taxonomists. Typically, the single columnar stem may branch in old age. It reaches a height of up to 1ft and a stem diameter of 2–3 1/2in. It owes its species epithet *pectinatus* to the comb-like arrangement of the radial spines (pectinate spination). The flower tube is covered with white, glassy spines, and the flower may be up to 4 3/4in wide when fully open. The petals are pinkish mauve, paler toward the mouth, where the color may shade to yellow. The fruit is a round berry covered with tufts of fine spines.
In the wild, it occurs over huge areas of terrain in many north Mexican states, where it grows both in the open, in full sun, and in the shade of shrubs and grasses. It shows a preference for colonizing flat woodlands or gentle slopes with a limestone substrate. It is a very common cactus in collections, but flowers rather less readily, and the seedlings take about 7 years to mature. It requires a well-drained soil mix, ideally with added minerals. The plants should not be overwatered during cold weather, otherwise they may quickly rot.

Echinocereus morricalii

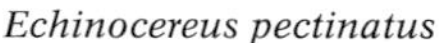

Echinocereus pectinatus

Echinocereus pectinatus f. *castaneus*

Echinocereus pectinatus f. *castaneus* ▣ ○

COLUMNAR

The classification of this plant still presents enormous problems; apparently it may be closer to *Echinocereus reichenbachii* than is indicated in this book. To most cactus growers, however, name used here is better known. It was given this name because of its brownish, comblike spines. The flowers of this forma are magnificent, up to 4in across, and often several of them appear on one plant at the same time.
The plant illustrated originates from the southern regions of the Mexican state of Coahuila, where the habitats of both species overlap, making correct classification even more difficult. Planting under either name is not nearly as complicated, if the seeds or plants are from a specified origin. Fortunately, catalogs contain offers specifying the locality where the seeds were collected.

Echinocereus pentalophus 

CLUSTERING

This plant is one of the procumbent, clustering members of the genus, and in the wild it forms rather unsightly clusters which often look damaged. Individual stems may grow to 1ft in length and 1 1/4in in diameter. The spines are unremarkable; the true glory of the plant is its flowers. Their purple-red color, with a contrasting creamy white mouth, attracts attention from a great distance. The large green stigma and yellow anthers serve only to complement a perfect color combination. In the wild, this cactus is found on rocky elevations and steep precipices, and from San Luis Potosí toward Rio Verde, its clusters skirt many lengths of highway. Cultivation is not difficult; only flowering presents problems. To ensure that *E. pentalophus* flowers, it must be cold-wintered in the light.

Echinocereus pentalophus ssp. *procumbens* ▣ ○

TRAILING

This classification corresponds to the latest definition of the genus, so most cactus growers may know this cactus under the separate species name of *E. procumbens*. This is a bushy, procumbent cactus, whose individual shoots grow to a length

Echinocereus pentalophus

Echinocereus pentalophus ssp. *procumbens*

of 8in, with a stem diameter of about 3/4in. There are 4–6 radial spines, and there may be no central spine, or 1 only, which may be anything from 1/4in to 2 1/4in long. The bud has a spiny flower tube, from which grows a pinkish mauve flower, 2 3/4in long and 3in wide, with a light-colored mouth. The green fruit ripens in 3–4 months and contains a large number of black seeds.

It can be found both in northern Mexico in the state of Tamaulipas, and also on US territory, in Texas. It favors flatter, more level terrain at a low elevation above sea level, and there are a number of collection numbers remaining from the past, under which it still circulates in collections – random examples are SB 0860, SB 1023 or HK 1281, or Rep 0408. Cultivation is the same as for the typical species. A large, shallow pan makes a suitable growing container. In the summer, plenty of water should be given, and a balanced type of fertilizer should be used several times during the growing season. Wintering should be absolutely dry and, if possible, in the light.

Echinocereus poselgeri

Echinocereus poselgeri ▣ ○

CLUSTERING

This cactus is bushy and branches out in various directions. Individual shoots are of pencil thickness over 3ft long. It forms distinctive roots like those of a dahlia. The inconspicuous ribs have clustered areoles, and growing from each of these there are usually 12 radial spines and 1 central spine. They are all small, with only the central one reaching lengths of up to 1/2in. It blooms on the upper parts of the stem with a large mauve-pink flower.

Difficult to find in the wild, because it is very well camouflaged in the tangle of bushes and other associated vegetation. It only becomes conspicuous from a distance when it produces its flowers. It grows mainly in the states of Coahuila, Tamaulipas, and Nuevo León, but also on US territory, in Texas. It favors deeper, sandy soils. Due to its roots, it is sensitive to watering at the wrong time. For this reason, cactus growers often graft it, but plants grown in this way grow too luxuriantly. It is important to grow plants on their own roots in deeper containers with drainage material at the bottom. A well-drained, mineral-high soil mix should be chosen; the cactus should be cold-wintered, preferably inlight and watered only when completely dry.

Echinocereus poselgeri ssp. *kroenleinii*

Echinocereus pulchellus

Echinocereus poselgeri ssp. *kroenleinii* ▣ ○

CLUSTERING

A rather shorter species, reaching a maximum height of 20in. This cactus, too, produces clambering stems, and its roots are heart-shaped tubers. The spines are thin, and the areoles on the upper part of the plant produce white down as well as spines. The flower is a beautiful pinkish mauve color, and is usually no more than 2in across.
At present its locality is known only in one place in the Mexican state of Coahuila, near the village of El Amparo, were it grows in deeper sandy soils. It is not very common in collections, especially under this name. Many cactus growers have this plant under collection number HK 0379. As regards cultivation, the same applies as in the case of the typical species.

Echinocereus pulchellus ▣ ○

GLOBOSE

This is one of the smallest members of the genus; the above-ground part of the stem does not usually grow more than 1 1/2in across and 1 1/4in high. However, the underground section may be up to 3in long and turns into a beet-like root. The inconspicuous radial spines, 3–5 in number, are only a fraction of an inch long. The plant in the photograph has rather more robust spines. The magnificent purple-red flowers grow from lateral areoles; they have a broad funnel shape, and are up to 2in across when fully open. But there are also forms which have white flowers from localities in the vicinity of Pachuca (Hidalgo, Mexico).

This is one of the species under relatively serious threat, because it colonizes localities which are mostly suitable for agriculture. Although the area in which it grows is relatively wide, extending from the state of Puebla to the states of Querétaro and Hidalgo, it is now encountered only in isolated localities. An interesting feature is its geophytic growth, which allows it to survive drought with its stem contracted completely underground. The stem does not emerge above the surface until the first rains; it then flowers and produces fruit. It is undoubtedly one of the most attractive representatives of the genus, and is kept in collections as a splendidly blooming miniature. It blooms relatively quickly from seed, when its stem is about 3/4in in diameter. Because of the special structure of its stem, with a large underground part and beet-like root, it is rather difficult to grow. It is important that it should be placed in a deep pot filled with a free-draining soil mix, with a drainage layer at the bottom. Grafting onto a great variety of rootstocks can also be recommended, but the

Echinocereus pulchellus var. *amoenus*

plants then grow to a much greater size and may form quite a number of offsets – e.g. when grafted onto *Pereskiopsis*. It is propagated from seed. It tolerates dry, cold wintering.

Echinocereus pulchellus var. *amoenus* ▣ ○

GLOBOSE

Precise classification of this varietas and its placing within the species is problematic from the outset, but the plant is in circulation in collections, and this is why it is mentioned here. Unlike the type, this variety has a more robust stem and is more spiny. There is also great variability in the coloring of the flowers, which ranges from light pink to deep pinkish mauve.
This cactus grows in the state of San Luis Potosí, where it favors grassy meadow communities. During dry periods, its stem shrinks and retracts almost completely below ground, which makes it very difficult to find. Cultivation is the same as for the type, because this variety, too, has a beet-like root.

Echinocereus pulchellus ssp. *sharpii* ▣ ○

GLOBOSE

This subspecies is distinguished from the type by its rather finer but longer spination, greater number of ribs and spines, and especially by its large creamy white flowers, which sometimes have a delicate pink tinge.
The habitat was until recently unknown, but now it is clear that this cactus grows on hilly meadowland at an altitude of about 6,500ft above sea level in the state of Nuevo León. It has spread quite rapidly in cactus collections, but remains a rarity, which it is advisable to keep as a graft until there are enough seeds for experimentation.

Echinocereus pulchellus ssp. *weinbergii* ▣ ○

GLOBOSE

A very attractive plant, distinguished by its sturdier, thicker and more substantial spination compared to other members of the complex. The flat or flattish globose stem grows to a diameter of up to 5 in with concave crown. The wide funnel-shaped, pink flower is up to 1 1/2in wide and grows from lateral areoles near the crown.
It colonizes flat grassland in the state of Zacatecas. As a result, they are all plowed up since these are areas suitable for agriculture. It is neither common nor rare in collections. The sensitive, beet-like roots need a well-drained, slightly alkaline, mineral-rich soil mix. Self-rooted seedlings flower in five years, and are a great asset to any *Enchinocereus* collection. Cold wintering in the light is a requirement for abundant flowering the next year.

Echinocereus pulchellus ssp. *sharpii*

Echinocereus pulchellus ssp. *weinbergii*

Echinocereus rigidissimus

Echinocereus rigidissimus ▣ ○

COLUMNAR

Another rather variable *Echinocereus*. It forms columnar stems, usually 8in high, but plants nearly 20in tall have also been recorded. The stem diameter can be 4in at the most, but is usually less. From the oval areoles grow 15–23 radial spines pressed against the plant; they do not exceed 1/2in in length, and their color varies from yellowish through ocher to reddish brown. Central spines are entirely missing. The flower tube is covered with fine spines. The flower grows on the upper parts of the stem, and is about 3in across. The typical pinkish-mauve color of the petals shades into creamy white in the flower mouth. The anthers are yellow and the stigma green.
This cactus is found in Mexico and the USA. It grows in grassy regions with a limestone substrate in eastern Sonora, the western part of the state of Chihuahua, and also in southeast Arizona and southwest New Mexico. In collections, it is one of the more widespread species; many cactus-growers may know it only under field numbers, of which the best known are L 096, SB 0155, SB 0246 and SB 1777. Cultivation is the same as for most members of the genus. A decorative effect is provided by a group of these cacti planted together in a large pot, where they grow and flourish splendidly.

Echinocereus rigidissimus ssp. *rubispinus* ▣ ○

COLUMNAR

This taxon, too, has gone through complex combinations, but cactus growers and catalogs still tend to identify it by its original field number, L 088. The columnar, single stem may reach a height of 7 1/4in and a diameter of about 2in. It is a striking cactus with its comb-like spination, which, especially on younger areoles, has a distinctive red color. This is one of the reasons for its separate classification. The flower is splendid, light purple-red in color, with a cream-colored mouth and green stigma.
Another important factor which played a role in its taxonomic classification is the isolation of the single habitat, which is situated in the west of the Mexican state of Chihuahua in the very inaccessible Sierra Obscura range, in the Cañon de Barbarocas valley. When Alfred Lau first collected it, it was obviously a beautiful novelty that was bound to arouse the interest of growers. It is now quite widespread in collections, and has become widely available in commerce in recent years. Cultivation is the same as for other "pectinate" *Echinocereus*. Important requirements are a well-drained soil mix, cold, light wintering, and adequate water and ventilation in summer.

Echinocereus rigidissimus ssp. *rubispinus*

Echinocereus scheeri ssp. *gentryi*

Echinocereus scheeri ssp. *gentryi*

TRAILING

These procumbent cacti have a branching habit, with individual stems up to 1ft long, divided into 4–7 ribs. The rather short radial spines are about 1/16in long, but plants with spines up to 2in long are not unknown. As a rule there is no central spine. The flower has a markedly elongated funnel shape, and may be up to 5in long. It is deep pink, sometimes with an orange mouth.
It grows in the inaccessible mountains of Sierra Obscura, where it was collected by A. B. Lau, who introduced it to collections under collection number L 087. It also occurs on the borders of the Mexican states of Sonora and Chihuahua, in the Cañon Saucito. It grows on rocky outcrops and in very exposed places. It is one of the relatively common representatives of the genus in collections, because of its unique habit and the fact that it is quite easy to grow. In summer it needs light, tolerates quite generous watering, and grows well, provided it is planted in a shallow pan in which the soil mix can dry out thoroughly and there is adequate space for the root system to develop.

Echinocereus schereri

COLUMNAR

The columnar stem, which is usually solitary, may grow to a height of 8in and diameter of 2 1/4–4in. There are usually 11–16 ribs, which are densely covered with areoles; growing from each of these, there are usually 13–22 radial spines. The growing buds are covered with wisps of down and tiny black spines. The flower is up to 4in across when fully open, and pinkish purple in color.
The species was only recently described, and is actually known only from a few localities in the Mexican state of Durango, not far from Mina Navidad, where it grows in meadows at altitudes of about 5,500ft above sea level. Experience with cultivation so far shows that it is relatively easy to grow, and may flower in about 7 years provided the basic requirements are met. It should be cold-wintered in the light, in absolutely dry conditions.

Echinocereus schereri

Echinocereus stramineus

Echinocereus stramineus 

CLUSTERING

This cactus forms large clusters, often more than 20in across. The individual stems are about 1ft long and up to 3in in diameter. The spines on extremely spiny individuals may be up to 4in long. Most of them are gray, but become more colorful near the top of the plant. This species blooms in spring and summer with large flowers up to 4 3/4in long and across, and pinkish purple in color, with yellow anthers and a green stigma.
E. stramineus occurs in practically all the arid regions of northern Mexico in a number of forms and ecotypes. It is therefore important to know its variable origin of spination, and the longest the seeds from which collectors' plants are grown. Cultivation is not difficult, and the plants react very favorably to applications of fertilizer, after which they develop thick, beautifully spined stems. Only larger plants produce flowers, and like all bulky *Echinocereus*, they need space. Planting in large containers is therefore recommended.

Echinocereus subinermis

Echinocereus subinermis 

GLOBOSE

A species that cannot be mistaken for any other *Echinocereus*, especially when it flowers. Its stem is globose, 2 3/4–4in in diameter, in collections becoming slightly columnar. The epidermis is gray-green, turning to black in some places as a result of excessive sun. There are no central spines, and the radial spines are quite variable in length and number; there are 5–20 of them, and they may be 1/8 to 1/2in long. The beautiful flowers bloom near the top of the plant; they are deep yellow in color, and their stigma, as in most *Echinocereus*, is green. The flower may be an unbelievable 4 3/4in across when fully open.

Echinocereus subinermis var. *aculeatus*

The species occurs in many isolated localities within the territory of the states of Sonora, Chihuahua, and Sinaloa. It grows at altitudes between 1,500 and 4,000ft above sea level. It is a great favorite for cultivation, not only because it is undemanding, but also because of its attractive flowers, which are quite exceptional for this genus. Bringing plants into flower calls for some patience, but is not at all difficult. The seeds should preferably be sown in a propagator, and the plants transferred to a greenhouse later, when they are big enough. This plant tolerates light shade when in growth during summer; wintering may be very cold.

Echinocereus subinermis var. *aculeatus* 

GLOBOSE

A taxon extremely similar to the typical species, and often treated as being identical with it. Perhaps the only features that distinguish it are the more prominent spination and, in the wild, a more globose shape, which is not found in cultivated plants. The material for description was collected near the village of La Bufa, in the west of the state of Chihuahua, at altitudes of about

2,000ft above sea level. Cultivation is exactly the same as for the type.

Echinocereus subinermis ssp. *ochoterenae* ▣ ○

GLOBOSE

This is a plant with prominent spination, with a tendency to offset freely, but in other respects it resembles the typical species. The bud, as in the basic species, has a downy covering, and the flower tube is covered with tiny spines.
According to the published description, the type locality of this subspecies is Cerro de la Cobriza, situated in the province of Concordia in the Mexican state of Sinaloa. Cultivation is the same as for the species.

Echinocereus subinermis ssp. *ochoterenae*

Echinofossulocactus arrigens ▣ ○

GLOBOSE

In terms of classification, it is the most problematic genus in the entire family. It is extremely variable even in single localities. Validated in 1935, all the species were re-assigned to the genus *stenocactus*. However, most cactus growers use the former genus name *Echinofossulocactus*. *E. arrigens* produces 2 3/4–3in in diameter and height stems with anything from 24 to 55 ribs. There are usually 3 or 4 central and 6–8 radial spines. The flower is 3/4in–1 1/4in wide, with a mauve-red streak in the middle and white petals.
Information on the locality is very scarce, according to specialists. Typical plants of this species might be found on flatter terrain with a limestone substrate in the vicinity of Pachuca, town in the state of Hidalgo. Cultivation is the same as for other species in the genus. Keeping small seedlings in the shade and applying fertilizer occasionally when in active growth is advisable.

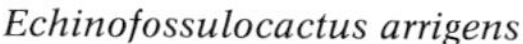

Echinofossulocactus arrigens

Echinofossulocactus coptonogonus, cultivated

Echinofossulocactus coptonogonus ▣ ○

GLOBOSE

The stem is usually globose and solitary, and in natural habitats the epidermis has a green-gray color. Of all members of the genus, it has the fewest ribs, only 15–20, and they are slightly wavy. From each areole grow 3–5 spines of a reddish color, 1/2–2in in length. The flowers appear in early spring; the petals are white with a mauve-red streak in the middle.
The flat plains around the town of San Luis Potosí (Mexico) are, in places, full of these cacti, but their future is very uncertain, because they grow on land which is quite suitable for agriculture. Some colonies are made up of plants which have a stem partly hidden underground, and others consist of huge plants with stems up to 8in in diameter. In collections it is a clearly recognizable species, so it is usually cultivated as an unhybridized form. It requires wintering in the light at temperatures around 50 °F, a soil mix which should preferably be slightly alkaline and well-drained, and the sunniest possible position during the summer. Some growers even recommend keeping the plants under cover (e.g. polycarbonate) during the summer.

Echinofossulocactus coptonogonus, wild

Echinofossulocactus erectrocentrus

Echinofossulocactus erectrocentrus ▣ ○

GLOBOSE

The globose stem usually grows to 2 3/4in, and there are about 50 corrugate ribs. This species, like others in the genus, is extremely variable. The spines may be up to 2in long, but we know of individual plants in the wild with thorns over 6in long. The flowers are white, and individual petals have a mauve-red streak.
In the wild, it is one of the most beautiful representatives of the genus, because its central spines may be very long, and are often curved too. It grows in the flatter regions of the state of Nuevo León. Cultivation is the same as for other *Echinofossulocactus*. Even small seedlings are able to produce beautiful spines, and it is therefore advisable to have plants of a specified origin. All species in this genus have been grown for decades without regard to whether or not they are hybrids. In view of the fact that they hybridize very often, individual species must be kept in complete isolation when in flower.

Echinofossulocactus lloydii ▣ ○

GLOBOSE

This species produces a globose stem, about 4 3/4in in diameter. The numerous corrugate ribs have light-colored areoles, from which grow about 8 radial and 3 central spines, and the up-

Echinofossulocactus lloydii

ward-pointing spine at the middle is up to 4in long and often curved. The flowers are white, with a mauve streak in the middle of each petal. The fruit is a green berry which later reddens, containing spherical black seeds.

F. E. Lloyd first collected this plant on 7 August, 1908 in a locality near the town of Zacatecas in the state of the same name. The species grows on flatter terrain, often in the shade of accompanying shrub vegetation. Cultivation is the same as for other members of the genus. In view of its enormous degree of variability, it is important that only plants of known origin should be included in the collection. Only in this way can the collection be of great botanical value. These plants should not be crossed with other examples of the species from a different locality.

Echinofossulocactus multicostatus ▣ ○

GLOBOSE

E.multicostatus is characterized for its large number of ribs. The globose stem is up to 4in in diameter, and the prominent corrugate ribs number up to 100. The yellow spines range from short to 2in long. The flowers with white petals and a red-mauve streak appear on the top of the plant. It grows in the mountains between the states of Coahuila and Nuevo León, but also finds reported in Durango. It colonizes areas in light shade, and clearings in open pine forest. In summer it is placed in full sun, and the epidermis is lighter green in this case. The soil mix may be slightly acid, well drained, and it tolerates a large amount of water. Sowing the seeds in early spring is advisable, so that the seedlings are sufficiently mature by the first winter.

Echinofossulocactus multicostatus

Echinofossuloactus phyllacanthus

Echinofossulocactus phyllacanthus ▣ ○

GLOBOSE

There is no end to the variability of this species, and finding a uniform-looking colony in any locality is virtually impossible. The plants produce single, unbranched, flattened globose stems, up to 3in in diameter, which, in the wild, are often one-third retracted into the ground – mainly during the period of dormancy, when the plant's intake of water is minimal. Older specimens have a stem divided into roughly 35 ribs with wavy edges. The circular areoles produce white down, which is retained mainly in the area of the crown. The number and length of the spines are extremely variable. Although the species epithet *phyllacanthus* means "flat-spined" or "with spines in the form of a leaf," this is not necessarily accurate. Usually, however, there are 1–3 central, thicker, flat spines of a brownish color growing from each areole, and 2–5 white radial spines. The flower is yellow, about 3/4in across, often with a darker streak in the middle. The fruit contains about 30 small, dark brown to black seeds.
The area of distribution of the species is relatively wide, and it is found mainly on flat terrain in the states of San Luis Potosí, Zacatecas, Hidalgo, and Guanajuato. It is very important to obtain collection material from a specified source. The availability of seeds from plants of specified origin has now increased, which means that a collection built up on this basis is very likely to be of considerable botanical value. The actual cultivation of the species does not differ from cultivation of other members of *Echinofossulocactus.*

Echinofossulocactus sulphureus ▣ ○

GLOBOSE

The flattened globose stem is about 3in in diameter, and its epidermis is dark green. The number of ribs is, once again, very variable (26–40), and si-

Echinofossulocactus sulphureus

Epithelantha micromeris

milar variability is seen in the number and length of the spines. There are usually 3 or 4 central spines and a similar number of radial spines. The flowers are yellow and appear in early spring.
Perhaps the best-known localities for this species are in Barranca de Tolimán in the state of Hidalgo, where Felipe Otero and Jorge Meyrán were among the notable collectors of this plant in the past. The species grows at altitudes of 4,000–4,500ft above sea level. In collections, the distinctive color of its flowers distinguishes it from related species. Its cultivation, however, is the same as for other species.

Epithelantha micromeris ▣ ○

GLOBOSE

This globose plant is a miniature, the largest specimens of which reach a maximum diameter of 2 1/4in. The stem is divided into small mammillae, on which fine, white, bristly spines grow from the areoles; the length of the spines does not usually exceed 1/8in. In spring and summer, small pink flowers (light pink, pinkish white to dark pink), about 1/2in across, emerge from the thick down at the crown. The fruit are decorative, too – red, slenderly club-shaped berries up to 3/4in long. The area of distribution of this species is very wide; it is found in the southern USA and the northern states of Mexico. As a rule it favors stony, rocky terrain. In its habitats, it is very variable. It often appears in collections, and is hardly ever missing from any collection of Mexican cacti. Cultivation is the same as for other members of the genus. Its main requirements are cold wintering and a well-drained, slightly alkaline substrate. Grafting is certainly possible, but plants grown in this way lose their typical character.

Epithelantha micromeris var. *greggii* ▣ ○

GLOBOSE

Distinguished by its rather larger size (up to 3in in diameter) and denser spination, which is characterized by the presence of several longer central spines of a glassy white color. Apart from this, the flowers are slightly smaller, and often dark pink.
The variety grows in the state of Coahuila. In collections it is usually treated as a separate species. Cultivation is the same as for the previous taxon.

Epithelantha aff. *unguispina* ▣ ○

GLOBOSE

For many years, this plant took the place of the true *Epithelantha unquispina* in collections. Not found in the wild for several decades until the end of the 1990s in the area of Saltillo in the state of Coahuila. It produces black central spines only in the region of the growing point, and later loses them. *E. unguispina* is distinguished by the feature: its pitch black central thorn, which may be up to 1/2in long.

Epithelantha micromeris var. greggii

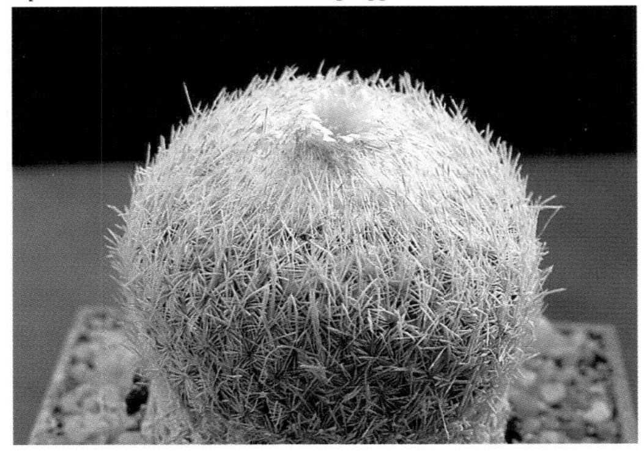

Epithelantha aff. unguispina

Escobaria asperispina

Escobaria asperispina ▣ ○

GLOBOSE

The matt green, globose stems may grow to a diameter of 2 1/4in. Each stem is divided into conical mammillae, tipped by small areoles bearing approximately 10 soft radial spines. The flowers appear in early summer; they up to 1 1/4in wide, and they have a yellow color which is sometimes tinged with pink. In some plants there is a darker central streak on the outer petals.
The habitats of the species are relatively small regions in the Mexican state of Coahuila, where it grows at higher altitudes above sea level. *E. asperispina* is propagated mainly by grafting; until recently it was represented in collections mainly by hybridized plants which did not have the typical features of the species. It needs a well-drained, mineral-high soil mix and full sun.

Escobaria chaffeyi f. *viridiflora*

Escobaria chaffeyi f. *viridiflora* ▣ ○

COLUMNAR

This plant is distinguished from the typical species by its denser spination and also the green color of the flowers, which grow from the upper areoles. Taxonomically, it has not yet been assessed, so the name used here is a provisional name referring to the specific color of the flowers.
In the wild, it grows as a marginal form in the Mexican state of Chihuahua near Flores Magon, where it colonizes limestone rocks and stony outcrops. It does not feature very widely in collections, but its cultivation is the same as for other members of the genus.

Escobaria grata ▣ ○

GLOBOSE–COLUMNAR

The species was not described until 2001, and its discovery aroused justifiable attention, because this is a splendid cactus, as the species name indicates: *grata*, meaning agreeable, charming, lovely. The stem is initially oval, and later slightly columnar, with a base which forms a number of offsets. Only the radial spines reach lengths up to 5/8in; they are very dense, practically covering the epidermis of the plant. The flower appears in sum-

mer, and is up to 1 1/4in wide. The outer petals have a downy, fringed edge, and the inner petals are pinkish mauve.
The type locality of the species is the Sierra el Burro range in the north Mexican state of Coahuila, where it grows on limestone hills at an altitude of about 4,000ft above sea level. There is little information on cultivation, because it is not very widespread among growers. It is clear, however, that it benefits from cold wintering in the light, and very careful watering during the hottest summer months, because it does not tolerate excess humidity caused by overwatering at too high a temperature.

Escobaria zilziana ▣ ○

GLOBOSE–COLUMNAR

The plant illustrated is by no means typical, and is perhaps more reminiscent of the mysterious, virtually unknown *E. robertii*. The stem clusters to a limited extent, and becomes slightly columnar in old age. The radial spines are needle-like and light-colored, while the central spines (of which there are usually 1–3) are up to 1 1/4in long and either entirely dark, or dark-colored at the tip only. The flower is about 1in across, pale pink, with a darker central streak.
Recent investigations have established a certain amount about the habitat of this escobaria, but, clearly, many localities remain to be discovered. There are known localities in the Mexican state of Coahuila, and also in the state of Durango, where Steven Brack collected it (SB 602 and SB 603). It grows mainly on limestone, on rocky outcrops. Cultivation is the same as for other members of the genus, and this has proved one of the easiest species to grow.

Escobaria zilziana

Escobaria grata

Ferocactus chrysacanthus ▣ ○

BARREL-SHAPED

This is definitely one of the most beautifully spined cacti (*chrysacanthus* = golden-spined). Its stem may grow to a height of 3ft and a diameter of about 14in. The color of the spines varies from yellow to brick-red; in the past, this species has been treated as a varietas (var. *rubispinus*). The yellow flowers, often with an orange streak on the inner petals, take many years to appear.
This species has a small area of distribution, being endemic to just a few islands off the coast of Baja California (San Benito and Cedros). Because of the limited availability of seeds, it appears relatively rarely in collections, and in any case it is not easy to grow. Important requirements are a relatively high winter temperature, and wintering in the light. This cactus if often grafted onto a slow-growing rootstock.

Ferocactus chrysacanthus

Ferocactus echidne var. victoriensis

Ferocactus echidne var. *victoriensis* ▣ ○

COLUMNAR

The cylindrical stem of this cactus usually grows to a height of 20in–2ft and a diameter of 1ft. The slender, fan-like ribs do not usually exceed 15 in number, and this is the main feature distinguishing this varietas from the type. The spines are thin and whitish or yellowish brown. The flower is yellow, and may be up to 5/8in across when fully open.

This form grows on the eastern slopes of Sierra Madre Oriental, and the best-known populations are on the lowlands near the towns of Jaumave, San Antonio, and Ciudad Victoria in the Mexican state of Tamaulipas. It is very often grown in greenhouses, and young specimens are very often among the easy-to-grow plants in any cactus grower's collection.

Ferocactus flavovirens ▣ ○

CLUSTERING

According to N. P. Taylor, expert on the genus *Ferocactus*, this species is, in evolutionary terms, one of the most primitive, from which there developed the most specialized barrel-shaped representatives of the genus. This clustered cactus forms clumps up to 6 1/2ft wide, whose individual stems usually grow to a height of 12–16in with a diameter of about 8in. Depending on the age of the plant, there may be 11–13 prominent ribs. The 12–20 radial spines are soft and tend to be bristly; the central spines (4–6 in number) are light brown, and the longest of them grow to 3in. The flower appears on the youngest areoles, and is about 1 5/8in wide and reddish orange in color. The elliptical fruit, which is red when mature, is covered with brown scales and contains dark brown seeds.

The species was first scientifically collected at some time during the years 1828–1832, but was not kept as type material. G. Lindsay therefore made a collection, in 1955, of material originating near the settlement of Zapotitlan de Salinas in the state of Puebla. The species is most widely distributed here, but its localities extend from the south-eastern part of the state of Puebla as far as the northern regions of the state of Oaxaca, where it grows on flatter terrain with a limestone substrate. It is not grown very often in collections, but cultivation is not difficult. It requires the same care and the same conditions as other mainland

Ferocactus flavovirens

Ferocactus glaucescens, cultivated

Ferocactus glaucescens, wild

members of the genus (those from Baja California and nearby islands form a distinct group).

Ferocactus glaucescens ▣ ○

GLOBOSE

This cactus forms individual or clustering stems which grow up to 27in high. It is very elegant with its glaucous, waxy-coated epidermis, which contrasts splendidly with the straw-colored spines and light yellow flowers.
The area of distribution of this species is relatively wide, extending to the states of Hidalgo, Querétaro, and San Luis Potosí, where it favors limestone subsoil and relatively rocky terrain. It is a great favorite among growers, and reasonably priced flowering specimens are now widely available. Its cultivation does not entail any difficulties; like all members of *Ferocactus*, this species is propagated exclusively by seed.

Ferocactus gracilis 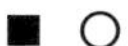

BARREL-SHAPED

The largest specimens reach heights up to 8ft, with a stem diameter of 14in. Mature specimens have roughly 24 ribs, and prominent red spines up to 2 3/4in long, pointing toward the base of the plant, which may be hooked. Its red flowers are about 1 1/2in across. The fruit is a yellow, juicy berry.
The species grows from Sierra San Miguel to Baja California in a mineral-high substrate on a granite bed. Cultivation entails warm wintering in the light. Older plants are low tolerant for any extreme; they are often seen grafted, for instance onto *Pereskiopsis*.

Ferocactus gracilis

Ferocactus gracilis var. *coloratus*

Ferocactus gracilis var. *coloratus* ■ ○

BARREL-SHAPED

Very similar to the type species in its habit and distribution. It is distinguished, however, by its smaller stature, and its very variable, denser spination, with hairy radial spines in most cases entirely absent. It shares part of its area of distribution with the species *F. peninsulae*, to which the intermediate species are also very similar. The type locality is the southern region from Laguna Chapala to Baja California.

Ferocactus hamatacanthus

Ferocactus haematacanthus

BARREL-SHAPED

In the largest specimens, the sturdy, cylindrical stem may grow taller than 3ft, with a diameter of about 16in. The species epithet indicates that this is a plant with blood-red spines. The color is es-

Ferocactus haematacanthus

Ferocactus histrix

pecially striking in the new spines, but later fades. This cactus has very attractive reddish purple flowers, which appear on older plants near the crown.
Distribution is limited to a relatively small territory on the borders of the Mexican states of Puebla and Veracruz, where it colonizes limestone hills at an altitude of about 8,000ft. The species is relatively uncommon among cactus growers, and has only recently begun to appear gradually in collections.

Ferocactus hamatacanthus ▣ ○

COLUMNAR

Many cactus growers know this species better under the genus name *Hamatocactus*. The hooked spines gave it its species epithet of *hamatacanthus*; in the most prominently spined specimens, the central spine may be more than 6in long (but is usually shorter). The size of the stem is also very variable, and the largest specimens reach heights of about 30in. The pleasantly scented flower, up to 3in across, takes many years to appear on plants in cultivation.
The species grows in the central and northern regions of Mexico, and the most northerly colonies extend into the southern regions of the USA. In collections, young specimens are the most successful; older plants do not take kindly to repotting.

Ferocactus latispinus

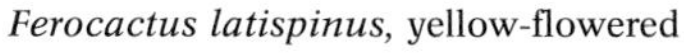

Ferocactus latispinus, yellow-flowered

Ferocactus histrix 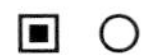

BARREL-SHAPED

The flattened globose to short columnar stem may exceed 3ft in height, but specimens taller than 27in are rare. The number of ribs varies considerably, between 20 and 40, with lower central spines up to 2 1/4in long. The dark yellow flower is only 1 5/8in across.
The area of distribution of the species is relatively wide, extending into several central Mexican states (Aguascalientes, Durango, Guanajuato, Hidalgo, Querétaro, etc.). Cultivation does not entail any difficulties; the main thing is to keep the plants in the shade in early spring, because they scorch very easily.

Ferocactus latispinus 

FLATTENED-GLOBOSE

This cactus tends to grow flat, or in a flattened-globose shape, and the maximum stem diameter may be as much as 16in. The epidermis is dark green. The stem is divided into about 20 ribs, and thick woody spines grow from the elliptical areoles. The unusually thick, flat central spine is a prominent feature that is characteristic of this species. It may be up to 2 1/4in long, and is hooked. The beautiful flowers are dark purple in color, but on rare occasions, specimens with yellow flowers have been observed in the habitat.
Red- and yellow-spined forms grow in wild localities in the central states of Mexico, often in a mixed community. Cultivation does not present problems. Beautifully flowering specimens are now available as imports at reasonable prices.

Ferocactus peninsulae

Ferocactus pilosus

Ferocactus peninsulae ■ ○

BARREL-SHAPED

In the wild, the columnar stem may grow 8ft tall, while the diameter does not usually exceed 16in. The radial spines are relatively thick and woody, but the thickest of all is the bottom-most central spine, which is up to 6in long, with a hooked tip. At the crown, all the spines are strikingly reddish-colored. The flowers, up to 2 1/4in across, appear in summer; they are orange-red with a darker streak in the middle.

As the species epithet *peninsulae* indicates, this is a peninsular species, originating in Baja California. It grows in the central part of the peninsula, on the east coast. In recent years there has been an increase not only in the availability of seeds, but also in the trade of plants raised in cultivation. However, the species is not suitable for complete beginners. Although seedlings grow without too many problems, older specimens are usually intolerant of poor cultivation. It should be borne in mind that this cactus needs rather warm wintering, at temperatures above 50 °F.

Ferocactus pilosus, detail of flowers

Ferocactus pilosus ■ ○

BARREL-SHAPED

The species epithet, meaning "hairy," refers to the fine, whitish, bristly spines in the areoles of older specimens. The species is one of the large members of the genus; the largest specimens may reach heights of more than 6 1/2ft, with a stem diameter of 20in. In the wild, it forms a large clump, several feet in diameter. An attractive feature of the plant is its red, thick, woody spines which grow together with white hairy spines from the relatively large, elliptical areoles. The flowers are about 1 1/2in long, and their color ranges from dark yellow to orange-red. The fruit is scaly, very sour, and contains up to 1,000 seeds.

In Mexico, it grows over quite a wide area, through San Luis Potosí and Durango as far as Nuevo León and Coahuila. This species is popular with growers, because of its problem-free

Ferocactus recurvus

growth and its beauty. Specimens of flowering size are now available in the nursery trade.

Ferocactus recurvus ▣ ○

COLUMNAR

The columnar stem may reach heights of up to 18in, with a diameter of roughly 8in. The prominent ribs, up to 2in deep, have oval areoles from which the spines grow. The most conspicuous of these is the flat central spine with a hooked tip. The flowers, up to 2in across, are produced near the crown of the plant, and their color varies between pink and purplish, often with a darker central streak.
The species grows in the south Mexican states of Puebla and Oaxaca, on higher ground with a limestone substrate. Among growers, it is one of the relatively widespread members of the genus, and growing specimens on their own roots usually presents no problems. However, it prefers quite warm wintering (the temperature should not fall below 54 °F) in good light.

Ferocactus reppenhagenii ■ ○

GLOBOSE

The largest specimens grow columnar, but most of the plants, both wild and cultivated, are globose. The diameter of the stem does not usually exceed 20in. The prominent spination is accentuated by the length of the central spines, which is up to 3in. The flower, 1 1/4in across, is usually yellow, or, less frequently, orange.
This cactus is seen relatively seldom in the wild, because it grows in a region which is less well-known to cactus specialists, in the Mexican states of Colima and Michoacán. For growers, this cactus presents quite serious problems, for several reasons. It has very fine seeds which are practically unobtainable. The seedlings grow slowly and require quite warm wintering.

Ferocactus robustus

Ferocactus robustus ▣ ○

CLUSTERING

One of the few clustering members of this genus: its cluster of stems may grow to a diameter of several yards. The height of such a group is often more than a yard, with hundreds of individual "heads." The deep ribs have prominent areoles, from which grow thinner radial spines and very thick, woody central spines. The flowers are deep yellow and appear about 15 years after germination.
The species occurs in southern Mexico, around the town of Tehuacan in the state of Puebla, and also in the northern regions of the state of Oaxaca. Cultivation does not initially present any problems, but older plants react sensitively to growers' mistakes. An important requirement is wintering at quite a warm temperature in the light; this applies especially to specimens of flowering size, which would not otherwise produce flowers.

Ferocactus reppenhagenii

Ferocactus setispinus

Ferocactus setispinus 

COLUMNAR

Most cactus-growers still know it by the invalid genus name of *Hamatocactus*, and keep it in collections under that name. Although it does not reach anything like the large dimensions of other members of the genus, *F. setispinus* is a striking species, both because of its prominent spines and because of its large flowers, which may be up to 2in across. Another attractive feature is the red fruits, which ripen about 3 months after the flowers have finished blooming. The flowers appear about 5 years after germination.
The species occupies an extensive region in the north of Mexico, with some populations extending as far as US territory (Texas). *F. setispinus* is one of the commonest cacti kept by growers. An interesting phenomenon is that its pollen can be used to stimulate the stigma of a cactus belonging to another species or genus. After being stimulated in this way, the cactus may fertilize itself with its own pollen.

Ferocactus wislizeni var. *herrerae*

Ferocactus wislizenii var. herrerae 

BARREL-SHAPED

A smaller number of ribs (usually about 13), a lower height, and the main central spine less flattened and thick – these are the main differences from the type species.
This varietas occurs on the western slopes of the Sierra Madre Occidental massif in Mexico, up to an altitude of 4,000ft above sea level.

Gymnocactus beguinii 

GLOBOSE

The problems presented by this entire complex are under constant discussion; the above name is the most widely used among growers. Other synonyms in use are, for example, *Neolloydia smithii* or *Thelocactus beguinii.* The slightly columnar stem grows to a height of up to 6in, with a diameter of about 2 3/4in. There is extremely wide variation in the spines, and on the basis of this, several disputed variants have been described. The flower is usually mauve-pink and 1 1/4–1 1/2in across.

In the wild, this cactus is found over a wide area extending from the north Mexican state of Coahuila, through Nuevo León, to San Luis Potosí. It grows both in the flatter areas and in the mountains, but always at high altitudes above sea level. Growers are usually over-concerned about the requirements of this cactus, and it is therefore most often seen as a graft. Grafting is entirely superfluous, provided a few basic principles are followed. These are: full sun, cold wintering, and allowing the soil mix to dry out between waterings; when pricking out seedlings, allow any damage to the roots to dry out before potting up.

Gymnocactus beguinii var. *senilis* 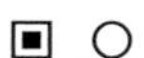

GLOBOSE

A taxon invalidly described whose name is designated a "nomen nudum" ("naked name," one published with neither description nor diagnosis). Distinguished from the typical species by their thicker, much finer and darker color spines. However, these are no more than local variants, and individual specimens with such spines are evidence of the natural variability of the taxon in different localities.

Gymnocactus horripilus ▣ ○

GLOBOSE

This cactus grows up to 4in in diameter, often forms large clumps. There are roughly 15–18 ribs divided into densely dark green skin clustering mammillae. As a rule there are 15 radial spines and a single 1 1/4in long central spine. The elegant reddish purple flower is about 1 1/4in wide, and appears in late spring or summer. Barranca de Metzitlan state of Hidalgo is the principal, best-known locality of this species. It grows there on slopes and rocky outcrops with a limestone substrate. Splendid specimens can be grown on their own roots. The main rule is that the plant should be grown in a free-draining, slightly alkaline soil mix.

Gymnocactus horripilus

Gymnocactus beguinii

Gymnocactus beguinii var. *senilis*

Gymnocactus knuthianus

Gymnocactus knuthianus 

GLOBOSE

A solitary plant – in rare cases, clustering – with a globose stem up to 4in in diameter. The bright green epidermis is densely covered with spines which are initally glassy white, later turning gray. There are roughly 20 radial spines, and most frequently a single central spine. In early spring it produces pink flowers, about 1 1/4in across, which appear near the crown.
The natural habitats are not extensive, and are limited to the Mexican state of San Luis Potosí. Beautiful plants can be seen near the small town of Guadalcazar, where they grow in mountain meadows, and often in the undergrowth of open woodland. This cactus is a favorite with growers because it is so easy to grow. The only sensitive phase lasts until the seedlings reach a height of about 1/2in; otherwise this cactus has the typical requirements of Mexican cacti.

Gymnocactus mandragora

Gymnocactus mandragora 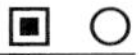

GLOBOSE

One of Mexico's greatest cactus mysteries, whose rediscovery is the result of exploration of the terrain in recent years. These are gray-green, globose little plants, usually 1 1/2–2 1/4in wide. They have a characteristic large, beet-like root, which is the reason for the species epithet *mandragora*. Growing from areoles on the clustered mammillae, there are about 12 radial radial spines, and 2 central spines which are 3/4in long and darker in color than the radials. The flowers, which are 3/4–1in in diameter, are produced from the crown of the plant. The outer petals have a typical greenish white color with a brownish central streak, while the inner petals are white.
The plant was described by A. V. Frič, but it is no longer known whether he also discovered it, or received it in a consignment which reached him in 1925. The habitat was a complete mystery, because nobody found it for many decades. The locality where the species grows is, even now, a very long way from civilization, and its rediscovery was a real piece of detective work by many cactus specialists. It is found some tens of miles from the town of Parras de la Fuente in the Mexican state of Coahuila. Here the species grows on some strange, furrowed hills (often on vertical surfaces). It inhabits only a few hills that have a specific kind of substrate containing fragmented slate; it can be found nowhere else in the vicinity. In collections it usually appears in the most varied hybrid forms, and few can claim to own the true *G. mandragora*. In recent years, however, the first grafted seedlings have begun to appear, and because the seeds germinate well, re-introduction of this cactus to collections can be expected soon. Growing the self-rooted plants is quite difficult, and at present, while plant material is scarce, grafting onto a slow-growing rootstock is recommended.

Gymnocactus subterraneus 

GLOBOSE

A great rarity among cacti, this is an interesting plant, not only because of its morphology, but also because of its habit. The stem, on a narrow neck, grows from a relatively large tuber, and is initially narrow and rod-shaped, only later beginning to form the typical, densely spined head. It has obviously adopted this strategy because it grows among

Gymnocactus subterraneus

tufts of grass, which it has to penetrate quickly in order to reach the light. The stem, up to 2in in diameter, is covered with glassy white radial spines, with pairs of black central spines protruding through them. The flower is a splendid sight, reddish purple, and usually 1 1/4in across. Looking for this species in the wild is like searching for a needle in a haystack. It occurs in a limited area in the state of Nuevo León, and even there it is very hard to find, because it is so well camouflaged in the tufts of grass. It is not often seen in collections, either, and growing it is no easy task. Seedlings grow quickly at first, but are sensitive to overwatering. Growth slows down while the underground tuber is forming. Grafted plants are altogether less interesting in appearance, but are easier to care for.

Gymnocactus subterraneus ssp. *zaragosae*

Gymnocactus subterraneus ssp. *zaragosae* ▣ ○

GLOBOSE

The club-shaped stems are up to 1 1/2in in diameter (or more in the case of cultivated plants) at their widest point, but have only a narrow neck at the base. The cactus clings to vertical surfaces by means of long tuberous roots. Growing from each areole, there are 21–25 white radial spines, and about 3 central spines, which are more rigid and, in every case, darker at the tip. They may be up to 3/4in long. The flowers are usually dark yellow with a dark pinkish brown central streak. The locality where these plants grow has given its name to the subspecies: they grow on rock faces around the town of Zaragosa in the state of Nuevo León. Apart from the moss-like *Selaginella lepidophylla*, it is often the only plant seen growing on this substrate. This cactus recommended to complete beginners, because its roots are quite sensitive to excessive watering at the wrong time. It needs an alkaline, well-drained soil mix, and adequate sun and ventilation. It should be wintered at a cold temperature, in the light. Raising from seed and growing plants on their own roots may present problems, because the seedlings form their underground parts first, and the aboveground part only grows slowly in the first few years. *Eriocereus jusbertii* or *Myrtillocactus geometrizans* can be recommended as rootstocks, but plants grafted onto them grow to an excessive size.

Gymnocactus viereckei

Gymnocactus viereckei, L 1159

Gymnocactus viereckei

GLOBOSE

This plant was named after Hans Viereck, who collected cacti for the Haage Erfurt company in the 1930s. It is not a large plant; the stem, which is usually globose, does not exceed 2 3/4in in diameter. The elegant spines, white down at the crown of the plant, and pinkish mauve flowers, make a beautiful color combination.

The type locality is considered the town of Jaumave in the state of Tamaulipas. The plant in the right-hand photograph is a specimen collected by Alfred Lau, designated by field number L 1159, and clearly differentiated by its spination and smaller flowers. This species is one of the less demanding members of the genus, and with a little patience, plants of flowering size can be grown on their own roots in 3–5 years.

Gymnocactus ysabelae, cultivated

Gymnocactus ysabelae

GLOBOSE

It was originally described under *Thelocactus*, but its classification within *Gymnocactus* is clearly correct (some authorities consider it a member of *Turbinicarpus*). The flattened-globose stem grows to a diameter of up to 3 1/2in, and its crown is covered with white down. The spirally arranged mammillae bear elliptical areoles, from which grow 16–20 radial spines and 1 central spine, bent toward the top of the plant. The bell-like flowers are about 5/8in long and 1/2in wide. They are creamy white in color, and appear on the plant in spring. The berry-like fruits split when ripe lengthwise and release spherical black seeds about 1/16in in diameter.

In the past, there were prolonged searches for the type locality. From the time when the plant was discovered in the 1930s until the end of the 1980s, nobody saw it in the wild. The author of the description had reported the place of discovery incorrectly. Rancho El Vergel and its surroundings were searched many times, without success. The locality of this species was discovered by chance, by Czech cactus specialists, in the vicinity of the town of Tula in the state of Tamaulipas. It grows on limestone hills there, not far from the town, and recent explorations of the terrain have revealed that the species is at significant risk from the effects of water erosion. It is not so long since it was a sought-after rarity, but in recent years, thanks to an adequate supply of seeds, it has again found a place, perhaps permanently, in collections. It can be grown on its own

Gymnocactus ysabelae, wild

roots, though this is not recommended for beginners. It is advisable to graft it onto a slow-growing rootstock, and experience has shown that the most beautifully spined plants, without any distortion of their growth, are those grafted onto *Trichocereus pasacana*. In terms of its other requirements, it is the same as most of the other members of *Gymnocactus* without taproots.

Hertrichocereus beneckei ■ ○

COLUMNAR

In collections this is known mainly as a columnar plant, but old specimens in the wild may be prostrate. The individual stems can be up to 10ft tall. A noteworthy feature is the color of the youngest parts: a striking gray-blue color, due to wax, which is seen not only in the wild but also in collections. As a rule there are 5 or 6 radial spines; there is usually only 1 central spine, which is black. The creamy white flowers, up to 2 1/4in long, open at sunset.

In the wild, this cactus grows in the mountain regions of the Mexican state of Guerrero, which is otherwise relatively poor in cactus flora. It tends to form an understorey among stands of taller shrubs and trees. In view of its natural habitat, it needs warm wintering at temperatures around 60 °F. In summer it benefits from full sun, fairly generous watering, and occasional applications of fertilizer.

Isolatocereus dumortieri 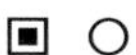 ○

COLUMNAR

Sometimes known under the genus name *Lemaireocereus*. This is a tree-like species, which can grow more than 50ft tall. Individual stems can be more than 6in diameter. The trunk branches are about 3ft above ground level. Older branches only produce small spines, while seedlings have fine, elegant spination. The yellow flowers with reddish-brown outer petals grow in rows one above another from densely clustered areoles reaching up to 2in long and 1in across. Puebla, Oaxaca, Morelos, and some other Mexican states are the areas of distribution of this interesting species. Due to its size, it is not often grown in collections. They grow without the slightest difficulty, and within a few years they make an impressive centerpiece for any greenhouse. They require quite warm winter temperatures.

Hertrichocereus beneckei

Isolatocereus dumortieri

Lemaireocereus chende

Lemaireocereus chende ▣ ○

COLUMNAR

This cactus was previously classified in a separate genus, *Heliabravoa*, named in honor of the Mexican botanist Helia Bravo, who devoted his entire career to cactus research. It grows to a height of about 13ft, with a trunk diameter of up to 10in. The individual stems are divided into 7 or 8 prominent ribs bearing circular areoles, each with 5 or 6 short radial spines which are brown, later turning to gray. The flowers, which appear on the areoles near the top of the plant, are about 2in long and up to 2 1/4in across, and pink in color. An interesting characteristic is their unusual, sweet scent. The fruit is a spherical, reddish purple berry.

The habitat of this species is in central and southern Mexico in the states of Oaxaca and Puebla, where it grows on flatter terrain on a limestone substrate. It only appears rarely in collections, despite the fact that cultivation is not difficult. It requires temperatures around 54 °F for wintering, without any prolonged exposure to winter temperatures below 50 °F. To ensure good growth, it should be planted in a fairly large pot, and should be given about two doses of a balanced fertilizer when in active growth.

Lemaireocereus hollianus

Lemaireocereus hollianus ▣ ○

COLUMNAR

This columnar cactus may grow as tall as 13ft; individual stems branching from the ground are 2–3in in diameter and have 8–10 prominent ribs. Newly developing spines have a brilliant red color, which soon fades to gray. The radial spines are relatively short (about 3/4in), while the 3 or 4 central spines are up to 4in long. The white flowers, which open in the daytime, are about 4in in diameter. The spherical fruits are edible and have a sweet taste.

In the wild, this cactus grows in a relatively restricted area in the central Mexican state of Puebla, in the Tehuacán valley, where it grows on flatter terrain. It is not at all common in collections, although its cultivation is not difficult. It requires a slightly alkaline soil mix, a fairly large pot, occasional applications of a balanced fertilizer, and relatively warm wintering with no prolonged temperature drops below 54 °F.

Leuchtenbergia principis ▣ ○

COLUMNAR

At first glance, this species does not even look like a cactus. Especially in the wild, it looks exactly like a tuft of dry grass, while in collections it seems more like a kind of agave. This is because the stem, up to 20in tall, is divided into long, three-sided mammillae, up to 4 3/4in in length, each tipped with an areole from which grow about 6 radial and 1 or 2 central spines. All these spines are

Leuchtenbergia principis

very soft and papery, and in some ecotypes they form a thick tangle. The magnificent, bright yellow flowers are up to 2 3/4in across, and bloom in early summer.

It is not easy to find this plant in the wild. Although it grows over a wide area, it is not an abundant species anywhere. Its center of distribution is the Mexican state of Coahuila, where it grows on hilly terrain, showing a strong tendency to camouflage itself among the rosettes of bromeliads of the genus *Hechtia* and in clumps of an agave plant of the genus *Dasylirion* or in tufts of grass. This unique plant is probably represented in every collection. This is partly because it is a real rarity (as regards habit), and also because it is relatively easy to grow, provided the principles of growing Mexican cacti are followed. In collections, it has even been possible to grow an intergeneric hybrid between *Ferocactus* and *Leuchtenbergia*, known as x *Ferobergia* 'Gil Tegelberg'. The hybrid, however, is infertile; unlike both its parents, for which seed propagation works best, this hybrid has to be propagated in vitro from tissue cultures.

Lophophora diffusa ▣ ○

GLOBOSE

The stem is initially solitary, but usually clustering in old age; it has a gray-green epidermis, often with an unusual yellowish tint. The spineless stem is very soft, fleshy, 4 3/4–5 1/2 in wide, merging into a bulky, beet-like root below ground. The flowers, which grow from the areoles on the concave crown, are white, but may also have a yellowish or pinkish tinge. They are not usually more than 3/4in across. The species is found on the sandy clay alluvia in the state of Querétaro (Mexico), where, mainly among whippy shrubs, they form large clumps that are often more than 18in across. The cultivation of this species is rather difficult because of the soft stem, which is very prone to rot. Handle these plants with care, because their unarmed stems put them at a distinct disadvantage as compared with densely spined cacti. They should preferably be wintered in the light at temperatures around 50 °F.

Lophophora diffusa

Lophophora fricii ▣ ○

FLATTENED-GLOBOSE

The species was named after the Czech cactus expert, traveler, and ethnologist A. V. Frič, who collected specimens in 1923. This is evidently the largest representative of the genus, whose individual stem may grow to a diameter of 7 1/4in. It usually grows as a solitary plant, but very old clustering specimens are also found in the wild. There are up to 14 low, flat ribs (usually 9-12), and the skin is yellowish gray-green. The author of the description stated that the plants bloom with a crimson flower, but it is now known that *L. fricii* also blooms in the wild with a white or pinkish or light mauve flower.
In the wild, this species occurs in a relatively small area around the small town of Viesca in the Mexican state of Coahuila, where it grows on the nearby mountains, often in cracks in the rocks. It has become widespread among cactus growers, but other cacti have constantly been in circulation under the name *L. fricii*. It is true here, too, that the source of the plant material you want to include in your collection is very important. In terms of cultivation, it is one of the more demanding cacti – a very well-drained soil mix with good drying properties is very important, and it should be watered only when completely dry.

Lophophora fricii

Lophophora williamsii ▣ ○

FLATTENED-GLOBOSE

The above-ground part of the plant is flat or flattened-globose, reaching a diameter of roughly 4in. It gradually merges underground into a robust beet-like root. 5–10 ribs usually form on the plant; the downy areoles have no spines growing from them.

Lophophora williamsii

Only the very small seedlings have thin spines about 1/16in long, which soon drop off, and stop growing altogether in older plants. The flowers grow from the depressed center of the plant covered in thick down, and are whitish pink in color.
The indigenous people in Mexico know this cactus as "peyote" or "peyotl," and, especially in the past, it served as an aid to meditation, ceremonies, and communication with the souls of ancestors. This hallucinogenic species is surrounded by a great variety of myths and superstitions, as has been discovered from the surviving evidence and travelers' experiences. Collection and use of this cactus is now prohibited, and cultivated plants have nothing like the effects of the wild plant. This cactus grows over a wide area from Texas and New Mexico in the USA, through the Mexican states of Coahuila, Chihuahua, Nuevo León, San Luis Potosí, and Zacatecas, as far as Durango. It is found in flatlands and also in rocky areas, where it grows mainly in the shade of scrub vegetation.
The genus *Lophophora* is so attractive to cactus growers that there are collections devoted exclusively to it, where no other plant has a place in the collector's greenhouse. Cultivation is not difficult, provided a little care is taken with the soft stem and the thick, taproot in the soil mix.

Lophophora williamsii var. *koehresii* ▣ ○

FLATTENED-GLOBOSE

The green part of the stem grows to a diameter of about 1 1/2in and a height of 3/4–1 1/4in. The underground section which is not green may be up to 4in long and gradually merges into a beet-like root. The varietas has a matt gray-green epidermis and is entirely spineless, but has striking flowers which may be up to 1 5/8in across.
This varietas inhabits a relatively small area near the town of Las Tablas in San Luis Potosí, Mexico, where it grows on the flat beds of lagoons. Cultivation is the same as for the type spe-

Lophophora williamsii var. *koehresii*

Machaerocereus eruca

cies, but it is important to maintain a non-hybrid line in the collection.

Machaerocereus eruca ■ ○

TRAILING

An extremely interesting cactus with a trailing type of stem, which local people nickname "creeping devil." Individual stems may grow to a length of 10 ft, constantly putting out roots but dying away at the base after a while. The prominent spines are grayish, and the dagger-like central spine may reach 2 3/4in long. This is an endemic species of the Mexican peninsula Baja California, where it grows on sandy and poor soils over a very limited area on the west coast. A year or two ago it was an unattainable rarity. In terms of propagation, there are the options of vegetative reproduction (offsets, cuttings), germinate well, even when they have been kept for many years. Relatively warm temperatures are needed over winter, with no prolonged drops below 54 °F.

Machaerocereus gummosus ■ ○

COLUMNAR

The prolifically branching stem forms a dense shrub, up to 6 1/2ft tall. Individual shoots are 1 1/2–2 3/4in in diameter and usually about 3ft long. On the older parts, the dark green skin becomes corky. The spines are short; the longest central spines reach 2in long. Its splendid flowers grow about 6in long and 3in wide. The fruit is a favorite food for the local people, who call it "pitahaya agria."
This species grows all over Mexican Baja California from north to south. In Some places, it forms very dense outcrops, in association with a variety of succulent vegetation. However, it is not usual to find this species in greenhouses due to its demands for space. Growing from seed or from rooted offsets is not difficult. Relatively warm wintering is important.

Machaerocereus gummosus

Mammillaria albilanata

Mammillaria albilanata ▣ ○

COLUMNAR

The stem of this *Mammillaria* grows in a globose shape initially, and later becomes slightly columnar, and also forms offsets in old age. The small mammillae have a large number of short radial spines, and on some plants there are 2, or at the most, 4 central spines, but these are unremarkable in terms of length and color. The crimson flowers are about 1/2in across and grow in a garland around the crown. Later they develop into red, club-shaped fruit.
The most precise information about the occurrence of this species is as follows: 134 miles along the Oaxaca-Mexico D. F. highway, but it also grows around the town of Tlatizapán in the Mexican state of Morelos. Cactus specialists often grow this species under a different name, and sometimes confuse it with the similar *M. supertexta*. Its cultivation requirements are a sunny position, well-drained soil mix, and wintering at temperatures around 50 °F.

Mammillaria baumii

CLUSTERING

A quick-growing species which begins to form offsets when mature. Individual stems may be about 2in in diameter, and the clusters they form may be up to 8in in diameter. The light green stem is often concealed by dense white spines. The radial and central spines are the same color and almost the same length (1/2–3/4in). The lemon yellow, relatively large flowers are a splendid sight; they appear in early summer and open in the daytime.
The species originates in the Mexican state of Tamaulipas, where it grows at altitudes between 2,300 and 5,000ft. It often grows in the shade of associated vegetation, and observers who found it near San Vincente say it is often completely shaded by dense bushes. So, in cultivation, it needs at least partial shade on the hottest summer days, although, in a well-ventilated greenhouse, the plants can be in full sun throughout the growing season. It can be propagated either from offsets or from seed. Wintering: cold and, as far as possible, in full light.

Mammillaria bocasana ▣ ○

GLOBOSE

One of the commonest species for starting a collection. It is extremely elegant and also undemanding. It is admired for its globose stem, which is up to 2in in diameter and clothed in fine hairy spines. These grow as radial spines from the areole, and there are also 1 or 2 central spines growing from each areole, which are reddish brown, and hooked at the tip. The flowers are light yellow with a central red streak, and they appear regularly every summer. When mature, the plant forms clumps, which are really very impressive.
Paradoxically, it is not an abundant species in the wild, and its habitats are confined to a few localities in the Mexican state of San Luis Potosí, where it grows on gentle limestone hills. As indicated above, this species is grown even by complete non-specialists who have only limited interest in cacti. Cultivation and propagation are easy, but relatively cold wintering is needed. It can be propagated from offsets; allow cut surfaces to dry out before potting up.

Mammillaria baumii

Mammillaria bocasana

Mammillaria candida

Mammillaria bombycina 

CLUSTERING

This is classed with the "hooked" *Mammillaria*, and the name *bombyca* (silky, shiny) was not chosen at random – the radial spines are indeed very fine and shiny. When mature, it forms clustering stems, and individual plants may be almost 8in tall and roughly 3in in diameter. Growing from each areole, there are up to 40 silvery, shiny radial spines, which usually grow to 1/4–1/2in. There are up to 4 central spines, but 1 of them, facing away from the stem, is reddish brown and up to 1in long, with a hooked tip. Pink flowers, about 5/8in across, appear on older plants; this species does not bloom very readily.

For a long time its habitat was unknown, and many thought it had become extinct in the wild before it was rediscovered in the 1990s. Its habitat is in the state of Aguascalientes in central Mexico, and extends to the border with the state of Jalisco, into the Sierra de Laurel range. It is a very great favorite among growers, because of its elegant appearance. It is usually grown on its own roots in collections, although it is quite sensitive to prolonged damp, especially during colder weather in early spring or in the fall. It is wintered in the light, at temperatures around 54 °F.

Mammillaria bombycina

Mammillaria candida 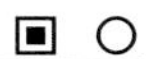

GLOBOSE

An extremely elegant and popular *Mammillaria*, with a history dating from 1838, when it was validly described. The globose stem usually grows to a diameter of 4in, but in the wild there are colonies with larger individuals. The length, number, and color of the spines are extremely varied. Colonies are found with short spines, long spines, and white or almost brown spines. The flowers are relatively uniform, whitish pink in color, with a darker streak in the middle of the petal. Plants with ripe fruit are very decorative. The club-shaped, bright red berries, up to 3/4in long, appear in a garland near the middle, in spring of the following year.

In the wild, this *Mammillaria* is found in many states of central and northern Mexico, in a slightly different form in each place where it grows. Extremely interesting plants with brown spines can be found in Noria de las Flores, and there are dwarf, clustering forms around the town of Guadalcazar (San Luis Potosí). It can perhaps be found in every collection, because it is a "traditional" species. But it is necessary to know the origin of cultivated plants for the collection to be of genuine botanical value. Cultivation is the same as for the usual Mexican species.

Mammillaria capensis

Mammillaria capensis ▣ ○

CLUSTERING

One of the *Mammillaria* that produces columnar clusters. Initially it grows in solitary form, but when mature it begins to form offsets from the base. It grows to a height of about 10in, with a stem diameter of 1 1/2–2in. There are usually 13–16 radial spines and, as a rule, a single central spine with a reddish brown point, which in some cases is bent into a hook. The elegant, whitish pink flowers are relatively large, about 3/4in across, and some of the petals have a pink or greenish pink central streak. The fruit is a club-shaped, orange or red berry.

This species, originating on the Baja California peninsula, has been collected many times, but its variability and transitional forms mean that it is still a rather mysterious cactus. The town of Puerto de Bahia de los Muertos is regarded as the type locality, but we have not found any plants of this kind there. In collections, special care must be taken not to overwater the soil mix, especially on colder days. A position in full sun, and wintering in the light at about 50 °F, are necessary conditions for flowering the next year.

Mammillaria carmenae

Mammillaria carmenae 

GLOBOSE

Until recently, this *Mammillaria* was the dream of every cactus grower, and an unattainable rarity. The plants form small clumps, in which each stem measures about 1 1/2in in diameter and twice as much in height. Growing from the areoles, there are 120–180 fine, soft spines, yellow in color, completely covering the stem. The flowers appear near the center, usually individually, but sometimes in a garland; they are most often white (less frequently yellowish or pinkish), and about 5/8in across.

The species was first described in 1953, but until 1977 hardly anyone had any idea where this cactus actually grew. Its locality was not re-established until A. B. Lau and W. Repehagen wrote their report. The location is in the Sierra Madre Oriental in the state of Tamaulipas, where this species colonizes inaccessible precipices. Its exceptional appearance gave rise to a real mania among cactus enthusiasts, prompting a feverish search for this rare beauty. Anyone who found it would graft it, for fear of losing it, and as a result, many of the older specimens seen in collections are grafts. Now that there is enough plant material available, and *M. carmenae* is one of the commonly available species, it is not necessary to resort to grafting. Plants on their own roots have a much more natural appearance and flower more readily. With seed propagation, the most difficult period is the first six months of the seedlings' life. Propagation from offsets is also possible. The plant tolerates very cold wintering with temperatures falling to 32 °F.

Mammillaria coahuilensis ssp. *albiarmata* 

GLOBOSE

Some cactus growers may know it by the older name of *M. albiarmata*, *M. coahuilensis* var. *albiflora*, or *Porfiria schwarzii* var. *albiflora*. It grows in solitary form, and its globose stem is about 2in in diameter. At the tips of the mammillae, there are large, sparsely woolly areoles, from which grow 20–25 white or pinkish radial spines. The flowers grow near the top of the plant and are creamy white in color, and the outer petals have a greenish brown or greenish red streak in the middle. The width of the flowers when fully open is about 3/4in. The fruit is a long, narrow, red berry, containing small dark brown or black seeds. The plant originates from the Mexican state of

Mammillaria coahuilensis ssp. *albiarmata*

Coahuila, where it grows near the capital city, Saltillo. This subspecies represents the easternmost distribution of plants in the *M. coahuilensis* range. Because the plant produces thick, fleshy roots, it must be watered very carefully. Once again, the principle applies: it is better to give a little water three times, than a lot once. This principle must be followed particularly during summer when growth slows down. Use a slightly alkaline, very well-drained soil mix, and overwinter in cool conditions, preferably in full light.

Mammillaria compressa 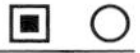

CLUSTERING

A typical representative of the "green" *Mammillaria*, whose stem, when mature, produces many offsets and creates dense, compressed clusters (hence the name *compressa*, meaning compressed), up to 3ft across. The spines of this species are extremely variable; usually, 2–6 white radial spines, 3/4–2 3/4in long. Grow from areole. The flowers grow in a garland around the middle; they are pink, with a lighter edge to the petals.
In the wild it can be found on limestone hills among stones in the central states of San Luis Potosí, Hidalgo, and Querétaro. Cultivated plants are crossed with related taxa; only in recent years have plants of a precise origin appeared in collections. In terms of cultivation, it can be recommended to every beginner.

Mammillaria crucigera 

COLUMNAR

The plant produces solitary stems initially, but these soon begin to divide forming several tips (dichotomous division). The stem is columnar, up to 2 3/4in high and 2in in diameter, slightly depressed at the crown. Short, thick down forms in the axils; growing from the areoles, there are roughly 25 radial spines, only 1/16–1/8in long, and 4 central spines arranged in a cross, of a maximum 3/16in long. The flower is red or reddish purple and about 1/2in long. The species is rare, but it is known to occur on the border of the state of Puebla and Oaxaca, where it grows on limestone subsoil. It is an undemanding species to grow, requiring full sun, a well-drained, mineral-rich substrate, and wintering at about 54 °F.

Mammillaria compresa

Mammillaria crucigera

Mammillaria deherdtiana

Mammillaria deherdtiana 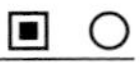

GLOBOSE

Another hit in its time, classed with the "large-flowered" *Mammillaria*. In maturity, these globose plants form offsets, with individual stems reaching a diameter of about 2 1/4in. The conical mammillae, about 1/2in long, have an areole at the tip, from which grow about 30 glassy white radial spines. Central spines are either missing, or may be present in quite a large quantity (up to 8), which is a clear sign of the high degree of variability in the spines of this taxon. Every cactus grower has been enticed by the magnificent flowers, and the desire to have this plant in one's collection was so great that people spent quite large sums of money on it 30 years ago. The flowers appear in early summer. They are up to 2 3/4in long and 2in across, light crimson in color, with long whitish filaments and deep yellow anthers, making a splendid contrast with the color of the flower.

The habitat of this *Mammillaria* was kept secret for a long time, and was even deliberately mis-reported by some experts. In the end it came to light that it colonizes the soft limestone north of the town of Mitla in the Mexican state of Oaxaca. Older plants in collections are usually grafts, but now growers are trying to cultivate this species on its own roots. The soil mix may be slightly acid. It is important that wintering should be at relatively warm temperatures between 54 and 60 °F. Propagation by seed is one way of obtaining a large number of plants, but the seeds are relatively poor germinaters.

Mammillaria deherdtiana var. *dodsonii*, wild

Mammillaria deherdtiana var. *dodsonii* 

GLOBOSE

This variety is distinguished from the type species mainly by its spination, which is rather "wilder," with a larger number of longer central spines, and a smaller number of coarser radial spines. Certain

Mammillaria deherdtiana var. *dodsonii*, cultivated

Mammillaria densispina

differences can also be seen in the seeds, and another interesting feature is the prominent white style.
The habitat is relatively isolated, and lies to the north of the town of Oaxaca in the Mexican state of the same name. The plants colonize pockets in rocks with a limestone substrate, roughly 9,000ft above sea level. In cultivation, this varietas is quite sensitive. It should preferably be watered only sparingly, but often. It needs full sun when in active growth, and when dormant temperatures should not drop too low, or for too long below 50 °F.

Mammillaria densispina □ ○

GLOBOSE

The stem is divided into bare and tipped conical mammillae with an areole. From this grow the radial and central spines, which are roughly of the same length (1/2–3/4in) and color, and which completely cover the stem. In summer, broadly funnel-shaped flowers appear near the crown.
This plant is found on rocky outcrops of limestone hills in the states of San Luis Potosí, Querétaro, and Zacatecas. It is seen mainly in specialists' collections, but is not particularly difficult to grow. It needs adequate light, water preferably given often in small amounts, and wintering in the light at temperatures of 41–50 °F.

Mammillaria dixanthocentron ▣ ○

COLUMNAR

It is easy to see why the authors of the description chose the apt species epithet *dixanthocentron*, which means "with two yellow central spines." Plants in the wild are less columnar; in collections, they form distinctive club-shaped columns up to 1ft tall. In the axils and on the areoles, a fine, dense down forms. The radial spines, of which there are usually 20, grow from the areole in a uniform circular arrangement. There are 2 yellow central spines (in exceptional case, up to 5). The flower is scarlet and about 5/8in across. Another appealing feature is the cylindrical striking red fruit, 5/8in long. There are also colonies in the wild with red central spines. These plants have also been designated *M. dixanthocentron* var. *rubrispina*, but this classification is rather superfluous, due to the many mixed yellow-spined and red-spined populations found growing in association.
This *Mammillaria* grows in Tomelin Cañon in the state of Oaxaca, in foothills at altitudes of about 2,000ft. This is not a particularly sensitive species. It should be allowed to dry out between watering, and relatively warm wintering is also important; the temperature should not drop for long below 50 °F.

Mammillaria dixanthocentron

Mammillaria duwei

Mammillaria duwei ▣ ○

GLOBOSE

This is one of the Mexican miniatures, because its globose stem is on average no more than 2in tall. Growing from each areole, there are about 35 fine, downy radial spines, and usually 2 central spines about 1/4in long, often with a hooked tip. The flower is approximately 5/8in across and whitish yellow in color, and the red, club-shaped fruit are also an impressive sight.
A distinctive feature of the northeast part of the town of San Luis de la Paz (Guanajuato) is the occurrence of many species of cactus, including this *Mammillaria*. It grows at an altitude of roughly 3,000ft above sea level, where it colonizes limestone rocks, on which it forms clumps. Its cultivation is complicated by the beet-like roots, which rot quite easily, especially if overwatered. However, it can be recommended to beginners who are able to devote adequate care to the plants. The flowers appear either in fall or in early spring. Growing from seed is not difficult, and the plants bloom in the second year.

Mammillaria elongata

Mammillaria elongata 

CLUSTERING

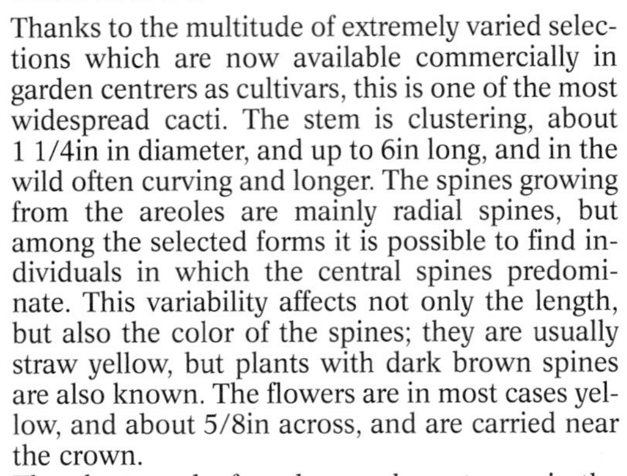

Thanks to the multitude of extremely varied selections which are now available commercially in garden centrers as cultivars, this is one of the most widespread cacti. The stem is clustering, about 1 1/4in in diameter, and up to 6in long, and in the wild often curving and longer. The spines growing from the areoles are mainly radial spines, but among the selected forms it is possible to find individuals in which the central spines predominate. This variability affects not only the length, but also the color of the spines; they are usually straw yellow, but plants with dark brown spines are also known. The flowers are in most cases yellow, and about 5/8in across, and are carried near the crown.
The plant can be found on rocky outcrops in the Mexican state of Hidalgo, where it often forms a dense, pendulous curtain. Thanks to commercial nurseries, and its undemanding nature, it is a permanent part of growers' collections, and also adorns the windows of non-specialists. Perhaps the only important thing to remember is that it needs rather cold wintering to ensure flowering next year.

Mammillaria elongata var. *echinaria* 

CLUSTERING

This cactus resembles the type species, but its stem is much more luxuriantly spiny. The central spines are especially prominent. However, the validity of this varietas is now in doubt, and some authorities consider it to be simply an extreme form of the basic species.

Mammillaria fittkaui 

CLUSTERING

This was first described quite recently, in 1971, by the American cactus specialists Glass and Foster. The plant forms quite large clusters, but individual stems are no more than 4in high and 2in in diameter. The stem has no down at all, and the white areoles bear radial and central spines. There are usually 7–10 radial spines, and in most cases 4 central spines, 1 of which has a hooked end. The light pink flowers appear near the top, and the plant produces a great abundance of them, and is also capable of flowering all summer.
This *Mammillaria* is found in Jalisco, a state which is generally less interesting for cacti, and this is possibly why it remained unknown to botanists for so long. It is not difficult to grow, and

Mammillaria elongata var. *echinaria*

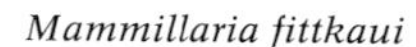

Mammillaria fittkaui

novice cactus growers master its cultivation without difficulty. It is important to give the plant enough light, but beware of bright spring sunshine, which can scorch it badly. It is propagated by seed, but to a lesser extent, offsets can also be used for propagation; these often take root even on the parent plant.

Mammillaria formosa

GLOBOSE

The stem extends slightly into a column in old age, bears short, pyramid-shaped, very densely clustered mammillae. Short down forms in the axils, and growing from the areoles there are small radial and short central thorns, which completely cover the plant. Pink flowers with darker central streak petals, about 5/8in across, appear in summer.
In the wild, it stretches extensively across the gently hilly Mexican terrain from San Luis Potosí to Nuevo León. The American cactus specialist Charles Glass even reported a habitat of this *Mammillaria* in the state of Zacatecas on open terrain, on the flatter peaks or on foothills. It is a great ornament to any collection with its fine, elegant spination. It tolerates full sun, cold wintering, and, during summer, quite generous watering. The seedlings grow without problems in a slightly alkaline soil mix with a sufficiently high mineral content (antuka, slate, etc.).

Mammillaria formosa

Mammillaria geminispina

Mammillaria geminispina 

CLUSTERING

A very elegant species both in the wild and in collections. The stem grows to a maximum of 8in tall and is usually about 3in in diameter, and it forms mounds. The white, downy axils and areoles, together with the white spines, all combine to make a beautiful plant, and as the species epithet indicates, it has two central spines (*geminispinus* = with twin spines). The flowers grow in a garland around the crown, and they are purplish red, while the inner petals have a lighter edge. The ripe fruit, which thrust out from the axils of the mammillae when the plant is mature, are red, and make a splendid contrast with the white color of the stem.

Mamillaria glassii var. *ascensionis*

In the Metztitlan valley (Hidalgo, Mexico), where it grows on limestone rocks in a community with many other cacti, it forms large clustering mounds But it occurs over a much wider area, and is to be found in other valleys, e.g. in Barranca de Venados, or on hillsides along the Rio Amajaque. To ensure that this cactus produces beautiful spines, it must be placed in the lightest part of the greenhouse. Because of the great variability in the length and density of the spines, selected long-spined clones are often grown in collections. When this cactus is propagated by seed, a wide range of seedlings is produced, from which the most beautiful individuals must be selected.

Mammillaria glassii var. *ascensionis* 

GLOBOSE

This varietas only produces miniature, clustering stems, hardly more than 3/4in high; it is remarkable for its white, delicate spination. The flower is pink, and quite large, up to 5/8in across when fully open. The fruit is decorative too; it is quite large, about 5/8in long, and its color ranges from greenish to greenish red.

It is found both in the southeastern regions of Nuevo León, and in the state of Tamaulipas, around the town of Jaumave. It was formerly very rare, and its discoverers even described it as a separate species. It has now spread to collections to such an extent that can easily be obtained from any supplier of quality plants or seeds. It can be increased easily, either by seed or offsets. During cultivation, beware of scorch caused by early spring sunshine.

Mammillaria grusonii ■ ○

GLOBOSE

This is one of the larger species of *Mammillaria*, because its globose or slightly columnar stem can grow as tall as 10in. The spines are first pinkish brown, and later gray. In summer it blooms with quite large flowers about 1 1/4in across, which have a pale pink color; in some ecotypes, there is a dark central streak on the inner petals.
The habitat of this species is in the Mexican state of Coahuila, where it favors slightly undulating or level terrain. Usually it grows under the cover of a herb or woody plant. In collections, however, it needs full sun, a slightly alkaline soil mix, and general routine care.

Mammillaria guelzowiana ■ ○

GLOBOSE

In collections, the stem is usually solitary, and in exceptional cases clustering, and is as wide as it is tall, approximately 2 3/4–3 1/2in. The cylindrical mammillae are bare, as is the axil, and growing from each areole, there are about 70 very delicate, hairy radial spines, white in color. The central spines are reddish brown or yellow, and end in a hook. The splendid funnel-shaped flowers have a distinctive reddish purple color, and their size also attracts attention, because they may be up to 2 1/4in across when fully open.
The habitat of this *Mammillaria*, which many cactus specialists still know under the former genus name of *Krainzia*, is in the Mexican state of Durango, in the locality of Puente Rio Nazas. It grows on rocky outcrops of limestone hills, usually in cracks between stones. This is a short-lived plant, which should be replaced with new seed-

Mammillaria grusonii

Mammillaria guelzowiana

lings in the course of 10 years in a collection. Seedlings grow without serious problems, but older plants are quite sensitive to overwatering. The flowers appear at the end of May, and are among the highlights of any collection.

Mammillaria haageana ssp. *conspicua* 

GLOBOSE–COLUMNAR

Classed as a subspecies of *M. haageana*. It is distinguished from the subspecies below primarily due to its rougher spination, the presence of several brown central spines, and also its bulkier stem is generally 6in high and about 4 1/4in in diameter.
It is found in the central states of Puebla, Oaxaca, and Morelos, where it grows on a limestone substrate at various altitudes from 2,000 to 8,500 above sea level. Cultivation is the same as for the subspecies below. The slower growth rate of the seedlings should be taken into account; it is advisable to plant the seeds in early spring or at the end of winter, using a propagator, so that the plants are as large as possible when the time comes for wintering.

Mammillaria haageana ssp. *conspicua*

Mammillaria haageana ssp. elegans

Mammillaria haageana ssp. *elegans* ▣ ○

GLOBOSE-COLUMNAR

In the past, this cactus was also distributed under the invalid name *M. collina*. A very elegant subspecies, which does not grow to large dimensions. Its stem is usually 2 1/4–2 3/4in in diameter, and its height is only slightly less than this. It only rarely forms offshoots, and its beauty lies mainly in its fine, elegant spination. The 16–18 radial spines are white, varying in length between 1/16 and 5/16in. There are, at the most, two central thorns, and they may be missing altogether. The dark red flowers grow in a garland near the top of the plant. The fruit is a small red berry with brown seeds.
The distribution of this subspecies is rather limited, and reliable reports of its occurrence in the wild come from collectors who found this cactus between the town of Tehuacan and Los Combres in the Mexican state of Puebla. It grows at altitudes of about 7,500ft, where it colonizes rocky terrain with a limestone substrate.

Mammillaria hahniana

Mammillaria hahniana 

GLOBOSE

The globose stem, up to 4in in diameter, is divided into small mammillae, about 5/16in long, at the ends of which there are areoles producing hairy spines about 1 1/2in long. In their old age, many plants are completely enveloped in these spines. In some, there is also a short central spine. *M. hahniana* blooms near the top, with a garland of purplish red flowers which are full of yellow anthers. If the cactus is injured, white latex flows from the wound.
Finding this *Mammillaria* in the wild is not difficult, because its habitats are found in many places in Sierra de Jalpan (Guanajuato, Querétaro), where it grows on rocky slopes and in precipices. In the 1920s and 1930s, it was perhaps the most collected cactus in the whole of Mexico. Cactus enthusiasts now grow it successfully from seed, and provided the usual principles are observed, no problems arise in cultivation.

Mammillaria hernandezii ▣ ○

GLOBOSE

A beautiful representative of the genus, this is one of the large-flowered miniatures. The stem does not usually grow more than 1 3/4in in diameter. Very short down forms in the axils, in the flowering zone only. There are 7–25 radial spines; these are a fraction of an inch long, and are arranged in a spidery pattern on the oval areoles. The splendid purple-violet flower measures about 3/4in in length and the same across. The stamens, and the style with the stigma, are yellow. The fruit contains only a few black seeds.
Only a couple of cactus expeditions so far have been lucky enough to find the species in the wild, because the locality is quite a closely guarded secret. It occurs in the Mexican state of Oaxaca at heights of 7,500ft above sea level. It grows on limestone hills in Sierra Mixteca, near San Miguel

Mammillaria hernandezii

Astatla and San Antonio Abad. During drought, it is very well camouflaged, and most of the stem is retracted below ground during such periods. The great majority of cultivated plants are kept as grafts in collections, but some skilled growers are able to grow hundreds of them on their own roots. However, growing such plants calls for considerable experience. It is important to give due attention to the thick, fleshy roots and the fact that the plants often flower even in late summer. If pollination and fertilization have taken place, transfer the plant, before wintering, to a warmer place where the flower will be able to dry out without beginning to rot, which usually has harmful effects on the whole plant.

Mammillaria herrerae ▣ ○

GLOBOSE

When plants of this species first appeared in commerce, they caused quite a sensation among cactus enthusiasts. The small stems, only about 1 1/2in wide, are initially globose, and later grow into a slight column, but they have very prominent spination, made up of numerous fine, white, non-prickly spines. About a hundred of them grow from a single areole. The reddish purple flowers are beautiful, too; they are up to 1 in wide, with a large number of yellow anthers and a greenish stigma.

Well camouflaged in the wild, since it grows on limestone hillsides where there are many white stones, becoming completely invisible. The habitat is near the town of Cadereyta in the state of Querétaro. Due to its sensitivity, it is very rarely seen a large number of specimens on their own roots in a collection. It is usually grafted onto a slow-growing rootstock, and because cultivation of seedlings also presents problems, it is propagated from offsets from a stock plant that is specially grown for this purpose. But take care! – Constant vegetative propagation significantly reduces the genetic variation, and this may in turn lead to degeneration of the clone.

Mammillaria herrerae

Mammillaria herrerae var. albiflora

Mammillaria herrerae var. *albiflora* ▣ ○

GLOBOSE

This varietas is very similar to the species, but is distinguished by its white flowers, and also by its habitat, which is hundreds of miles from the habitat of the type.
This variant was rediscovered in the wild by the Austrian cactus expert W. Reppenhagen, a specialist on the genus *Mammillaria*. The cultivation requirements are identical with those of the basic species.

Mammillaria huitzilopochtli ▣ ○

GLOBOSE-COLUMNAR

This is quite a distinctive, unmistakable species, both in habit, and in the position of its flowers. The stem is up to 6in tall, and its diameter is usually no more than 3in. It usually grows solitarily, and may divide in old age. The numerous radial spines (15–30) are glassy white, regularly distributed around the areole, and 1/8–3/16in long. The central spine may be absent, or may be very long; its color also varies, between brown and pitch black. The flowers grow on the side of the plant, and this, too, makes it a very distinctive, striking species. The crimson flowers are only about 5/8in across. The club-shaped red fruits contain very small brown seeds.
This *Mammillaria* has its habitat in the border regions of the Mexican states of Puebla and Oaxaca, on the hills of the Tomelin valley. However, there is a great difference in altitude between the two, i.e. 1,500ft and 7,500ft respectively. Cultivation is not demanding, and this species is easy to grow. It prefers full sun to shade, and tolerates high summer temperatures very well. But care must be taken to avoid too steamy an atmosphere around the plants due to inappropriate watering during the summer dormant period, when most cacti stop growing.

Mammillaria laui f. *subducta* ▣ ○

GLOBOSE

Named after A. B. Lau, expert on cactus flora; the forma *subducta* was then distinguished on the basis of its more elongated stem. This is usually about 2in in diameter, and in old age slightly co-

Mammillaria huitzilopochtli

lumnar. Growing from each areole, there are about 30 spines, hardly distinguishable into radial and central. They are all straw yellow and about1/2in long. The scarlet flowers, about 1/2in wide, grow near the crown.
The Minas de Asbestos region (Tamaulipas, Mexico) is regarded as the type locality. It can most often be found on rocky outcrops or in cracks between stones. The cultivation requirements are the same as those of the commonly grown *Mammillaria*. They must be placed in a well-lit position and generously watered in summer. The species flowers in late summer or early spring.

Mammillaria laui f. *subducta*

Mammillaria longiflora

GLOBOSE

Kept for some collectors under the former name *Krainzia*, but it is now classed within *Mammillaria*. It is distinguished, as the species epithet *longi-flora* indicates, by its long flower. Growing about 2 3/4in in diameter, the stem rarely produces offsets. Adorned with their 20–30 radial spines and about 3 central ones, usually 1 of these pointing toward the base of the plant and a hooked tip, the *Mammillaria* are about 1/2in long, without any down in their axils. The splendid, light mauve flowers with a darker central streak grow near the top of the plant, and usually open in succession.
Clearings and glades in oak and pine woods are the natural habitat of this species. It occupies a relatively small area in the Mexican state of Durango, and the most precise information refers to the area around the small town of Santiago de Papasquiaro. Because this is a mountain species, most greenhouses are too hot for it in summer. It needs a sunny location with good air circulation, but should not be exposed to a constant draught. The plants reach flowering potential in the third year after germinating, and their flowers are a highlight of any collection.

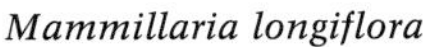

Mammillaria longiflora

Mammillaria longimamma

Mammillaria longimamma ▣ ○ ⊙

CLUSTERING

Formerly classed within the genus *Dolichothele* because of its flowers and distinctively shaped stem. The flat stem grows to a width of 2–4in and produces an abundance of offsets, which spread to form low, cushion-like clusters, up to1ft wide. Each of the long, conical mammillae is tipped with a small areole, from which grow the rather soft, yellow spines. Here are usually 8–10 radial spines, and 1 central spine, up to 1 1/4 in long. The elongated yellow flowers are 1 1/2–2 1/4in across when open, and after being pollinated and fertilized, they turn into a yellowish fruit with brown seeds.

This species originates in the states of Hidalgo and Querétero, where it grows at altitudes of 3,000–7,000ft. It colonizes rocky valleys and gullies, but also grown on flatter terrain. It is definitely a cactus deserving greater attention from growers, because of its interesting habit and beautiful yellow flowers. The growing technique is very simple. Offsets can be used for propagation, but it is also possible to plant seeds, which germinate freely when fresh.

Mammillaria marksiana

Mammillaria marksiana

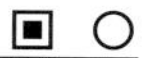

GLOBOSE

In terms of habit, this is a rather unique *Mammillaria*, due to its prominent yellow spines and slightly concave crown full of whitish yellow down. It usually grows in globose form, but in maturity extends slightly into a column, and begins to form offsets. The species has interesting, broadly funnel-shaped flowers of a lemon yellow color, about 5/8in across.

The habitat of this species lies in the hills of the mountain massif of Sierra Madre Occidental, extending in a north-south direction in the west of Mexico in the states of Sinaloa and Durango. In collections, it is one of the problem-free members of the genus, and it does not need to be placed in the best-lit part of the greenhouse. It is propagated from seed, and takes 5–6 years to mature.

Mammillaria melanocentra

GLOBOSE

A *Mammillaria* of globose habit, popular among growers due to its distinctive, eye-catching flowers. The stem grows to a height and diameter of approximately 8in, but may be larger in the wild. The radial spines are about 1/4in long, apart from the lower radial spines, which are up to 3/4in long. The single central spine is slender and tapering, dark-colored, and roughly 2–2 1/4in long. The flowers grow in a garland near the top of the plant, and are pink-colored with a darker or lighter tinge. When fully open they are up to 1in across.

The habitat of this *Mammillaria* is in several states (Coahuila, Nuevo León, and Durango). It grows most readily in cracks in rocks, and on stony outcrops on flatter terrain. In cultivation, it does not need the best-lit position in the greenhouse, and does not mind light shade. It is advisable to use a pan for growing, so that the plant can extend its shallow root system, and the soil mix can dry out as quickly as possible. Cold wintering can be in shade. Propagation is by seed.

Mammillaria melanocentra ssp. *rubrograndis* ▣ ○

GLOBOSE

This subspecies is distinguished from the type species mainly by its denser but finer radial spines, flatter stem, and the somewhat different shape of its buds. It occurs in many localities in the states of Nuevo León and Tamaulipas, where it grows mainly on flatter terrain; the highest localities are at altitudes of up to 8,000ft above sea

Mammillaria melanocentra

level. Cultivation is the same as for the species above.

Mammillaria mercadensis 

GLOBOSE

Not grown to large dimensions, and its diameter and height do not usually exceed 2in. Some plants produce offsets, forming small clusters. Each of the conical mammillae is tipped with a circular areole, from which grow about 30 radial spines and usually 4–7 dark central spines, one of which is longer and has a hooked tip. Light pink flowers are more common on these plants, but plants with almost white flowers are known in cultivation. The appearance of the plant is enhanced by its fresh, cylindrical red fruit, about 3/4in long.

The habitat, Cerro de Mercado, after which the species was named, is situated near the town of Durango in the state of the same name. *M. mercadensis* is an endemic species confined to volcanic soils, and for this reason its occurrence is very restricted. As a cultivated plant, however, it does not require special conditions, although in the wild it is a plant with rather specific needs. Cold wintering, in the light if possible. It needs full sun when in active growth; in the case of plants from locations about 6,500ft above sea level, there must be adequate air circulation to prevent overheating.

Mammillaria melanocentra ssp. *rubrograndis*

Mammillaria mercadensis

Mammillaria microhelia

Mammillaria microhelia ▣ ○

CLUSTERING

A variable taxon, for which, especially in recent times, several clones have been selected; these are, in a way, extreme forms, and cactus growers take pleasure in propagating them. The stem is up to 6in tall and 1 1/2in wide. It forms clusters with several offsets, and it may happen that the original parent plant is completely submerged. The central spine may be entirely absent, or with up to 4 central spines, usually dark, or competely black. Broadly funnel- or bell-shaped flowers, about 5/8in in width and length, grow near the top of the plant. The petals are yellowish green, and inside the flower is full of yellowish white anthers, from which protrudes a yellowish green stigma.

The habitat of this *Mammillaria* lies in the stony slopes of Sierra San Moran in the state of Querétaro, where it grows at an altitude of 5,000–6,500ft. It is often grown in collections, and is popular for its undemanding nature and tolerance of growers' interference. It thrives in a slightly alkaline, mineral-rich soil mix, and older plants benefit from being treated, at least once a season, with a fertilizer containing trace elements.

Mammillaria mystax ▣ ○

GLOBOSE

An extremely variable species, for which in a single locality can be found plants with short or long spines, solitary plants, and that produce offsets. Usually, however, they are solitary, and the largest specimens may reach a diameter of up to 6in. From the axils grow white, non-prickly, very twisted spines, which are more like bristles. The radial spines are short, straight, 1 1/2–3in long, while the longest central thorn may grow to nearly 4in. The plant blooms with a garland of scarlet flowers, which are 3/4in across when fully open.

M. mystax commonly occurs in flatter regions of

Mammillaria mystax

the state of Puebla, where we observed it, for example, not far from the settlement of Zapotitlan de Salinas. However, its area of distribution is wider, and extends along the entire Tehuacan valley, as far as the north of the state of Oaxaca. Growing cultivated plants does not entail any problems; they like a sunny position, and generous watering in summer. Propagation from seed is very easy, and allows the option of choosing the most beautifully spined individuals for the collection.

Mammillaria orcutii ▣ ○

FLATTENED-GLOBOSE

A flat-growing cactus, forming stems about 6in in diameter. The mammillae are conical, and the upward-facing axils are full of short, thick down. Growing from each areole, there are radial spines only 1/8in long, and usually 4 gray-black central spines. The mauve-pink flowers appear in summer near the growing point. The fruits are club-shaped red berries with brown seeds.

This species originates from relatively restricted localities in the state of San Luis Potosí. It occurs mainly in limestone glades among dense shrub vegetation in Valle de los Fantasmas. It grows at altitudes of 4,000–7,000ft. It was introduced into collections in the years before the Second World War, and remains one of the common representatives of the genus. At first glance, its rather robust and imposing appearance catches the attention, and its large flowers are equally impressive. In cultivation, it is one of the species that are easy to grow; apart from cold wintering, it needs an alkaline, well-drained soil mix, and in summer, full sun and occasional applications of fertilizer. It benefits from being planted in quite a large, shallow pan, and it is propagated by seed.

Mammillaria orcutii

Mammillaria pectinifera

Mammillaria pectinifera 

GLOBOSE

The complicated story of the classification of this species begins with its first description, when it was classed in the genus *Pelecyphora* – apparently because of its elongated areoles and comb-like arrangement of spines . Later, the separate genus *Solisia* was proposed, but it has subsequently been classed within *Mammillaria*. It has a solitary stem, only 2in in diameter, divided into mammillae, each tipped with an elongated areole a fraction of an inch long. The radial spines are regularly spaced around the longitudinal axis of the areole and form a dense mass, entirely concealing the epidermis. The flowers appear on the upper third of the stem and range from whitish to light pink in color, and the inner petals always have a darker streak.
The habitats of this superb *Mammillaria* are situated in a relatively small area south of the town of Tehuacan in the Mexican state of Puebla, and isolated localities where it is found extend to the border with the state of Oaxaca. In these places it colonizes low hillocks, or the lower slopes of hills, where there is a limestone substrate. In the wild, it is one of the cacti under serious threat. It is quite difficult to grow on its own roots, so most cactus growers graft it onto a slow-growing rootstock. It is interesting to see that it retains its authentic appearance, and does not form many offsets. If you have made up your mind to grow it as a self-rooted plant, the essential requirements are a slightly alkaline, mineral-high soil mix and a position in full sun. It tolerates cold wintering, but must be wintered in the light, because it flowers in early spring.

Mammillaria perezdelarosae

Mammillaria perezdelarosae 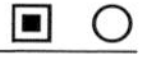

GLOBOSE

This splendid *Mammillaria* was first described quite recently (1985), and owes its rather unusual name to the director of the forestry research institute in the town of Guadalajara (Jalisco), A. Perez de la Rosa. The usually solitary, club-shaped stem grows, in the wild, to a height of about 2 3/4in and a diameter, at the top, of about 1 1/2in. The numerous fine spines, arranged in a circle around the areole, and the dark reddish black central spine, combine to give this cactus its beautiful spination. The whitish yellow to whitish pink flowers appear near the top of the plant, growing from the downy axils in spring. The fruit is light pinkish mauve and about 5/8in long.
Although the type locality is taken to be the area of the Cuarenta pass in the Mexican state of Jalisco, this cactus has also been found near the capital city of the state of the same name, Aguascalientes. Here, it colonizes stony outcrops on the peaks of relatively steep but low rock formations, where it grows in crannies filled with organic and mineral debris. The methods of cultivation are similar to those used for *M. bombycina,* to which it is closely related; it is rather more demanding in terms of wintering in the light, and greater care should be taken with watering, especially on colder days.

Mammillaria pottsii 

COLUMNAR

The narrow cylindrical stem (up to 8in high and roughly 1 1/4in in diameter) produces offsets, both from the base and from higher up the stem. It forms splendid groups of distinctively spined columns, which flower very beautifully. The spination varies considerably; there are up to 7 central spines and no more than 35 radial spines. There is great variation in the color too, from yellow through brown to gray. The flowers appear on the upper parts of the stem; they are bell-shaped, and have a distinctive dark red color, but may be lighter in some cases.
It grows over a huge area, extending from Texas as far as the central Mexican states of Zacatecas and Durango, but can also be found in Nuevo León and Tamaulipas. Usually, however, it favors rocky

terrain, where it often colonizes the most exposed places. A range of different selected clones is grown in collections, but for a certain amount of variation, it is also advisable to propagate it by seed. Extra care should be taken with the seedlings, which often rot after potting on, if the soil mix is overwatered.

Mammillaria rekoi ssp. *leptacantha* ▣ ○

GLOBOSE

Some experts on the genus *Mammillaria* regard it as a separate species, *M. leptacantha*. Individual stems grow to a height of about 4in, and their diameter is slightly less. The axils of the areoles are full of white down, which gradually disappears on the older parts of the plant. The name *leptacantha* indicates that this is a plant with fine spines. There are usually 27–30 white and non-prickly radial spines. The central spines are brown and slightly twisted, and grow to a length of 1–13/4in. The bell-like flowers usually grow in a garland near the crown of the plant, and their color ranges from pink to red.
It grows on the steep rock faces in hollows and crannies in limestone of the Mexican towns of Mitla and Oaxaca. The most precise details of the habitats refer to localities around the villages of El Camaron, Las Animas, and else where. Cultivation is not difficult, the plants flower within quite a short time. They should be watered carefully in summer; in winter, they should be kept in an environment where the temperatures do not drop below 50 °F. Propagation is by seed.

Mammillaria rekoi ssp. *leptacantha*

Mammillaria saboae f. *haudeana*

Mammillaria saboae f. *haudeana* ▣ ○

GLOBOSE

A small *Mammillaria* which usually grows in clusters. In the wild, it grows to a maximum of 1 1/4 in diameter, with the greater part of the stem hidden below ground. The fine white spines are regularly distributed around the areole, and there are usually 15–45 of them. It is rightly assigned to the group of large-flowered *Mammillaria*, because the flowers are long and trumpet-shaped, up to 2in long, and, when fully open, up to 2 1/4in across. They are a lighter or darker shade of pinkish mauve.

Mammillaria schiedeana

The southeastern part of the Mexican state of Sonora, where this species occurs, is situated at an altitude of 5,000ft above sea level, where it snows in winter and even freezes for a few days. The plant favors shallow rock crannies filled with plant debris. This cactus is difficult to grow, mainly because of its sensitive, fleshy roots. During prolonged damp periods, when the weather is cold, the plants very easily fail. Apart from this, grafted plants grow excessively vigorously, forming clumps. Propagation from offsets may, over time, lead to loss of vigor. Seeding is a much more natural method, but more difficult. Watch out for spider mite, which very readily attacks this entire complex of *Mammillaria*.

Mammillaria schiedeana ▣ ○

FLATTENED-GLOBOSE

In the wild, the flattened-globose stem grows to a diameter of about 2 1/4in. In cultivation, it tends to be larger. The long mammillae with bare axils are tipped with an areole from which about 70 fine, short spines grow, usually golden yellow in color. The flowers are creamy white, and about 3/4in across.
In the natural habitat, this species is found on rocky limestone terrain. An extreme habitat is the vertical gypsum rock faces near the small town of Xichú in the Mexican state of Guanajuato. This is certainly not one of the problem-free *Mammillaria*. It needs a very well-drained, slightly alkaline soil mix (with added limestone), full sun, and adequate water – but only when the soil mix has completely dried out. The plant can be propagated by seed or from offsets.

Mammillaria schwarzii 

CLUSTERING

An interesting *Mammillaria* with a cushion-like habit, capable of forming plants up to 8in across, with individual stems not usually exceeding 1 1/4in in diameter and height. The 35 fine white radial spines are often tangled with the central spines, which are only slightly thicker, and often have a reddish tip. The white flower, about 1/2in across, appears near the growing point, and its inner petals usually have a light pink streak.
Until recently there was no confirmation of the habitat which was reported by Fritz Schwarz, the discoverer of this species, who collected the plants in the north of the Mexican state of Guanajuato. This information has now been confirmed, and the plant still grows in the wild. It colonizes rocky outcrops with a fertile organic and mineral substrate, at altitudes of about 3,500ft. Formerly, these plants were generally grafted, but in the present state of knowledge, other methods should not present serious pro-

blems. It is important to water sparingly, but often.

Mammillaria schwarzii

Mammillaria sempervivi ▣ ○

FLATTENED-GLOBOSE

The flattened-globose stem, up to 6in in diameter, is divided into conical mammillae, with a rich growth of white down in their axils. The radial spines are inconspicuous, only a fraction of an inch long, and 3–7 in number. The central spines usually grow in pairs, and are only 1/16in long. The flowers, about 1/2in across, are creamy white, often with a pinkish streak in the middle of each petal. The elongated, club-shaped fruit has a red pericarp containing brown seeds.
This cactus grows in the central Mexican states of Hidalgo, Querétaro, Guanajuato, San Luis Potosí, and Nuevo León, so its area of distribution is quite wide. It is found most of ten in the moderate shade of whippy shrubs. From a number of collections, which are available as seeds from various companies, it is possible to build up a very interesting collection of these elegant *Mammillaria*. Cultivation is not difficult, but care should be taken with the fleshy roots, which easily rot during hot summer weather, or on cold days in fall, when it is damp. Germinating the seed is easy, and the seedlings grow quickly, but the plant does not produce flowers until maturity.

Mammillaria sempervivi

Mammillaria sheldonii

Mammillaria sheldonii ▣ ○

COLUMNAR

The plant in the photograph was originally called *M. alamensis*, but under the present taxonomic definition of the genus, this is a synonym for (*M. sheldonii*). It forms columnar stems, up to 6in high and 1 1/4–2 1/4in in diameter. There are 9–24 radial and 1–4 central spines bent in a hook shape. From the downless axils grow magnificent flowers; these may be entirely light or dark pink, but usually the petals have a dark pink center and almost white edge, which gives the flowers an extremely impressive appearance.
The habitat extends through northwestern Mexico, on the borders of the states of Coahuila and Sonora. This *Mammillaria* has been collected many times, and due to the relatively large area in which it grows, it exists in a variety of different forms, distinguished by their habit and the color of their flowers. Cultivation is not difficult. It is important to put this cactus in a sunny position, but during hot summer weather, its dormancy must be taken into account; at such times, watering should be restricted, so they do not rot.

Mammillaria solisioides ▣ ○

GLOBOSE

On the basis of its size, this cactus is called a Mexican miniature, because the individual stems do not exceed 2 1/4in in diameter. The stem is divided into small mammillae which are conical in cross-section, each of which bears about 25 radial spines pressed against the stem; central spines are entirely absent. The flowers grow from the older axils, and are usually yellowish, less often whitish pink in color.
Formerly, this *Mammillaria* was often confused with the related *M. pectinifera*, from which it is distinguished by several characteristics and also by its habitat. The only known habitat of this species was always reported to be in the vicinity of the town of Petlatzingo in the state of Puebla. The plant in the photograph is not entirely typical in its flower color, but the seeds from which it was grown are from a collection of wild seeds (collected in the 1970s). *M. solisioides* is certainly difficult to grow, and for this reason only rarely appears in collections; fine specimens can only be found among cacti grown by real specialists. It is usually grown as a graft, preferably on slow-growing rootstocks; it seems well-suited to *Myrtillocactus geometrizans*, on which it retains its typical shape and size. It is propagated by seed, but it is possible to graft offsets from plants from which the tip is removed.

Mammillaria sp. ▣ ○

GLOBOSE

An unusual plant, not yet taxonomically assessed, which is a sort of intermediate form between *M. carmenae* and *M. laui*. It has characteristics of both plants, but certainly not a cultivated hybrid. We had an opportunity to examine some interesting colonies of this plant in the state of Tamaulipas, northwest of the town of Ciudad Victoria, where it grows in the Cañon de Novillero, on rocky terraces and outcrops.

Mammillaria solisioides

Mammillaria sp.

Mammillaria sphaerica

Cultivation methods are comparable to those used for *M. carmenae.*

Mammillaria sphaerica ▣ ○

CLUSTERING

Many cactus growers still refer to it by the genus name of *Dolichothele*, but its classification within *Mammillaria* is, in our opinion, correct. In the wild, it grows in clusters, forming low cushion-like mounds up to 20in across. The individual stems are globose, about 2in in diameter, and growing from the circular areoles on the long mammillae are 12–14 radial spines, and usually 1 central spine, about 1/4in long. From the axils of the mammillae grow lemon yellow flowers, up to 2 3/4in across. The fruit is a green berry which later turns pink, containing small black seeds.

The main habitat possibly lies in the regions around Corpus Christi (Cameron County) in the US state of Texas, but also comes from Mexican territory, where this cactus grows around Ciudad Mier and north of Victoria. It certainly deserves to be more widespread in growers' collections than it is now. As a rule it found only in specialist collections, but its easy cultivation and beautiful flowers make it an ideal plant for beginners' collections, too. During the season, it should be given adequate light and ventilation. This plant is prone to spider mite attack.

Mammillaria spinosissima

Mammillaria spinosissima 

COLUMNAR

The stem, initially solitary, and later cluste ring, has a markedly cylindrical shape; the plants, when 1ft tall, have a stem diameter of about 4in. The species epithet means "very spiny," and obviously refers to the rather dense spines, usually yellow which protrude from the stem. The flowers develop near the crown, forming a garland; they are crimson-red, and roughly 5/8in across.

The species is found on rocky outcrops of hills, in cracks between stones, invariably on limestone rock. Its habitat is reported to be in the central Mexican state of Guerrero. It is very undemanding, and nowadays it is also grown in large quantities in commercial nurseries. The plants are quick-growing, elegant in appearance, and relatively tolerant of growers' mistakes. They should, however, be wintered at temperatures around 50 °F; this ensures that flowers will be produced in the next season.

Mammillaria surculosa

Mammillaria surculosa ▣ ○

CLUSTERING

This cactus still tends to be known in collections by its former genus name *Dolichothele*. The individual stems are small, not exceeding 2in in height and 1 1/4in in diameter. This is a distinctive plant because of its hook-tipped central spine, which is usually about 1in long. The lemon yellow flowers are splendid, too; they start to appear while the plant is still young. These flowers are remarkable for their delicate scent, which is especially noticeable in the late afternoon.

The large cushion-like clusters of this *Mammillaria* can be seen in Miquihiuany in the Mexican state of Tamaulipas, which is regarded as the type locality. But it also grows several hundred miles further south, in the state of San Luis Potosí. Although it was formerly one of the most widely grown cacti, today it can hardly be found anywhere in collections. In spite of its "ordinariness," it deserves to be grown more widely. Being easy to grow, it can be recommended to any beginner. But take care to avoid excessive overwatering, which may cause the fleshy roots to rot. Seed propagation is not necessary, because it can easily be propagated by dividing the clusters.

Mammillaria theresae

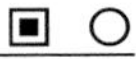

GLOBOSE

Another miniature representative of the genus, with larger flowers in this case. Because of these flowers, its arrival caused a real sensation among cactus growers, and it is still a sought-after rarity. The stem in wild plants is usually solitary, rarely clustering; its maximum height is 1 1/2in, and its diameter 1in. The plant has thick beet-like roots,

Mammillaria theresae

and the above-ground part is divided into 1/4in long cylindrical mammillae. In each areole there are about 25 very fine, feathery radial spines, and central spines are entirely absent. The beautiful, funnel-shaped flowers with their long trumpets grow from the older axils, and are pinkish violet to purple-violet in color.

This is a high-altitude species, which grows at about 8,000ft above sea level. There are very few habitats and localities where it has been possible to confirm its occurrence; knowledge is really very limited. The most specific information refers to the mountains near Coneto Pas in the Mexican state of Durango. The chance finding of this *Mammillaria* in 1966, and its description in an American cactus journal in 1967, aroused enormous interest among enthusiasts. Its unusual appearance and the exceptional beauty of its flowers make it a strong contender as a potential "beauty queen." But it is not easy to grow. On its own roots, its growth is very poor, and most seedlings soon rot. In view of constant failure to grow on enough seeds to allow experimentation, most cactus growers content themselves with grafting. Unfortunately, plants on rootstocks, however slow-growing, lose some of their characteristic shape and size, and tend to offset more freely. A white-flowered form is also in circulation among cactus growers, sometimes known as *M. theresae* f. *albiflora*. However, the establishment of this forma is problematic, because in the wild there are mixed colonies in a single habitat with a huge range of flower color. Nevertheless, this rarity is a sought-after cactus growers' "treat."

Mammillaria theresae f. *albiflora*

Mammillaria vetula ssp. *gracilis* ▣ ○

COLUMNAR

Over time, the low, clustering stems produce luxuriant mats. Individual stems may be over 4in tall and 1/2–1 1/4in in diameter. There are 11–16 white radial spines, which are about 1/4in long. Central spines are either absent, or present in small numbers, each being about 1/2in long. The relatively small flowers, about 1/2in across, are yellow or light pink, and their outer petals often have a darker streak.

In the wild, this cactus occurs in a small area in the Mexican states of Hidalgo and Querétaro, at altitudes of 4,000 to 6,000ft. Specific information about habitats refers to the area around the towns of Ixmiquilpan and Metztitlan, or on the way to the town of Joaquin. This is a cactus that can be seen on any non-specialist's windowsill, because its requirements are really minimal. It grows without difficulty, even in light shade, and is very easy to propagate by removing offsets, which root within a week or two; it is not fussy about the composition of the soil mix, and even tolerates quite clumsy treatment by the grower. In order to flower next season, it needs cold wintering in dry conditions. Growers have even developed a few clones which are quite distinct, but these are not new species, but selected forms.

Mammillaria vetula ssp. *gracilis*

Mammillaria winterae

Mammillaria winterae ▣ ○

GLOBOSE

Quite a variable species, but it always produces a flat or flattened-globose stem. It grows to a diameter of 8–12in, and is divided into flattened conical mammillae, which, in older plants, have axils full of white down. There are usually 4 spines, the longest of which may reach a length of 1 1/4in. The whitish yellow flowers grow in a garland near the growing point, and their outer petals have a darker streak. The fruit is a red, club-shaped berry with brown seeds.
M. winterae grows in the mountains near the town of Monterrey in the state of Nuevo León, and also in the neighboring state of Coahuila. Its localities extend over many tens of miles in an east-west direction between these two states; there is therefore a whole series of field numbers from a great variety of observers. In cultivation, it is one of the less demanding species. It thrives in a shallow bowl that dries out reasonably quickly. The species tolerates full sun, and cold wintering in low light levels. It is recommended to novice cactus growers.

Mammillaria zephyranthoides

Mammillaria zephyranthoides ▣ ○

GLOBOSE

Grown in shapes ranging from rather flat to globose, and the stem is up to 4in in diameter. It is divided into relatively large mammillae, which are 3/4–1in long, cylindrical, with a circular areole at the top. Growing from this, there are 15–20 white radial spines, and usually 1, or at the most 2, reddish brown central spines. The flower has whitish yellow inner petals, and the flower, when fully open, is up to 1 1/2in across. The long red fruit is a beautiful sight, especially in spring, when the plant releases ripe seeds.
This is another mountain cactus, growing in higher locations in some Mexican states, at altitudes of over 6,500ft. It is found, for example, in the states of Querétaro, Hidalgo, Guanajuato, Puebla, and Oaxaca. Because it comes from higher regions a good air circulation position is advisable. It grows well both in full sun and in moderate shade. After wintering, careful coaxing back into growth is needed; it is recommended to give only very small amounts of water initially.

Melocactus dawsonii 

GLOBOSE–COLUMNAR

A beautiful representative of the Mexican *Melocactus*, first described in 1965. Its stem is solitary, initially globose, only becoming slightly columnar when the plant is very old. There are about 14 ribs, which a light green epidermis. There are 9–11 radial rigid and woody spines. There are usually 4 central thick, prickly spines and up to 1 3/4in long. The terminal cephalium is usually 2 3/4in in diameter and 2in high, and consists of whitish gray down and bristle-like spines. From this cephalium grow quite large crimson flowers, up to 1 1/2in across. The club-shaped fruit, up to 1 3/4in long, is red in its upper part, shading to white at the base. It contains brownish black seeds, about 1/8in long.
Unlike the species below, which grows on the east coast of Mexico, *M. dawsonii* lives on the west coast in the state of Jalisco. The American botanist Yale Elmer Dawson first collected it near Barra de Navidad, but later it was found in other localities in coastal zones of the state of Jalisco, e.g. near Bahía de Tenacatita, Playa de Cuixmala, and near Playa de Careyes. As a representative of Mexican flora, it does not need such warm wintering as other *Melocactus*, but nevertheless winter temperatures should not drop below 60 °F. It is propagated from seeds, which readily germinate. However, the young plants grow quite slowly, and the first flowers take about 20 years to appear.

Melocactus dawsonii

Melocactus delessertianus

Melocactus delessertianus ■ ○

GLOBOSE

This species forms a stem no more than 4in in diameter. The stem is divided into 15 ribs bearing the areoles with spines. The spination is prominent and conspicuous. The radial and central spines are rigid, woody, and very prickly. The purple-pink flowers appear in summer and are about 3/4in across. The cephalium from which the flowers grow is about 2in in diameter, and its height is the same as its diameter, and in addition to the tiny bristles and down, thicker spines also form part of its structure.
One of the few Mexican members of the genus, it grows in the state of Oaxaca. Cultivation is less difficult than in the case of coastal species. The winter temperature is important (roughly 60 °F); water it sparingly once every two months.

Mitrocereus fulviceps ▣ ■ ○

COLUMNAR

This columnar cactus can grow to a height of 60ft. It often forms a low, woody trunk, which individual branches up to 1ft in diameter. The stems are divided into prominent ribs with woolly hairy areoles, and growing from each of these there are about 10 radial spines, and 3 central spines that are up to 6 in long. The creamy white flowers, up to 3in long, open at night.
The species occures in the hot regions of central Mexico, in the states of Puebla and Oaxaca, where, in some localities, it stands out as a dominant feature of the landscape. To grow, it needs adequate light, heat, and a large growing container. It is advisable to apply ferilizer several times during the season. Full-grown specimens are seen rarely in collections, but smaller plants are very decorative, too. In the northern hemisphere this cactus can take several decades to flower. It needs relatively warm wintering at temperatures between 54 a d 60 °C.

Mitrocereus fulviceps

Mitrocereus ruficeps ▣ ○

COLUMNAR

A beautiful columnar cactus which forms distinctive dominants, up to 50ft high. Some cactus growers may know it by its former name, *Neobuxbaumia macrocephala*. The individual stems are about 1ft in diameter at the base, and the main trunk may be up to 16in in diameter. It forms about 26 ribs. Only 1–3 spines, 2in long, grow from each areole. The areoles at the top form a denser tangle of spines, a sort of pseudo-cephalium, and from this, the whitish pink flowers grow; these are 2in across.

The species grows in central Mexico, in the Tehuacan valley in the state of Puebla. It is found mainly on a limestone substrate, on gently sloping hillsides. It is seen relatively rarely in collections, mainly because of its size. This is a shame, because it takes many years to reach full size, and its beauty is already apparent when it is a smaller plant. It needs full sun, cold wintering, and a large container.

Myrtillocactus geometrizans ▣ ○

COLUMNAR

An tree-like cactus which usually grows about 13ft tall. The epidermis of new branches is blue-green, contrasting with the short black spines which grow from large, light-colored areoles. The flowers, which appear at various times of year, are small, about 1 1/4in across, and when fertilized they turn into reddish purple fruit, which the local people call "garambullo." *M. geometrizans* can be seen throughout central Mexico; the southernmost edge of its habitat extends into Guatemala. In some localities it may grow in relatively dense stands. It has become popular with cactus growers lately, as one of the best rootstocks, because it does not cause grafted cacti to distort through overgrowth. The species needs plenty of space because it grows quickly; it is usually seen in glasshouses in botanical gardens, or in larger collections.

Mitrocereus ruficeps

Neobuxbaumia euphorbioides

Myrtillocactus geometrizans

Neobuxbaumia euphorbioides ▣ ○

COLUMNAR

The resemblance of its stem to some tree-like African spurges (*Euphorbia*) gave rise to the species epithet *euphorbioides*. The plants grow about 16ft tall, and the individual stems may be up to 4in in diameter. The prominent ribs, of which may be 8–10, have the areoles along their edges. Growing from aeroles, there are dark gray to black spines pointing outward from the stem of the plant; these are no more than 1 1/4in long. The dark red, upward-facing flowers are narrow and tubular, up to 3in long.

In the flat regions of the state of Tamaulipas, where the vegetation is quite dense, *Neobuxbaumia euphobioides* grows in the shade of the shrub layer; only older specimens grow taller than the surrounding vegetation. It is not often in cactus growers' collections, but in the Cereus collections in botanical gardens. It is not difficult to grow, and if the picked-out seedlings are placed in shade, they might grow quite quickly into elegant plants. In most collections, however, they seldom reach flower-bearing size.

Neobuxbaumia mezcalensis

Neobuxbaumia mezcalensis ▣ ○

COLUMNAR

A distinctive element of the cactus flora of central Mexico, this cactus has columnar stems growing as high as 23ft, each roughly 1ft in diameter. The radial spines (6 or 7) are relatively short for such a large stem, growing to about 1/2in. The central spine is only slightly longer and thicker. The spherical buds open into long, white, tubular flowers, about 1 3/4in across and 2 1/4in long; their outer petals are enveloped in brownish down. The crimson fruit contains a large number of small black seeds.

The species occurs in the states of Puebla and Oaxaca. The type locality is reported to be in the region near Mezcala. However, it also grows in other places, e.g. Cañon de Zopilote, where it was observed by Curt Backeberg, who brought back several 6ft specimens to the botanical gardens in Hamburg in the 1950s. In collections, it is very

Neobuxbaumia polylopha

elegant while still young, just a foot or two high. Cultivation of this species does not pose any problems, but it should be borne in mind that in cool climates, the plants hardly ever flower, because in order to reach flowering size, they need plenty of space and time to mature. To ensure that they grow well, they should be placed in a large pot, and given fertilizer roughly twice per season.

Neobuxbaumia polylopha  ○

COLUMNAR

A very tall cactus, whose stems may reach a height of 42ft and a diameter of 16in. The number of ribs varies greatly according to the age of the plant; on younger plants, for instance, there are only 20 ribs, while on old plants, there are about 50. Growing from the oval white areoles, there are short radial spines, and a single central spine which is up to 2 3/4in long; all the spines are yellow. The narrow, scarlet tubular flowers open toward evening, and are up to 2in long.

The species occurs on the slopes of some valleys in the state of Hidalgo, where it is a dominant species, giving the landscape a distinctive appearance. The seedlings usually grow in the shade of shrubs and grasses, and only mature plants rise above this layer, so that their crowns are in full sun. In collections, seedlings grow relatively quickly in moderate shade. However, they take many years to reach flowering size, and in collec-

Neolloydia conoidea

tions they usually do not flower at all. They should be given enough space to develop their root systems, either in a large container, or in the greenhouse bed.

Neolloydia conoidea ▣ ○

COLUMNAR

The species epithet *conoidea* (conical) indicates that the plantlets are moderately columnar in shape. Offsets often grow from the base, but this only happens at a later stage, when the largest plants are 6in high and 2–3in in diameter. There may be 15–18 radial spines, and in most cases there are 3-5 central spines, which are slender and tapering, verging on black in color, and up to 1 1/4in long. The beautiful flower, when fully open, is up to 2in across, and the petals are pinkish mauve with a darker or lighter tinge.
This cactus grows in the north states of Coahuila, Nuevo León, Tamaulipas, San Luis Potosí, Hidalgo, Zacatecas, and Querétaro, but its habitat extends as far as Texas, USA. It occurs in various localities, but in most cases these are localities with a limestone substrate. Although in the wild it is certainly not one of Mexico's rarities, cultivation of this species is rather difficult. It needs full sun, preferably just below glass; plants from mountain regions, and from more northerly localities, are very well suited to open-air cultivation under a glass roof. For growing, it is essential to use a very well-drained soil mix with good drying properties, with additional lime. Propagation is by seed, but the seedlings grow slowly, and many of them are lost in the first years of life.

Neolloydia grandiflora ▣ ○

COLUMNAR

The columnar stem is usually solitary, but may sometimes form a few offsets. It does not usually exceed a height of 6in and diameter 23/4in. The conical mammillae, which, on their upper side, have a groove filled with down, are arranged in spirals, and have downy areoles at their tips. Growing from each areole, there are up to 25 radial spines, 1 1/4–2 1/4in long. Central spines are usually absent, but there are colonies of plants which have 1 or 2 black central spines. In summer, large funnel-shaped flowers appear, up to 1 1/2in across when fully open. The petals are reddish violet, and the stamens and stigma are yellow.
This *Neolloydia* occurs in a relatively small area, bounded by the Jaumave valley and extending southward to Tula in the Mexican state of Tamaulipas. Because the species is quite variable in the wild, and a number of cactus specialists confuse it with the even more variable *N. conoidea*, its distribution is given incorrectly in a number of publications. It grows on flatter terrain on sandy loam alluvia, often in the moderate shade of shrub vegetation. It is one of the more difficult species to grow; sometimes plants without visible signs of previous distress become blighted and die within a few days. More experienced cactus specialists grow them in a slightly alkaline soil mix in full sun; less skilled growers and beginners would be well advised to graft them. However, plants on rootstocks grow unnaturally large.

Neolloydia grandiflora

Nopalea nuda

Nopalea nuda ▣ ○

BUSHY

An interesting species, sometimes classified within *Opuntia*, with a remarkable flower. It usually grows to larger dimensions than specified in the original description. There are plants as tall as 6 1/2ft, made up of pads about 6in long and roughly 2in wide. The large, densely woolly areoles have no spines; fleshy stipules appear only on young pads, and soon drop off, as in most other *Opuntia*. The red flower always has a style considerably longer than the petals; this is one of the distinguishing features of the species.

N. nuda occurs in northern Mexico. Provided the plants have enough water in summer, and adequate reserves of soil nutrients, they grow very quickly, and flowering specimens can be expected in less than 10 years. The only significant drawback is the considerable demand for space.

Nopalxochia phyllanthoides ▣ ■ ⊙

EPIPHYTIC

The botanical classification of this species is quite problematic, and there are strong grounds for including it in the genus *Epiphyllum*. We use the genus name *Nopalxochia* advisedly, because this is the name under which these beautiful cacti, with their pinkish mauve flowers, are grown; meanwhile, the specialist discussions about their origin and taxonomy continue unabated. This is one of the flat-stemmed cacti which are incorrectly called "leaf cacti".

The habitat is unknown; none of the published sources gives a location more specific than Mexico. Cultivation is not difficult, and is comparable to the cultivation methods for members of the genus *Epiphyllum*.

Obregonia denegrii ▣ ○

FLATTENED-GLOBOSE

The genus, which to date contains only one species (a monotypic genus), was discovered by the Czech traveler and cactus specialist A. V. Frič in 1923. It was described in 1925. Frič himself considered it his greatest botanical discovery. The flattened stem is divided into spirally arranged mammillae, each tipped with a downy areole from which grow 3 or 4 flexible spines, 1/4–5/8in long. The white or whitish yellow flower grows from the growing point, which is enveloped in thick, yellow-brown down. The berry contains about 40 black seeds.

The habitat was originally a closely guarded secret, and the exact whereabouts was still unknown to the members of many expeditions a few decades ago. The information about the locality was very imprecise, and simply referred to the Jaumave valley. The locality is now well known, but very carefully guarded by the local people. Although the plant is one of the cactus species at greatest risk, its survival in the wild is very satisfactory so far, and the greatest danger is large-scale water erosion caused by excessive grazing. The cultivation of *O. denegrii* entails certain difficulties; in the past it was grown mainly as a graft. Bearing in mind that in the wild it grows in the moderate shade of taller vegetation, the cactus grower should provide partial shade, especially for the young seedlings. A well-drained soil mix, and watering only when completely dry, are the essentials of successful cultivation. Nevertheless, this species represents one of the greatest challenges for the cactus grower, and with mature specimens, in particular, growers are regularly faced with the problem of root rot.

Nopalxochia phyllanthoides

Obregonia denegrii

Opuntia auberi 

BUSHY

A tall, tree-like species, whose stem may grow 26ft tall. It consists of long elliptical pads which are up to 18in long and only 3in wide. These are easily shed, and take root near the parent plant. It produces tiny glochids and 2 or 3 spines. The flowers grow on pads which are two years old, or older; they are pinkish red, and the stigma and group of stamens always protrude from them.

This *Opuntia* occurs over an area from southern Mexico to Guatemala and Honduras. It is hardly ever seen in collections, mainly because of its heavy demands for space. Otherwise it is easy to grow, and is even suitable for winter gardens, because it tolerates quite a high winter temperature of about 60 °F.

Opuntia azurea 

BUSHY

This is one of the lower-growing, bushy *Opuntia*, which usually produce a short main stem above ground, and then branch out. An interesting characteristic is the striking gray-blue color of its epidermis, which makes a splendid contrast with the flowers. Each of the flat pads is ellipsoid in shape,

Opuntia azurea

Opuntia auberi

and up to 6in long. Growing from the areoles, there are tiny glochids and 1–3 spines, which do not exceed 1 1/4in in length. The flowers usually grow on two-year old pads; they are deep yellow in color, with an orange-red mouth, and are about 1 1/2in across; when fertilized, they turn into a oval, crimson-colored fruit, thickly studded with areoles with miniature glochids.

This *Opuntia* grows in many places in the Mexican state of Zacatecas, and is also reported to occur in the state of Durango, though this has not been confirmed by us. It grows at low altitudes above sea level, on hills with a limestone substrate. As with most other members of the genus, cultivation is relatively easy. It must be given enough sunlight, and preferably a large container or a position in the greenhouse bed, where it can then grow to a large size. Unfortunately, like other *Opuntia*, this species is quite demanding as regards space, and if it is to flower, it must be wintered at low temperatures in the light. Propagation is easy, by rooting indvidual pads; they should be allowed to dry out for at least 3 weeks in a warm but shady place, and then planted in a light rooting medium.

Opuntia durangensis ▣ ○

GLOBOSE

This cactus does not usually grow taller than 5ft, forming a branching bush. The elliptical pads are quite large, growing up to 8in long. Growing from each areole, there are 3–5 spines and a large number of yellow or brown, microscopic glochids. The flower is yellow or orange, or even red. The fruit is eaten by the local people, who call it "tuna blanca," which is the name also given to the fruit of the most closely related species, *O. spinulifera.*

It grows in northern Mexico in the arid regions of the state of Durango, but is not endemic there. Because the local people grow it for fruit, it has now spread to many other regions. However, it is not grown in "nopalerias," as the large fields are called, but simply serves as a supplement to other species of *Opuntia* which are grown for their fruit. Cultivation does not present problems; it can be propagated very easily by the vegetative method – rooting individual pads. To enable the plant to form a more spreading clump, it should be placed in a large pot, or directly into the greenhouse bed. Only under these conditions is there any hope that the plant, when older, will produce flowers and fruit.

Opuntia imbricata ▣ ○

BUSHY

A many-branched cactus, eventually a small tree, of which many variants and forms have been described. The type species may grow as tall as 10ft, and forms a short, woody trunk. The cylindrical pads are divided into regular tubercles, on whose tips there are areoles with a small number of glochids and several pointed, sheathed, prickly spines. The large flowers are usually reddish purple, but shades of color ranging as far as red and orange are also known. When fully open, the flowers are 1 1/2–3in across.

The plant occurs in the north states of Chihuahua and Coahuila, but also extends into the southern states of the USA. Dried pieces of these cacti are admired as beautiful creations of nature; sections are cut from the sieve-like cylindrical structures of lignified fibers, which remain after the plants die. Cactus growers sometimes cultivate this species to lend some variety to uniform collections, e.g. of globose cacti. But take care when handling them – the sharp spines with their harpoon-like tips are not so easy to remove from the skin. Cultivation is the same as for other *Opuntia* of the less demanding kind.

Opuntia durangensis

Opuntia imbricata

Opuntia kleiniae

▣ ○

BUSHY

Taxonomists assigned this species to the large genus *Cylindropuntia*, which consisted mainly of species with narrow, cylindrical pads. The stem of this cactus branches into a bush, becoming woody at the base. It reaches a maximum height of 10ft, and individual pads are 2–6in long and about 1/2–3/4in wide. Small glochids, and in most cases a single spine, usually 2in long, grow from each areole. The Scarlet or orange-yellow flowers appear in summer, opening in the daytime.
The relatively large area of distribution of this species extends from Texas to central Mexico. It is found in practically all types of locality and at a widely differing altitudes above sea level, which is a clear sign of the versatility of this taxon. For cultivation, the same general principles apply as with other *Opuntia*. A certain amount of space is necessary for full appreciation of the beauty of the plant.

Opuntia leptocaulis

▣ ○

BUSHY

A bushy *Opuntia* of relatively variable habit; in some places it grows to 3ft, and elsewhere to 6ft. The individual pads are narrow, up to 1/2in across, but they may be 6 or 8in long. Growing from the areoles, there are tiny, ocher-colored glochids, and also 1–3 very prickly spines, up to 2in long. The whitish yellow flowers are about 3/4in across, and bloom on summer days. When fertilized, they turn into fruit whith a distinctively red-colored pericarp; the surface of the fruit is covered with very prickly but microscopic glochids.
O. leptocaulis occurs over large areas of northern Mexico and in the southern states of the USA, where it grows on the plains and on mountainous terrain – one of the hardiest of all cacti. It is almost impossible to beat a path through these bushes without injury. They are especially dangerous because they are very well camouflaged among fine-leaved, whippy bushes, and you are not aware of them until you have spines in your skin and broken-off pads firmly attached to your clothing. Not many growers devote themselves to cultivating this plant. However, this is a very elegant species, distinctively different from "ordinary" cacti. The seeds are slow to germinate, but individual pads take root and grow very well. The requirements are very cold wintering, full sun during active growth, and a large pot to allow adequate development of the root system.

Opuntia kleiniae

Opuntia leptocaulis

Opuntia leucotricha

Opuntia leucotricha ▣ ○

BUSHY

An tree-like *Opuntia* whose stems may grow 16ft tall. The lower part consists of a woody trunk, which branches freely about 3ft above the ground. The oval pads are quite large, up to 10in long, and about 2in across. White hairs, yellowish glochids, and also 1–3 long, woody spines grow from the areoles on the youngest pads. The beautiful yellow flowers appear in summer, and are up to 3in across when fully open. The fruit is a large, reddening berry, full of light-colored, hard seeds.
The area of distribution of this *Opuntia* is quite wide, covering a large number of arid regions of central Mexico. We saw a herdsman feeding his hungry goats with sliced pads of this *Opuntia* during the catastrophic drought which afflicted some regions of the state of San Luis Potosí in the year 2000. Although it goes against common sense, the goats were eating these prickly mouthfuls with great relish. This cactus is often grown as a centerpiece in larger greenhouses, where its beautiful flowers and interesting habit make it a real highlight of the collection. It needs o be grown either in the greenhouse bed or in a large container, because otherwise it does not achieve desired size and, over time, becomes completely stunted. Cultivation is very easy, and propagation is the same as for all the undemanding *Opuntia*.

Opuntia microdasys

Opuntia microdasys 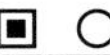

BUSHY

This species can definitely be ranked among the most popular cacti, because its oval or rounded pads, studded with numerous glochids, are really beautiful. The plant does not grow very large – a 3ft specimen is very tall. In the wild, there are many local forms which have been described in the past, and which differ from each other in size, color of glochids, habitat, and overall habit. The flowers of this *Opuntia* are deep yellow and 1 1/2–2in across.
It occurs in many localities in northern and central Mexico, where it grows both on the plains and in the mountains. It is very often grown in collections, although it is not at all pleasant to handle; even with the most careful handling, it pricks the skin with large numbers of glochids which are very difficult to remove. Despite this drawback, this is a very popular species in wholesale nurseries, and, thanks to the efforts of gardeners, a large number of mass-produced cultivars have been developed. Cactus growers still cultivate it under many different names; plants whose glochids differ in color are called, for example, *O. microdasys* var. *albispina* (white glochids), *O. microdasys* var. *pallida* (narrower pads and yellow glochids), *O. microdasys* var. *rufispina* (reddish brown glochids). Cultivation and propagation are very easy, but it flowers relatively rarely in collections.

Opuntia stanlyi 

CLUSTERING

The clumps, about 1ft high, consist of individual oval pads, which may grow to a length of 6in, though most are smaller, being only about 2in long. They form a sort of tubercle, at the top of which there are downy areoles with numerous small glochids, but they also have long, rigid spines which reach a length of 1 1/4–2 1/2in. The flowers are up to 2in across, usually yellow, sometimes with a darker or lighter tinge of a different color. The fruit is yellow and oval-shaped.
This is a very variable species, which occurs in many localities in the north of Mexico, extending into the USA. It grows mainly in flatter regions, and individual colonies may be distinguished by their size or spination. We know of plants from the north of Sonora on which the young spines have a distinctive red color. In terms of cultiva-

Opuntia stanlyi

tion, this *Opuntia* does not present many problems, and it is quite widespread among cactus growers. There are a number of local forms which can make a fine collection, showing the enormous range of variation in this species. It needs full sun, cold wintering, and fairly frequent potting on. The plant in the photograph has been grown in a small bowl as an indoor bonsai; excessive growth would be undesirable.

Opuntia stenopetala ▣ ○

BUSHY

Due to its creeping habit, this can be classed as one of the smaller *Opuntia*. Its pads tend to spread horizontally, and in exceptional cases grow erect above ground level. The individual flat pads are circular or oval, and may grow to a length of 8in. Growing from each areole, there are 2–4 spines which reach 2in long, and also a very large number of glochids, which are retainedmainly on younger pads. The flowers, which grow from the areoles on the edges of the pads, are orange, and 1 1/4–1 1/2in long. Later they turn into a spherical fruit with quite large seeds.
This is one of the commonest cacti in many localities and, as a rule, dense colonies of this *Opuntia* are practically impenetrable. It grows from the north of Mexico as far as the states of Hidalgo and Querétaro. It is noticeably less common in collections. Although one of the smallest *Opuntia*, it needs plenty of room, and most cactus growers constantly struggle to find space. However, it is not difficult to grow, and is recommended to complete beginners. Like all *Opuntia*, it is advisable to plant it in a greenhouse bed, not in a container.

Opuntia stenopetala

Opuntia tunicata

Opuntia tunicata 

BUSHY

This cactus belongs to the subspecies *Cylindropuntia*, but in the latest taxonomic works, it can be found under the species name *O. rosea*. It forms low, branching shrublets, only about 1ft high. The individual pads have oval areoles 1/4in long and 1/16in wide, from which grow very prickly spines up to 1 3/4in long, enclosed in a white membranous sheath. Like other members of the genus, this species has barbed spines. The flowers are funnel-shaped, up to 2 1/4in across, and the petals are pink.

It occurs in many localities in northern Mexico, and, according to the literature, it extends into the USA. A brush with this species is always very unpleasant, and its spines can easily pierce the soles of sports shoes. The embedded thorn can then cause an inflammation which heals badly in field conditions. In collections, it is one of the less commonly cultivated species, but it is certainly as beautiful as many other cacti. It needs a large pot and the best-lit position in the greenhouse. With cold wintering and occasional application of fertilizer, there is some hope that the plant will bloom, though in cool climates flowers appear very rarely, and only on older plants.

Ortegocactus macdougalii, cultivated

Ortegocactus macdougalii 

GLOBOSE

This remains a rare species, and is the only representative of the genus. The small, clustering stem, only 1 1/4–1 1/2in in diameter, has a gray-green epidermis. The small white areoles have about 8 radial spines and usually 1 central spine. All the spines are initially a black-red color, and gradually change to dark gray or even white. Yellow flowers, 3/4–1 1/4in across, with a greenish yellow stigma, grow from the youngest areoles.

Only a few devotees have seen this species in its natural environment in the mountains near San José Lachiguirí in the state of Oaxaca. It grows in an inaccessible region, on rocky terrain. Given the difficulty of cultivation, most cactus growers have it in their collections as a graft, usually on *Myrtillocactus geometrizans*. In this form, it grows without any problems; it simply needs to be protected against scorch by the spring sun, and against spider mite, which shows a strong tendency to attack it. The key to successful cultivation is wintering at relatively high temperatures,

Ortegocactus macdougalii, wild

Pachycereus pecten-aboriginum

because the plants, if too cold, develop brown patches and gradually die. The propagation method is either by seed – after which, the pricked-out seedlings are grafted onto *Pereskiopsis* and later regrafted – or cuttings.

Pachycereus pecten-aboriginum ▣ ■ ○

COLUMNAR

A tree-like cactus, up to 26ft tall; it forms a woody trunk about 3ft high, which subsequently grows branches. Its diameter may be up to 1ft, and individual branches are usually 4–6in in diameter. The large gray areoles usually have 8 radial spines and 2 longer central spines. The tubular flowers, 3–3 1/2in long, open in the daytime, and are white in color. Also of interest are the fruits, which when ripe are covered with densely clustered straw yellow spines. They contain large black seeds.
The species grows in the coastal zones along the Pacific coast of the Mexican mainland, and is also widespread on the Baja California peninsula. It usually grows sparsely among stands of open woodland or among underbrush. In collections, the seedlings grow extremely quickly, and their growth does not slow until about five years have passed, by which time they may be over 10in tall. They need a light, well-drained but fertile soil mix, full sun, and wintering preferably at quite warm temperatures with no prolonged spells below 54 °F.

Pachycereus pringlei 

COLUMNAR

A tall columnar cactus, whose stems grow more than 40ft high. The trunk, which branches about 3ft above ground, may be up to 2ft in diameter. The gray-green stems are divided into 10–16 rounded ribs. About 20 radial spines grow from the areole, and for a cactus of this size, they are quite short – usually only about 3/4in. The 1–3 central spines are only slightly longer. The flowers, which open at night, are white, and are roughly 3in in width and length. The fruit is a spherical berry, about the size of a table tennis ball, covered with yellow spines. This species has some of the largest seeds in the whole cactus family.
It occurs both on the Baja California peninsula and in the Mexican state of Sonora, where it grows on flatter terrain and forms a prominent feature of the landscape. The seedlings grow unusually quickly, and can be pricked out soon after germination. During winter the temperature should not drop for prolonged spells below 54 °F.

Pachycereus pringlei

Pachycereus weberi

Pelecyphora strobiliformis, cultivated

Pachycereus weberi 

COLUMNAR

The symbol of southern Mexico, where it grows into huge plants up to 30ft high, whose thick trunks branch about 3ft above the ground. The individual branches are about 4in in diameter, and are divided into straight, prominent ribs. The areoles on the edges of the ribs have black-brown radial spines about 3/4–1 1/4in long. The beautiful, funnel-shaped flowers, which are yellowish inside, open at night, and when fertilized, turn into a round fruit full of small black seeds.
Quite extensive territories in the south of the state of Puebla, and also areas in the state of Oaxaca, are covered with fairly dense xerophytic vegetation, of which one of the dominant columnar species is *P. weberi.*
It is not difficult to grow; it should be wintered at temperatures not dropping for prolonged periods below 54 °F. The seedlings, as young plantlets, are very attractive, and their growth rate is not too rapid, so the fear of soon outgrowing an ordinary greenhouse is dismissed as unfounded.

Pelecyphora aselliformis

Pelecyphora aselliformis 

GLOBOSE

Pelecyphora is a very popular genus, which numbers only two species. *P. asseliformis* has been known for longer, and is perhaps more widely grown. The stem is partly hidden underground, and grows up to 4in high, with a diameter of up to 2in. It is covered with hatchet-shaped mammillae, on which there are fine white spines in a comb-like arrangement. The flower is up to 1 1/2in across and purple-red in color.
It the wild, it is very well camouflaged, and finding it is always a matter of luck. It grows on low limestone hills in the state of San Luis Potosí, and at present is under quite serious threat from highway construction and limestone quarrying. Like the species below, it is one of the jewels of any collection, but because of the difficulty of cultivating it, it is unlikely to become more widespread among cactus growers. Cultivation is the same as for *P. strobiliformis*. Take care, because both species are very prone to spider mite attack.

Pelecyphora strobiliformis 

GLOBOSE

This cactus still tends to be known to growers under the genus name *Encephalocarpus.* The small, flattened-globose stem does not grow more than 2 3/4in tall. With its scaly mammillae, the plant is unmistakable, and the resemblance to a pine cone is the reason for the species epithet *strobiliformis*. The small, whitish gray spines are retained only on the youngest parts of the plant, around the growing point. The reddish purple flowers vary from light to dark in their shade of color; they are about 1 1/2 across when open.
The species occurs in the Mexican states of Nuevo

Pelecyphora strobiliformis, wild

León and Tamaulipas, where it grows on gently sloping hills with a limestone substrate. It is a cactus growers' rarity, and its cultivation is relatively difficult. The only effective method of propagation is by seed followed by grafting onto *Pereskiopsis*. Plants on their own roots are seldom grown in collections. It tolerates cold wintering below 50 °F.

Peniocereus viperianus ▣ ○

BUSHY

Some specialists consider this a member of the genus *Wilcoxia*. This is a very unusual cactus, of interest not only for its stem, but also, its flowers. It grows as a shrub, and consists of many slender gray-green shoots, which scramble through surrounding vegetation. These shoots may be up to 10ft long, with a stem diameter of only 3/4in. The inconspicuous ribs and small black areoles bear small spines, only about 1/16in long. This is a very inconspicuous species in the wild, but can be seen from a distance as soon as its beautiful red flowers appear; these are 3in long and about 1 1/2in across.

We have seen the species a few times in the wild, but it is quite difficult to find when not in flower, although it is no miniature. Its slender stems are well camouflaged in the surrounding vegetation. It grows on flat terrain in the state of Puebla, together with many other interesting cacti. As regards cultivation, it is advisable to place it in quite a deep, roomy pot, in full sun. In cultivation, flowers can only be expected when it has formed an extensive root system and fairly long shoots.

Peniocereus viperianus

Pilosocereus tehuacanus  ○

COLUMNAR

A tall columnar cactus, growing up to 30ft high. It forms a woody, branching trunk. The individual stems are about 2 1/4in in diameter, and light green in color, though the skin tends toward a blue shade on the youngest parts. The downy areoles, especially in the flowering zone, have spines accompanied by large quantities of hairs and down, giving the impression of a sort of false cephalium. The flowers are 1 1/2–2in long, tubular, and light pink or white. The flower is a round, blue-green berry containing a large number of small black seeds.

As the species epithet indicates, this species grows near the town of Tehuacan, but its distribution is much wider than this, extending throughout the Tehuacan valley in the state of Puebla.

Important requirements are relatively warm wintering, and adequate ventilation and sun in summer. Propagation from seed is not difficult, and the seedlings are very decorative even at three years old. Unfortunately, in cool climates flowers are produced only after several years.

Pilosocereus tehuacanus

Ritterocereus pruinosus

Ritterocereus pruinosus

COLUMNAR

Some handbooks also include this within *Lemaireocereus.* It is tree-like, growing to a height of about 23ft. The freely branching stem forms a thick, woody trunk. The individual branches are divided into 6 ribs, on which there are round areoles, each bearing 5–7 radial spines and 1 central spine, about 1 1/4in long. The long tubular flowers are up to 2 3/4in long and, when fertilized, turn into a fruit covered with woolly-hairy areoles and spines.
The area of distribution is relatively wide, comprising the central and southern of Oaxaca, Puebla, and Guerrero. It grows in the mountains and also on flatter terrain. It is not seen very often in collections, because it needs plenty of space in which to grow. The plants do not flower until they are about 10ft tall, so only a patient cactus grower with a large greenhouse can hope for flowers to appear. Cultivation is very easy; this species simply needs the basic conditions appropriate for less demanding cacti.

Stenocereus marginatus

COLUMNAR

This columnar cactus, which in the past was also known under the genus name *Marginatocereus,* usually grows to heights between 10 and 23ft. Its resemblance to organ pipes earned it the local Mexican name of "órgano común". The individual branches usually have 5–7 prominent, straight ribs with clustered areoles. From these grow short, brownish radial spines and 1 central spine, but the spines soon drop off. The white flowers, about 2in long, open during the day. The photograph shows how freely these cacti flower.
This Mexican cactus has now spread to many regions where it was not originally part of the flora. The local people often plant it as a living fence around their homes and, as the literature indicates, extracts from its stem are still used in the cosmetics industry as additives in the manufacture of special emollient soaps. Elsewhere, it is rare in cultivation, mainly because of its height, but this is a shame, because it takes a few decades to reach an enormous size. Cultivation is extremely simple, and even small seedlings look quite impressive.

Stenocereus treleasii

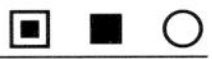

COLUMNAR

An tree-like, columnar cactus, growing to about 23ft. The number of ribs on the stems varies (12–20) with age. Growing from the small downy areoles, there are 7–9 short yellow radial spines; later, a single, longer, more rigid central spine may also appear. The flower has red petals, and opens in the daytime. Its length varies between 1 1/2 and 2in. This species grows in the Mexican state of Oaxaca,

Stenocereus marginatus

Stenocereus treleasii

where, in many places, it is a conspicuous, unmissable part of the landscape. Cactus specialists do not show much interest in growing it; generally it is of marginal interest to them. Cultivation is relatively simple, but calls for quite warm wintering.

Strombocactus disciformis

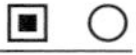

FLATTENED-GLOBOSE

An extremely interesting cactus, unusual in terms of its stem, and also its habitat. The stem which is visible above ground – ranging from rather flattened to top-shaped in shape – merges into quite a large, bulky underground part. Although this species is classed as a Mexican miniature, its stem may be up to 6in in diameter. The roots, however, are not beet-like, but long and wiry, to hold the plant firmly to the vertical surfaces where it grows. The spiral ribs are divided into tubercles, each tipped with an areole, from which grow 4 or 5 gray spines, which may be up to 1 1/2in long. The spines are retained on the younger parts of the plant, and later drop off. The flower may be up to 1 1/2in across, and is white or yellowish in color, often with a pink mouth. The fruit is an elongated-capsule that splits to release a large quantity of very small brown seeds.

The habitats are in the states of Hidalgo and Querétaro, where it grows on very steep or even vertical surfaces consisting of soft, crumbly slate. The population density is sometimes very high, and several dozen plants, ranging from seedlings to large flowering specimens, may be counted in a single square yard. Flowering self-rooted plants are the pride of every cactus grower. The ability to grow seedlings to a height of 1/2in – after which their growth improves – is a great cactus-growing skill, and there are not many growers who have mastered this method. It is best to germinate seeds by the Fleischer method, and then try to maintain the seedlings on their own roots, or graft them onto *Pereskiopsis*. In either case, this is quite a demanding species. The same applies to the recently described red-flowered *Strombocactus disciformis* ssp. *esperanzae*. Apparently it is even more difficult to grow than the type.

Strombocactus disciformis, cultivated

Strombocactus disciformis, wild

Thelocactus bicolor

Thelocactus bicolor ▣ ○

COLUMNAR

The tallest specimens may grow more than 20in high, with a stem diameter of up to 6in. The spination varies enormously and, together with other deviations, gives rise to a number of variants. From a taxonomic point of view, their validity is questionable, but their strikingly different appearance makes them very distinctive. They all bloom with a beautiful, shiny, crimson-pink flower, which is up to 3in across when fully open. The variability in habit is a reflection of the huge area of distribution of *T. bicolor*, extending from the southern states of the USA through practically the whole of northern Mexico. It is a very widespread species in collections. It is essential to know the origin of the seeds from which you intend to grow the basic plants for your collection. When pricking out and potting on seedlings, take care to avoid careless overwatering, which may cause most of the plants to rot during unfavorable weather.

Thelocactus bicolor var. *bolansis* ▣ ○

GLOBOSE-COLUMNAR

This varietas are distinguished easily from the type species. It is differentiated by its markedly conical stems and clustering, with plants producing offsets from the base and forming large groups. Most plants in the natural habitat have light-colored or white spines. The flower is very elegant, purple-red, and shiny.
The habitat of this varietas is reported as being the southwestern part of the state of Coahuila. It was named either after the Sierra Bola mountain range in which it grows, or after the vanished village of Cerro Bola, where we, too, have observed this cactus. Found on gentle slopes of limestone hillocks, where it grows with many other cactus species. A visit to this locality is quite an experience for the cactus enthusiast, because large numbers of cactus species and many other succulent plants, e.g. *Ibervillea sonorae*, can be seen within a relatively small area. It is, surprisingly, rather more difficult to grow than the type species. The larger plants, for unknown reasons, often rot, despite great care devoted to them by the grower. It is also true of this varietas that to be of botanical value material must have a specified place of origin, because this is the only guarantee that is has not been crossed with other variants.

Thelocactus bueckii ▣ ○

GLOBOSE

The skin of the flat or flattened-globose stem is usually brownish green or reddish. The cactus grows to a diameter of up to 7 1/4in. The low ribs are divided into prominent mammillae. The number and length of the spines are very variable. The flowers are up to 2in across when fully open, and are deep purple, light reddish violet, or even pink. They open on hot summer days.
The area of distribution of the species is wide; it is found on the hilly terrain of the central states of Nuevo León, Tamaulipas, and San Luis Potosí. Due to its variability, growing plants from a

Thelocactus bicolor var. *bolansis*

Thelocactus bueckii

known place of origin is recommended. Growing from seed is not difficult, and this species is grown in the same way as most Mexican cacti. It needs full sun, but beware of scorch in spring.

Thelocactus conothelos 

GLOBOSE

Perhaps the most robust representative of this complex. The globose stem may be up to 10in in diameter, and is divided into mammillae. The epidermis often has a reddish color. The spines are sharply differentiated into glassy white radial spines, and central spines ranging from reddish brown to brownish black. The flower appears in early summer and is usually reddish violet or purple, but may be orange or even pinkish white. In the wild, it favors gently sloping, rocky terrain, usually at altitudes of about 5,000–6,500ft. In Mexico it occurs in the states of Nuevo León, Tamaulipas, and San Luis Potosí. In cultivation, it is not an easy cactus to grow. Heavy losses occur, especially when the plants are pricked out and potted on. After removing them from the soil mix, the roots must be allowed to dry before replanting in a slightly alkaline, free-draining soil mix.

Thelocactus conothelos var. *aurantiacus* ▣ ○

GLOBOSE

The stem does not usually grow taller than 6in. The radial spines are glassy white and pressed against the stem, while the central spines are brown and protruding. The name of the varietas epithet means golden – from the yellow color of the flower, which is rare for *T. conothelos*.
The natural habitats are very limited, and this

Thelocactus conothelos

yellow-flowered variant is found only to the northeast of the small Mexican town of Aramberri. But, interestingly, we saw a mixed colony of *T. conothelos*, in which some of the plants had the typically mauve flowers, and some individuals had yellow flowers. The genus *Thelocactus* is also popular with cactus specialists because it is not difficult to grow. Plants do not need to be grafted; specimens on their own roots are much more compact and their spination is more beautiful.

Thelocactus conothelos var. *aurantiacus*

Thelocactus conothelos var. *macdowellii*

Thelocactus flavus

Thelocactus conothelos var. *macdowellii* ▣ ○

GLOBOSE

There have been problems with the systematic classification of this cactus – it is also known as *Echinocactus, Echinomastus,* or *Neolloydia*. It is a beautiful, slightly columnar cactus, usually taller than 6in, with a stem diameter of about 3–3 1/2in. The dense white spines envelop the stem so that the skin is hardly visible. The reddish violet flowers make a splendid contrast with the color of the spines.
Its habitat is a relatively small area in the Mexican states of Coahuila and Nuevo León, where it grows on limestone massifs, in rock fissures. Although it is not so unusual to see it in collections now, a group of self-rooted, flowering plants is the pride of every cactus grower.

Thelocactus flavus ▣ ○

GLOBOSE

A species discovered only recently, and still surrounded by controversy as to whether it is really a species in its own right, or, as we believe, just a form of *T. tulensis*. Some authorities even maintain that it shows signs of affinity with the *T. conothelos* group, but in the light of field observations, this view seems unfounded, too.
At present, the known localities for this cactus are near the small town of Santa Rita in the state of San Luis Potosí, where it grows on slopes with a limestone substrate. Cultivation is the same as for the other usual species of the genus *Thelocactus*; it requires full sun and cold wintering.

Thelocactus hastifer ▣ ○

COLUMNAR

In the wild, this cactus usually forms clusters, but in collections it offsets less freely. It grows to a height of up to 1ft, with a stem diameter of 1 1/2–2in. The spination is dense, especially on plants in the wild. One of the central spines stands out prominently from the stem, hence the

Thelocacus hastifer

species epithet *hastifer*, meaning spear-bearer. The splendid mauve-pink flower is up to 2in across when fully open, and seeing the flowering plants in the wild is quite an experience.
T. hastifer grows in a small area, and because it is so specialized, it is considered one of the most seriously threatened taxa in the genus. It grows on gentle limestone slopes near Vista Hermosa (Querétaro), and on the steeper slopes of the Sierra del Doctor mountains. Although its beauty, it is not very common in collections. The reason for this is the lack of commercially available plant material and seeds, and perhaps the rather difficult growing technique. Important requirements are a position in full sun, watering at frequent intervals in small quantities, and cold wintering in the light, at temperatures around 60 °F.

Thelocactus heterochromus

GLOBOSE

A sometimes flattened cactus, which owes its name either to its beautifully colored spination, with different shades of red alternating crosswise, or to its lovely flowers, whose color ranges from light pink to dark reddish violet.
Finding a colony of flowering plants in the wild is a fascinating experience, because this species undoubtedly has one of the most beautiful flowers in the whole cactus family. It grows over a wide area

Thelocactus heterochromus

Thelocactus hexaedrophorus

in the states of Durango and Chihuahua. Unfortunately, a number of hybrid plants are in circulation among cactus growers, and bear only a distant resemblance to the typical *T. heterochromus*. It is therefore important to know the source of the seeds used for growing plants in a collection.

Thelocactus hexaedrophorus

FLATTENED-GLOBOSE

The flattened stem, which may become globose in old age, has a skin of a striking gray-blue color, which strongly differentiates it from other members of the genus, as does its unusual and variable spination. Due to this spination, a large number of variants and subspecies have been described, while in fact most of these are local forms. The species blooms with a creamy white flower, roughly 2in across, but colonies are known where the flowers may even be deep pink.
The abundance of distinct local forms is a consequence of the wide area of the species, which extends from the state of San Luis Potosí, through Nuevo León, Coahuila, and Tamaulipas, roughly as far as Durango and Zacatecas. It usually favors flatter localities with a limestone substrate, where it grows not only in full sun, but also, in the shade of whippy shrubs of the genera *Larrea* or *Prosopis*. Botanically valuable plants are those for which the grower knows the place of origin, so that non-hybridized forms from clearly distinct regions are maintained in the collection. Seeds are now available in large quantities, and some firms now offer seeds from plants of certified origin. Cultivation does not present problems, but care should be taken to protect the plant's epidermis from scorch in spring.

Thelocactus lausseri

Thelocactus lausseri

GLOBOSE-COLUMNAR

Like *T. hastifer*, this is one of the least common representatives of the genus in collections. Its short columnar stem does not exceed 4in in height and 2 3/4in in diameter. There are about 10 ribs divided into inconspicuous tubercles, each of which is tipped with an areole; growing from this, there are up to 25 radial spines and, in most cases, 5 central spines, up to 4in long. The magnificent flower has white petals with a reddish violet streak in the middle.
A very inaccessible locality in the Sierra de Ovejas range, near the town of Cuatro Cienegas in the state of Coahuila, is, the only known habitat of this species. It grows on sunny limestone slopes, which are in some cases very steep. Cactus growers consider it a great rarity, because it was discovered relatively recently (1985). The seeds are hardly ever available, and vegetative propagation of these plants is practically impossible. They should be cold-wintered in the light. *T. lausseri* is usually grown as a graft on a slow-growing rootstock.

Thelocactus leucacanthus var. *schmollii*

CLUSTERING

The offsetting, cylindrical stems form clusters up to 20in across, made up of individual plants, which usually grow to 6in high and a diameter of 2 3/4–4in. The warty ribs have small areoles, from which grow regularly spaced radial spines (8–10), and there is often 1 central spine, up to 1 1/4in long, pointing away from the stem. The beautiful violet-red flowers appear at the growing point, and when fully open, are up to 2in across.
This varietas is distributed over a small territory north of the town of Cadereyta des Montes in the state of Querétaro. It is quite commonly seen in collections, and some cactus growers may know it by the name of *T. sanchezmejoradai*. Cultivation is the same as for other widely grown *Thelocactus*.

Thelocactus rinconensis

GLOBOSE

The flattened-globose stem grows to a circumference of up to 8in, and has a gray-green epidermis. It is divided into 20–25 ribs made up of separate tubercles, each of these is tipped with an oval areole covered with a tomentum. Growing from this, there are 4–5 rigid, woody spines, up to 3in long. The flower grows from the crown of the plant and is whitish pink.
The village of La Rinconada, near which the species was collected and from which it takes its name, is in the Mexican state of Nuevo León. The species grows on gentle limestone slopes there, often between rocks or in the moderate shade of shrubs or grasses. This is a beautiful *Thelocactus* which is relatively easy to grow, the only drawback being a reluctance to flower, which does not occur until it is about 10 years old. It is definitely one of the staples of any collection; however, great care should be taken to protect it from scorch in early spring, because plants damaged in this way regenerate very poorly, and the damaged parts take a long time to grow out.

Thelocactus schwarzii

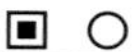

COLUMNAR

This cactus is very similar to the species *T. bicolor*, of which many authorities consider it a varietas. It differs, however, in that it lacks a central spine, and its habitat lies entirely outside that of *T. bicolor*. It occurs only in the state of Tamaulipas, and our actual observations of this species were made near the small town of Estanción Calles. The plants form beautiful groups of compact

Thelocactus leucacanthus var. *schmollii*

Thelocactus rinconensis

Turbinicarpus alonsoi

stems. The splendid, shiny, violet-red flowers are a real feast for the eyes. Cultivation is the same as for *T. bicolor*, and it is very widespread in collections.

Turbinicarpus alonsoi 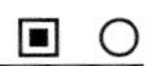

GLOBOSE

A sensational novelty and the great discovery made during the last journeys of the American cactus expert C. Glass, who lived in Mexico. The authors of the description named the species after the discoverer, a little Mexican boy called García Alonso. When a photograph of this cactus was published, it was obvious that this was once again a sensational discovery of a very distinct species. Its stem is globose, relatively large for *Turbinicarpus*, up to 2 3/4in in diameter, and divided into pyramid-shaped mammillae. From the areole grow 3–5 spines, which are about 3/4in long. Red-violet flowers, up to 1 1/4in across, are produced from the down-filled growing point.

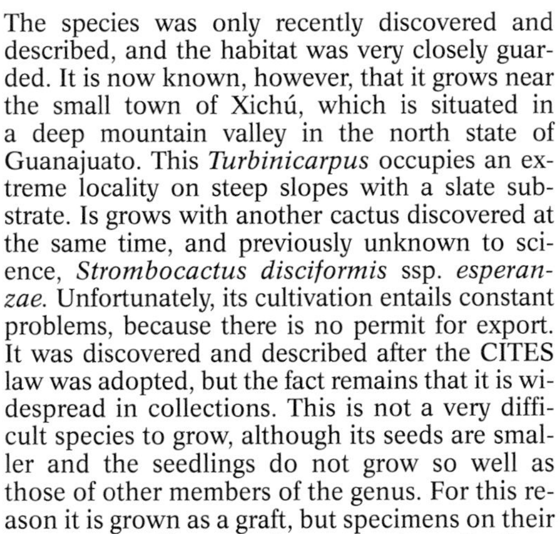

The species was only recently discovered and described, and the habitat was very closely guarded. It is now known, however, that it grows near the small town of Xichú, which is situated in a deep mountain valley in the north state of Guanajuato. This *Turbinicarpus* occupies an extreme locality on steep slopes with a slate substrate. Is grows with another cactus discovered at the same time, and previously unknown to science, *Strombocactus disciformis* ssp. *esperanzae.* Unfortunately, its cultivation entails constant problems, because there is no permit for export. It was discovered and described after the CITES law was adopted, but the fact remains that it is widespread in collections. This is not a very difficult species to grow, although its seeds are smaller and the seedlings do not grow so well as those of other members of the genus. For this reason it is grown as a graft, but specimens on their own roots will no doubt appear in collections soon.

Thelocactus schwarzii

Turbinicarpus flaviflorus ▣ ○

COLUMNAR

A columnar species, classed as a miniature. In the wild, it usually grows to a height of 1/14in and a diameter of 3/4in; in collections, the plants tend to be bulkier, especially when grafted. The epidermis is gray- to blue-green in color, and each of the conical mammillae is tipped with an areole, from which grow brown spines up to 1 1/4in long; these later turn gray and often drop off. The species epithet indicates the color of the flower: *flaviflorus,* meaning yellow-flowered. The flower is only about 5/8in long and 5/8in across.

The species was discovered by Alfred Lau, who gave it the collection number L 1185. The locality where it occurs is near the village of Santa Rita in the eastern region of the Mexican state of San Luis Potosí. It colonizes rock fissures and cracks between limestone rocks. Anyone interested in keeping this species can obtain it very easily from the many suppliers of seeds or plants, because it is now one of the very widespread representatives of the genus in collections. It is not particularly difficult to grow, provided allowance is made for heavy losses of small seedlings when raising from seed. The older seedlings grow well, and flower when the stem diameter is only about 1/2in. Soil mix and wintering are the same as for other members of the genus.

Turbinicarpus hoferi

Turbinicarpus hoferi ▣ ○

GLOBOSE

The species was discovered and described quite recently (1991). It forms flattened stems, which in grafted plants lose their characteristic habit and appearance. The cactus is 1 1/4–1 1/2in wide and has a gray-green epidermis. 1–7 gray spines grow from the small downy areoles; they are needle-like and their length ranges from 3/16 to 3/4in. The white flowers grow from the upper areoles, and are usually 1in across.

This is a strictly endemic species, occurring in a very limited area in the Aramberri valley, known for its very interesting cacti, in the Mexican state of Nuevo León. It can be seen on steep gypsum rock faces near Lampacitos, where it grows with just a few associated plant species, the most numerous of which are probably the moss-like *Selaginella lepidophylla* and *Thelocactus bueckii.* It is definitely not a common cactus, and is usually seen only in specialist collections. In cultivation, it needs a slightly alkaline, mineral-

Turbinicarpus pseudomacrochele, white-flowering

rich soil mix, careful watering, and a position in full sun. It thrives on a great variety of rootstocks, but generally loses its natural appearance when grafted. It is advisable to graft newly germinated seedlings on to *Pereskiopsis;* or you can try to root the scion itself directly into sterile perlite in moderate shade.

Turbinicarpus krainzianus ssp. *minimus* ▣ ○

COLUMNAR

A very small cactus, only about 1/2in in diameter and 3/4in high, whose above-ground part merges smoothly into a beet-like root, up to 2 1/4in long. The radial spines are small and soft, but the upper radial spines are relatively long, non-prickly, and twisted. The flowers, about 1/2in across, are yellow, as in the type species. The fruit is very small, containing only about 10 seeds.
For a long time the habitat of this miniature subspecies was a carefully guarded secret, and there was no precise information about its natural distribution. Only a few years ago, an isolated colony was discovered near the small town of Ixmiquilpan in the Mexican state of Hidalgo. It grows on limestone pavement, in rock fissures, and there are often so many plants that they fill an entire cleft. Like all members of the genus, *T. krainzianus* ssp. *minimus* is one of the more demanding cacti, with low tolerance for growers' mistakes. The basic requirements include a slightly alkaline soil mix, occasional watering, and cold wintering, if possible in the light.

Turbinicarpus pseudomacrochele ▣ ○

GLOBOSE–COLUMNAR

One of the most widely grown members of the genus. The stem forms a relatively small above-ground section, which merges into a large section below ground and a bulky beet-like root. The stems are usually 1 1/4in in diameter, but cultivated plants are larger. The inconspicuous ribs are divided into four-sided mammillae, each of which is tipped with an areole producing about 8 tangled, soft spines, usually brown in color. The flowers are 1 1/4–1 1/2in across and most often white with a delicate pink streak, but there are also forms with deep pink flowers, as the second photograph of the plant shows.
The area of distribution was first reported rather inaccurately as San Luis Potosí, but field observations have confirmed that the species occurs mainly in the Mexican state of Querétaro, not far from the Peñon de Bernal settlement, and that its habitats extend eastward to the state of Hidalgo, where it grows near the small towns of Cardonal and Ixmiquilpan. It favors low hillocks with a limestone substrate, where it occupies hollows and earth-filled clefts. To maintain plants on their own roots, give them a very well-drained, slightly alkaline soil mix; it is advisable to group a few plants together in a terra cotta bowl. They will then produce a sufficiently large root system, and the plants will thrive better. Seedlings grow rather slowly at first, and the first flowers may take about 5 years to appear. Flower-bearing capacity can be accelerated by grafting, but the plants lose their typical appearance. Cold wintering, and an active growth period in full sun, will guarantee good flower production.

Turbinicarpus pseudomacrochele, pink-flowering

Turbinicarpus pseudopectinatus

Turbinicarpus pseudopectinatus ▣ ○

GLOBOSE

Appearing occasionally in collections under the genus name *Pelecyphora* or, less often, *Normanbokea*. In terms of stem size, it is one of the Mexican miniatures; it does not usually grow to more than 2in in diameter. The ribs are divided into narrow hatchet-shaped mammillae, with elongated areoles on tips from which grow short white spines in a comb-like arrangement. Buds appear at the top of the plant in early spring, and these develop into white flowers, often with darker streaks, but ecotypes with pink or dark violet-red flowers as well; this variant is sometimes called *Turbinicarpus pseudopectinatus* var. *rubriflorus.*
Although the species was originally thought to occur mainly in the state of Tamaulipas, exploration of the terrain shows that this locality is only a marginal area. The center of distribution is mainly in the state of Nuevo León and partly in San Luis Potosí. The species grows on low limestone hills covered with xerophytic vegetation, and at higher altitudes above sea level, where, in many cases, there is a sparse covering of pine. It is grown on its own roots, but the requirements are even stricter than for other representatives of the genus. It is especially prone to rotting after overwatering during the dormant period in summer. It tolerates the sunniest position in the greenhouse, but needs adequate ventilation. As a rootstock for grafting, *Pereskiopsis* is recommnded; after a year, this should be cut, rooted, and grown on. It should be remembered that this species flowers very early in spring. The plant must be coaxed into growth as early as possible. Even so, there is often a problem with fruiting, because the pollen is often sterile due to incorrect lighting and temperature.

Turbinicarpus schmiedickeanus ▣ ○

FLATTENED-GLOBOSE

A lovely miniature species. Its flattened-globose stem grows to a diameter of only 1in, and is divided into prominent tubercles. Growing from the tomentose areoles, there are 2–4 central spines, 5/8–1in long. The youngest areoles at the top produce beautiful flowers about 1in across with narrow petals with a streak of pink. The fruit is a gray-green berry, which splits open lengthwise, with a few dozen matt black seeds.
Not easy to find in the wild; so far, the only known places where it grows are a few hills in the vicinity of the Miquihuana settlement in the state of Tamaulipas. It grows in fissures in limestone rocks there, or on screes on the southern slopes of hills. In collections it is rare in its non-hybridized form. Its rarity is due partly to the fact that it is relatively rare to grow, and to the shortage of seeds. This species produces few seeds because it flowers very early, and the pollen in the flowers is insufficiently developed, so that fertilization is not pos-

Turbinicarpus pseudopectinatus, var. *rubriflorus*

Turbinicarpus schmiedickeanus

sible. For this reason, the species should be in the sunniest position, and brought into active growth as early as possible in early spring.

Turbinicarpus schmiedickeanus var. *dickisoniae* ▣ ○

GLOBOSE-COLUMNAR

Described in 1982, and named after Shirley Dickinson of Texas, the cactus grower who discovered it. The stem grows to a maximum diameter of 1 1/4in. It is smaller in the wild; in collections, it often extends into a column, and its dimensions are larger. There are 18–23 radial spines, which are only a fraction of an inch long, and soft. There are 1–3 central spines, which are dark-colored or black, often twisted, and the longest of them is 1in. The flower is about 3/4in long, and white with yellow anthers and a light-colored stigma.
The Aramberri valley, is a much-visited place, full of cactus treasures. Three species of *Turbinicarpus*, and *Ariocarpus*, *Thelocactus*, and other interesting cacti all grow here within a small area. The above-mentioned varietas occurs in hollows in limestone rock, in the immediate vicinity of the town of Aramberri. There are shallow depressions in the rock where several dozen seedlings can be counted, all crowded together; only a few of these will grow into mature plants, bearing flowers and fruit. This cactus was grown mainly as a graft, but specimens cultivated in this way usually grow to an unnatural size. The slower method of cultivation on their own roots is preferable, because it results in much more impressive-looking plants. This cactus needs a slightly alkaline soil mix, full sun during active growth, cold wintering, and watering only when the soil mix is completely dry.

Turbinicarpus schmiedickeanus var. *klinkerianus* ▣ ○

GLOBOSE

Originally considered a separate species, but now usually regarded as a varietas of the highly variable *T. schmiedickeanus* range.
The slightly compacted, flattened-globose stem is about 1 1/4in in diameter, and has a crown covered with white down. It is divided into conical mammillae tipped with a downy areole, which produces 3 spines, but 1 or 2 of them soon drop off. The white flowers, often with pink central streaks, grow from the youngest areoles, and measure about 5/8in across. The small berry contains several dozen fine black seeds.
The author of the description believed these plants originated in the state of Tamaulipas, but, as field observations have shown, they occur in the vicinity of Entronque Huizache in the state of San Luis Potosí. They grow on limestone hillocks, often in cracks between rocks, or on flat screes and terraces on hills. There is usually a very rich range of associated vegetation growing with them; this consists of a number of other species and various scrub vegetation.
This cactus is recommended to less experienced growers.

Turbinicarpus schmiedickeanus var. *dickisoniae*

Turbinicarpus schmiedickeanus var. *klinkerianus*

Turbinicarpus schmiedickeanus var. *macrochele*

Turbinicarpus schmiedickeanus var. *macrochele* ▣ ○

GLOBOSE

The small stem grows to a diameter of 1 1/2in, and merges underground into a thick beet-like root. In the wild, only a small part of the stem protrudes above ground, and the greater part is hidden below the surface. The ribs are divided into mammillae with areoles a fraction of an inch wide, each with 3–5 spines growing from it. The older spines drop off. The flowers are white or pinkish. The fruit is a berry which splits to release fine black seeds.

This cactus occurs near the town of Matehuala in the state of San Luis Potosí. It grows on flat terraces of limestone hills or in clumps of grass and between rocks. It is very closely related to the varietas *klinkerianus* and even forms a transitional population which is very difficult to classify within one taxon or the other. When growing *Turbinicarpus* generally, it is important to make sure that plants included in the collection have a certified place of origin. This taxon is no exception. Only on this basis can the collection gain some botanical value. In some catalogs it is now possible to find seeds from a specified locality, which is very important information. Cultivation itself is not complicated. To beginners, grafting seedlings onto *Pereskiopsis* is recommended. They require full sun, a slightly alkaline, well-drained soil mix, and should be allowed to dry out between waterings.

Turbinicarpus schmiedickeanus var. *panarottoi* ▣ ○

FLATTENED-GLOBOSE

The taxon was first described in 1996 by the Czech cactus expert Jan Říha, who named it after the Italian specialist Paolino Panarotto, who discovered the locality of this varietas. The solitary stem is up to 2in in diameter and roughly 2 1/4in long, but two thirds of this are hidden in the ground. The above-ground part of the stem is green-gray. In older specimens, a single central spine grows from the areole, but in time even this drops off. The flowers appear from the youngest areoles at the growing point; they are about 1in across, funnel-shaped, and usually light pink with a darker streak in the middle of the petal.

According to field observations, the area of distribution of the species is limited, being confined to a small region south of the town of Tula in the state of Tamaulipas. It grows on gentle hillocks on limestone scree between rocks. The first plants in collections were grown as grafts, but since the species grows without great difficulty on its own roots, self-rooted plants are beginning to appear in collections, and these resemble the wild plants more closely in habit. For greater success with propagation, grafting germinated seedlings onto year-old shoots of *Pereskiopsis* is recommended, and, after a year's growth, rooting the grafts and growing them on as self-rooted plants.

Turbinicarpus schmiedickeanus var. *panarottoi*

Turbinicarpus schwarzii var. *rubriflorus*

Turbinicarpus schwarzii var. *rubriflorus* ▣ ○

GLOBOSE

For a long time this cactus was in circulation in collections under the name of the red-flowered *T. schwarzii*. In 1993 the varietas was finally given the valid description used here. The plant grows to a diameter of 1 1/4–1 1/2in, and, unlike the type species, should have slightly longer spines (1in), though this is certainly not true of every individual plant. The flower is usually pink, with a darker central streak, but individuals in a locality have flower colors ranging from white to dark pink, like the specimen in the photograph.

According to H. J. Bonatz, author of the description, the Cerros Blancos area in the state of San Luis Potosí was the original locality where the type material of this varietas was collected. The plants grow on gentle slopes of limestone hills at altitudes of about 4,000ft. However, we believe this varietas is overestimated, because colonies in the wild are far less uniform than some authors maintain. Large numbers of the most varied hybrids are in circulation among growers, and it is therefore necessary to obtain seeds from a certified source. Cultivation is moderately difficult, because the seedlings grow relatively slowly, and are sensitive to growers' mistakes. It is advisable to bypass this sensitive stage by grafting onto *Pereskiopsis*, and then root the graft. If allowed to continue growing on this rootstock, it may reach completely unnatural dimensions and become distorted. It requires full sun, cold wintering, and a slightly alkaline, very well-drained soil mix.

Turbinicarpus valdezianus 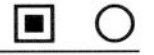

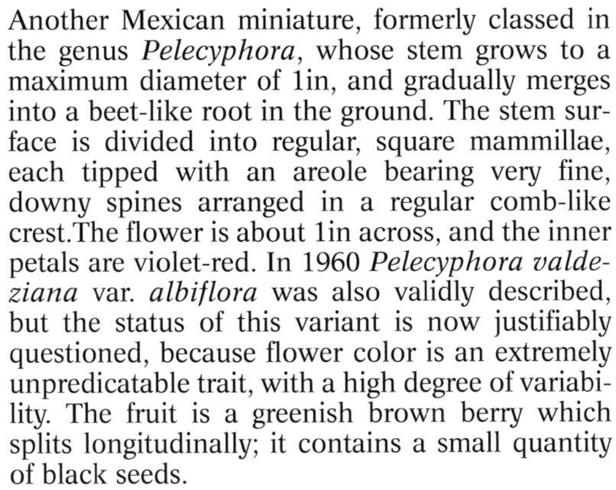

GLOBOSE

Another Mexican miniature, formerly classed in the genus *Pelecyphora*, whose stem grows to a maximum diameter of 1in, and gradually merges into a beet-like root in the ground. The stem surface is divided into regular, square mammillae, each tipped with an areole bearing very fine, downy spines arranged in a regular comb-like crest.The flower is about 1in across, and the inner petals are violet-red. In 1960 *Pelecyphora valdeziana* var. *albiflora* was also validly described, but the status of this variant is now justifiably questioned, because flower color is an extremely unpredicatable trait, with a high degree of variability. The fruit is a greenish brown berry which splits longitudinally; it contains a small quantity of black seeds.

The regions north of the town of Saltillo, and Monclova, are important localities. It grows all over these areas, between limestone rocks, usually without any shade from associated vegetation. Seed is practically the only way of propagating this plant, other than the grafting of offshoots from parent plants from which the top has been deliberately removed. Growing seedlings on is not at all easy, but self-rooted plants, when correctly tended, resemble the wild plants very closely. The requirements are a well-drained soil mix with added minerals, cold wintering, and full sun when in active growth. Due to of the sensitive roots, indiscriminate watering during the dormant period in summer should be avoided.

Turbinicarpus valdezianus

2. United States of America

The distribution of cacti in the USA is concentrated mainly in the south and southwest. Of course, cacti occur in other parts of the USA, and their localities extend as far as Canada. However, this distribution can be regarded as an extension to marginal zones, and apart from a few species of *Opuntia*, no other cacti are found so far to the north. On the other hand, in terms of cacti, the south and southwest are extremely interesting. In the USA there are some endemic genera which do not extend to Mexico (*Sclerocactus*, *Toumeya*, *Navajoa*), but there are also many species whose distribution extends unbroken from Mexico onto the territory of Texas, New Mexico, or Arizona. One of the largest cacti in the world, *Carnegiea gigantea*, is a sort of symbol of the American southwest; it is popularly known as saguaro, and these cacti are inseparably linked with the life of the Native American tribes, who have always used them for many purposes.
Cacti grow in semi-desert and desert regions of the USA, and there are also some very interesting localities in National Parks. Among these, it is worth mentioning the Organ Pipe Cactus National Monument in Arizona, and the Joshua Tree National Monument in California. The range of cactus species is much narrower here than in Mexico, but the cacti of the USA are real treasures. Their attraction for cactus enthusiasts lies not only in their beautiful spines, as seen in members of the genus *Sclerocactus*, but also in the fact that with some species, year-round open-air cultivation is an option worth trying, while other species tolerate wintering in an unheated greenhouse. A rockery with *Opuntia*, *Echinocereus*, or the very varied forms of *Coryphantha vivipara*, is a pleasure to see, and cacti grown in this way can be very evocative of cacti living in their natural environment. In cool climates, however, it is important to provide the right winter conditions for cacti, corresponding to conditions in their natural habitat; this means, in particular, very cold, freezing winters, but a minimum of rain and snow. Also typical of the American southwest is the presence of other interesting xerophytic and succulent species; among these, fine representatives of the genera *Agave* and *Yucca* can be admired in their natural settings. But, unquestionably, the greatest experience for the cactus enthusiast is finding one of the endemic species, e.g. a member of the genus *Sclerocactus* or *Pediocactus*: for example, *Pediocactus winkleri* in the Navajo desert or *Sclerocactus wrightiae* in the Abajo Mountains (Utah), under canopies of Ponderosa pine (*Pinus ponderosa*).
Cacti in the USA are very strictly protected, and as a rule the places where the cacti grow are also subject to this protection.

Left: *Carnegiea gigantea,* seedling in the foreground

Ancistrocactus scheeri ▣ ○

GLOBOSE

The globose or slightly columnar stem of this cactus is usually rather larger in cultivated plants than in the wild, where it only grows to these, and the green epidermis is practically invisible. The flower is about 1in across, and the inner petals are violet-red. The flower color is an extremely unpredicatable trait, with a high degree of variability. The fruit is a greenish brown berry which splits longitudinally; it contains a small quantity of black seeds. Growing seedlings on is not at all easy, but self-rooted plants resemble the wild plants very closely. The requirements are a well-drained soil mix with minerals, cold wintering, and full sun when in active growth.

Ancistrocactus scheeri

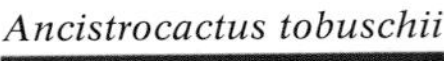
Ancistrocactus tobuschii

Ancistrocactus tobuschii ▣ ○

GLOBOSE

The smallest member of this genus; measuring only about 2in. The surface is divided into conical mammillae, each tipped with a round areole with yellow down. Growing from this, there are 7–12 yellow radial spines and about 3 central spines; the longest may be hooked at the tip. The yellow flowers are about 1 1/4in across and grow from the youngest areoles at the top of the plant. The fruit is a green berry, later slightly reddish, which contains black seeds a fraction of an inch long.
This is a rare plant which occurs in a limited area in the wild. It grows on a limestone substrate at altitudes of about 1,500ft above sea level, on Edwards Plateau near Vanderpool (Bandera County) in Texas. Cultivated plants are usually grown as grafts on a slow-growing rootstock; among the most suitable for this purpose are *Myrtillocactus geometrizans* or *Trichocereus pasacana*. Self-rooted cultivation is quite difficult: it needs to dry out between waterings, a well-drained, mineral-rich soil mix, full sun in the summer, and very cold wintering.

Carnegiea gigantea 

COLUMNAR

One of the best-known cacti, also known by the native American name "saguaro." It is famed for its height and its unique growing habits. Growing to over 60ft, it is said to be the tallest cactus in the whole family. The candelabra-like stem is characteristic of this species, and stands of saguaro in their natural habitat are a very impressive sight. The first flowers appear when the cactus is about 75 years old, and the oldest specimens are about 250 years old. The white flowers open at night, and are pollinated by bats and insects.
Wild saguaro cacti are found mainly in Arizona and California, and smaller localities extend to Sonora in Mexico. There is not much experience of growing this cactus in collections. It grows very slowly, and has low tolerance for growers' mistakes. It needs full sun, a very well-drained soil mix (with added drainage material at the base), and winter temperatures of about 50 °F.

Carnegiea gigantea

Carnegiea gigantea, detail

Coryphantha vivipara □ ○

GLOBOSE

Forms extensive clusters comprising as many as 200 stems. The individual plants are 2–6in high and 3/4–4in in diameter. 12–20 radial and 4 central spines, up to 3/4in long, grow from each areole. The purple flowers, up to 1 1/2in across, are a splendid sight. The fruit is a green berry with brown seeds.

This is probably the most widespread globose cactus in the USA, with a high population density in some areas. In the north, it extends as far as the southern Canadian provinces of Alberta and Manitoba, and in the southern USA it extends from Arizona through New Mexico to Texas. Some *Coryphantha* species are considered the most resistant of cacti, in terms of adaptability to cool climates. In rockeries with good drainage, they can be relied on to withstand the severest frost in winter and then flower beautifully in summer. This species is probably better suited to outdoor cultivation than to an overheated greenhouse. But for year-round cultivation, suitable plants with a known place of origin must be selected.

Coryphantha vivipara

Echinocereus chloranthus

Echinocereus chloranthus □ ○

COLUMNAR

This is one of the smaller species of *Echinocereus* with a cylindrical stem. It is usually solitary, or produces only a few offsets. It reaches heights up to 8in and a diameter of up to 2 3/4in. The spination is very variable according to where the plant originates. So far, three variants and a large number of local forms have been distinguished. The flowers grow roughly in the middle of the stem, and their color is highly variable, from yellowish green to brown.
Because the species occurs in climatically less favorable regions at high altitudes in the southwest (Texas, New Mexico), there are ecotypes which can tolerate wintering in cool areas, but they must be given the driest possible environment in winter.

Echinocereus davisii ▣ ○

COLUMNAR

Now classed as a separate species, but in the past it was usually considered a varietas of the closely related *E. viridiflorus*. The stem is usually solitary, or accompanied by a few offsets, and grows only 1 1/4–1 1/2in tall, with a stem diameter of 5/8–1in. The number, length, and color of the spines are quite variable. Usually, however, they are 1/4–5/8in long. The flower grows from the side of the plant, and is light yellow to greenish in color, and about 3/4in across.

Echinocereus davisii

The species occurs endemically in a relatively small area of the USA, in Texas (Brewster Co.), south of the town of Marathon. Cultivation is generally the same as for *E. viridiflorus*, but it does not tolerate outdoor wintering.

Echinocereus fendleri

COLUMNAR

Another highly variable species, which, on closer study, is fascinating for the diversity of its forms. The columnar stem, which is usually solitary, varies in height between 3 and 8in, with a diameter of 2–3in. Growing from the round areoles, there are 5–10 radial spines, and usually 1 central spine, up to 1 1/2in long.

Echinocereus fendleri

This central spine, unlike the light-colored radial spines, is gray-black or entirely black. The funnel-shaped flower opens from a pointed green bud, with a spiny flower tube. When fully open, the flower is 2 1/4–3in across; it is purple-red in color, and the yellow anthers contrast with the green stigma growing on a long white style.
The wide variation corresponds to the huge area of distribution. The species can be found in the states of Texas, New Mexico, Colorado, Arizona, and Utah, but also extends to the Mexican states of Chihuahua and Sonora. The very large number of collection numbers makes it a very attractive species for keen cactus growers, who try to document this variation and display it in the collection. Some types from the coldest localities can even tolerate low winter temperatures in cultivation, but the plants must be protected, above all, against excessive damp. SB 0134 from Bernalillo County (New Mexico) can theoretically tolerate lows of 0 °F.

Echinocereus x *lloydii* 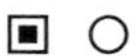

COLUMNAR

An unusual plant, showing features of the two parent species *E. dasyacanthus* and *E. coccineus*. It occurs in the USA in Pecos County, near Tuna Springs (Texas), from where it was collected by F. E. Lloyd in 1909. As yet, this population, with tetraploid chromosomes, is taxonomically unevaluated. The hybridized plants are extremely variable. The plant in the photograph is from seed

Echinocereus x lloydii

Echinocereus nichollii

collected at the end of the 1960s; its type of spination is more reminiscent of *E. coccineus*.

Echinocereus nichollii 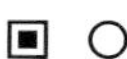

COLUMNAR

One of the closest relatives of *E. engelmannii*, with which it was formerly classified as a varietas or subspecies. It forms groups of up to 30 stems, the largest of which reach heights of up to 2ft 4in, with a diameter of 1 1/2–2 3/4in. Growing from the round circular areoles, there are 8–12 radial spines, 1/4–1in long, and 4–8 central spines, 1 1/4–2 3/4in long. Their color varies from white through yellow to light brown. The flower is pinkish mauve, often with a darker streak in the middle of the petals, and when fully open it is up to 2 3/4in across.
The habitats are mainly in the Sonora desert, distributed over US and Mexican territory. In the USA, it grows in Pima County, Arizona; in Mexico, the southernmost limit of its occurrence is in the north of the state of Sonora. As a cultivated plant, this cactus usually circulates under Steven Brack's collection references, SB 0148 and SB 1786. Cultivation is generally the same as for other *Echinocereus* of this group. The requirements are: as much light as possible, good ventilation, and careful watering during the summer dormant period, plus a well-drained, mineral-rich soil mix, and cold wintering in absolutely dry conditions. Propagation is by seed, and for this species, it is advisable to use seeds with a known place of origin.

Echinocereus reichenbachii ssp. baileyi

Echinocereus reichenbachii ssp. baileyi ▣ ○

COLUMNAR

Another extremely variable taxon that was formerly classified as a separate species. The columnar stem, which is usually solitary, grows to a height of up to 10in, with a diameter of about 2in. It is divided into roughly 15 ribs bearing oval areoles. From these grow the radial spines, varying in color from white to brown. The same variability is seen in the central spines. There are even forms in which central spines are entirely absent. The large flowers are up to 4in across when fully open, and purple-red. The fruit ripens about two months after fertilization; it is green in color, and contains a large number of small black seeds.

Occurrence is reported in two states of the USA: Texas, and Oklahoma, where it grows in the Wichita Mountains. It is often grown in collections, but individual plants differ widely. It is therefore necessary, in this case too, to grow plants of a proven origin, and at present, seeds under the following field numbers are commercially available: DJF 1308, DJF 1327, HK 1448, and SB 0211.

Echinocereus triglochidiatus

Echinocereus triglochidiatus □ ○

CLUSTERING

This cactus forms clustering stems, which are slightly spiraling in the wild plant; they may be up to 2ft 4in long, and up to 4in in diameter. The spination is very varied; the species has a number of local forms which may differ sharply. Usually, however, the number of spines is quite small, ranging from 2 to 5 in a single areole. The flower grows from the upper part of the stem, and is about 2 3/4in long and usually 2in across, and its color is a striking reddish orange.

There are a number of natural localities, almost all of them on US territory, with only a few extending into northern regions of the Mexican peninsula of Baja California. It grows on rocky ground and mountain massifs at altitudes of 4,000 to 7,000ft. It is a popular species because of its extreme variability. It flowers at an advanced age. Some ecotypes are frost-resistant, and provided the basic requirements are met, they can even survive winters in rockeries in cool climates.

Echinocereus viridiflorus □ ○

CLUSTERING

The short columnar stem grows in a cluster or individually, and may reach a height of up to 6in, with a stem diameter of about 21/4in. The spination is very varied, and differs according to locality, but most of the radial spines (up to 20) are pressed to the stem, being regularly spaced in a spidery arrangement around the areole. Central spines may be absent, or there may be only one. The flowers grow roughly at the mid-point on the stem, and, as the name viridiflorus indicates, they are greenish, or greenish yellow.

This typical representative of US cactus flora is the northernmost of all *Echinocereus*, in terms of its occurrence. It is distributed over many states in the southwest and midwest of the USA (New Mexico, Texas, Colorado, Oklahoma, Kansas, Dakota, and Wyoming). It usually occurs in grassland, or in the moderate shade of mountain forest. Because of its high variability and ease of cultiva-

Echinocereus viridiflorus

tion, it is very popular among cactus growers. There are growers specializing in the genus *Echinocereus*, who devote special attention to this complex. Some ecotypes tolerate wintering at temperatures below zero, but they also require absolutely dry conditions. The place of origin is very important in the case of this species, because plants of known origin are botanically very valuable.

Echinomastus intertextus □ ○

COLUMNAR

The cylindrical stem may grow to 6in in height, and half as much in diameter. The spines almost completely cover the epidermis of the stem, and this is why the species is called *intertextus* (interwoven). The flowers are about 1 1/4in across, and the color of their petals is variable; they may be creamy white, or light pink, or yellowish.
This cactus can be seen in the wild in many localities in the USA and Mexico. Plants originating in some regions of the USA tolerate frost, and if grafted onto a frost-resistant rootstock, *E. intertextus* can be grown through the winter in an unheated greenhouse. Plants on their own roots are still relatively rare, and most cactus growers prefer grafts.

Echinomastus johnstonii var. *lutescens* 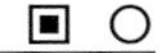 ○

COLUMNAR

Usually a solitary-growing cactus, whose stem, according to the description, is no more than 10in high, with a stem diameter of about 43/4in. In this varietas, the prominent radial and central spines, with their brown color, are a perfect foil for the greenish yellow flowers, usually with a darker streak, which appear in early summer.

Echinomastus intertextus

A relatively wide area where this cactus occurs is in the Mohave desert in the southwestern USA. However, this applies to the yellow-flowered varietas, and according to the latest field observations, this varietas does not mix with colonies of the red-flowered subspecies. Cactus specialists usually grow this cactus as a graft on *Pereskiopsis*, on which they graft it very early, just a day or two after germination. About a year later, the rootstock can be shortened so that the graft looks like a self-rooted plant.

Echinomastus johnstonii var. *lutescens*

Echinomastus mariposensis

Echinomastus mariposensis 

GLOBOSE

In the wild, the oval stem does not exceed a diameter of 2 1/4in and a height of 4in. It has roughly 20 ribs which are divided into tubercles. Each of these is tipped with a large downy areole, from which grow about 25 white radial spines, and about 7 gray-black central spines. The funnel-shaped flower is about 1 1/4in across, and the fruit is a longitudinally splitting berry.
The type locality is considered to be the southwestern extremity of Brewster Co., Texas, where the plants grow on low foothills at altitudes of 3,000–4,000ft. However, the area of distribution extends as far as Cuatro Cienegas in the Mexican state of Coahuila. This species has become more widespread among cactus growers in recent years, now that there are enough seeds available on the market. But this is still a rarity which should preferably be grafted, because self-rooted plants are sensitive to any mistake made by the grower. Because it produces buds in early spring, it requires cold wintering in the light.

Escobaria minima 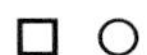

GLOBOSE–COLUMNAR

This plant owes its species epithet to its miniature size. However, it is still known to cactus growers under the name *E. nelliae*. The individual oval stems are no more than 2in tall, with a diameter of 3/4–1 1/4in. The plant produces offsets from its base. The spines are pinkish at first, and later turn gray or even white. The flowers, growing from the middle of the plant, are light purplish pink, and about 1in across.
It is very unusual to find this plant in the wild, because it only grows on a few limestone hills south of the town of Marathon, Texas, and the stems are very well camouflaged. Growing this miniature on its own roots is a very difficult task, so it is usually grafted onto slow-growing rootstocks, though the grafted plants differ in their growing habits from self-rooted specimens.

Escobaria minima

Escobaria sneedii var. leei

Escobaria sneedii var. *leei* ▣ ○

CLUSTERING

Another miniature member of the genus, whose small stems form luxuriantly spreading clusters. The slender cylindrical stem, about 3in high and 1 3/4in in diameter, is initialy solitary and later forms a many-headed group of offsets. The small radial and thicker central spines are whitish in color. The stem is divided into small mammillae which are completely hidden under the dense white spines. The color of the flowers is very interesting, and in very well-defined types it may be brownish pink, often with a darker central streak on the petals.
This cactus is part of the flora of the USA, where it grows in a limited area in New Mexico. In terms of locality this is a very rare species, and the whole area of its occurrence is limited to a few gullies to the west of the town of Carlsbad (Eddy Co.). In cool climates, it needs a position in full sun, as close as possible to the glass, and good ventialtion. If you decide to graft it, the rootstock you choose should be slow-growing, but even so, the grafted plant will grow to an unnatural size. Seed propagation is preferable, but vegetative propagation, using offsets, may also be considered. After removal from the parent plant, the offsets should be left to dry for about a week, and then inserted into clean perlite, in which the plants easily take root.

Ferocactus cylindraceus ▣ ○

BARREL-SHAPED

The columnar stem may grow to 10ft in exceptional cases, and its diameter does not exceed 16in. The number and length of the spines are very variable. The radial spines may be hairy, while the

Ferocactus cylindraceus var. *eastwoodiae*

Ferocactus cylindraceus

central spines are thick and woody, and sometimes grow to nearly 8in. The yellow flowers, up to 2 1/4in across, open in early spring.
The species can be found most often in a number of localities on the Baja California peninsula, but its area of distribution extends as far as southwestern Arizona, and to Sonora. For growing, a well-drained, slightly alkaline soil mix should be chosen. The species is sensitive to scorch by the spring sun. Wintering, as far as possible, should be in the light, with absolutely no water.

Ferocactus cylindraceus var. *eastwoodiae* 

BARREL-SHAPED

This barrel-shaped cactus, reaching a height of 10ft in extreme cases, may have a stem diameter of over 16in. It differs from the type species partly in its smaller number of radial spines, of which there may be 12–14 in each areole. The bottom-most central spine grows to a length of up to 3in, and is straw yellow in color. The flower is lemon yellow. Unlike the type, it grows only in the USA, where it can be seen in Arizona, e.g. in the western part of Pima Co., Gila Co., or in the mountains above Queen Creek. Cultivation is the same as for other *Ferocactus*.

Ferocactus viridescens

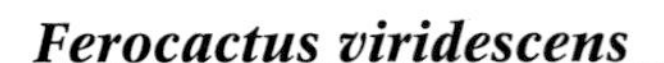

Ferocactus viridescens ■ ○

BARREL-SHAPED

Classed among the medium-sized *Ferocactus*, because its body grows to a diameter of roughly 1ft, and the height of full-grown specimens may be as much as 3ft, though in most cases it is less. The prominent central spines, arranged in a cross, are thick and woody, and may grow to a length of up to 6in. The flowers appear on relatively young plants (about 10 years old), and are yellowish green, and about 2in across when fully open.
The species grows partly in southwestern California, but also colonizes the dry northwestern region of the Mexican state of Baja California. It is now seen in collections much more often, because of its suitability for commercial production. Important requirements are relatively warm wintering, and full sun, but only when the plant has been acclimatized to the first spring sunshine (otherwise there is a risk of scorch).

Ferocactus wislizeni

Mammillaria wilcoxii

Ferocactus wislizenii

BARREL-SHAPED

This barrel-shaped species may be up to 6 1/2ft high, with a stem diameter of 32in. Spines grow from the areoles on the ribs; the bottom-most central spines grow to lengths of over 4in. The yellow-orange flowers are up to 2 1/4in across when fully open. After pollination and fertilization, they turn into oval fruit, up to 2in long.
This species occurs in the desert and semi-desert regions of the USA, from the westernmost part of Texas to southern Arizona, but it is also found in the northern regions of Mexico. Seeds are available almost every year, so there is always an adequate supply of healthy seedlings. They need the best-lit position in the greenhouse, and should be watered occasionally, but only after the soil mix has completely dried out.

Mammillaria wilcoxii

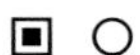

GLOBOSE

This species is closely related to *M. wrightii*, under which some authorities classify it as a subspecies. The stem, which is globose in wild plants, may take on a slightly columnar shape in cultivation. It is roughly 2in in diameter, and growing from the round, white areoles there are 14–16 radial spines about 1/2in long, and one brown, hook-ended central spine, up to 3/4in long. The beautiful flowers open on summer days, and there are usually a few of them on the plant. They are 1 1/4–1 1/2in across, pinkish mauve, with yellow anthers and a lighter-colored stigma.This is another species occurring both in the USA and in Mexico. It grows in the southern part of New Mexico and Arizona, but can also be found in Sonora and Chihuahua. It usually grows on flat terrain, in the moderate shade of grasses and other associated vegetation. In collections, it is one of the more sensitive species, and it is therefore necessary to choose the right soil mix with an adequate mineral content to ensure proper drainage. It tolerates full sun without any problems, but has less resistance to high summer temperatures in an overheated greenhouse. Germinating the seed is not difficult, but some growers graft the germinated seedlings onto Pereskiopsis, and root the scions later, when they have grown sufficiently.

Opuntia phaeacantha □ ○

SPREADING

This variable species tends to sprawl, but some forms may grow about 3ft tall. In the past, a large number of variants were described, which are now known only to a few experts on the complexities of this large genus. The pads are 4–6in long, and there is a variable number of spines. The lemon yellow flowers, which appear on pads at least 2 years old, are up to 2in across.

This species occurs in the states of New Mexico and Texas, where it grows high in the mountains. In the most diverse variants, it occurs in other American states – Colorado, California, and Arizona. This extremely wide area of distribution gives rise to the above-mentioned high variability of this taxon. Some forms are very resistant to low temperatures, and tolerate the relatively severe frosts of cooler climates without serious problems. Due to this, selected ecotypes are used as rootstocks for more tender species, e.g. from the genera *Echinocereus*, *Sclerocactus*, or *Pediocactus*. Cultivation is extremely simple: they can be grown outdoors without any cover, provided the soil is gritty and well-drained. Propagation is by removal of pads which have already rooted.

Pediocactus bradyi

Pediocactus bradyi □ ○

GLOBOSE

The very small stem, which very occasionally forms offsets, is initially globose, becoming oval when older; it is roughly 2in in diameter and 2 1/4cm high. It is divided into inconspicuous mamillae tipped with circular areoles. Growing from each of these, there are roughly 15 short white or yellow-brown radial spines; central spines are entirely absent. The flower grows from the youngest areoles on the top; it is about 3/4in across and is white or yellowish white.

P. bradyi is one of the cacti that is grown out of doors throughout the year. It grows in northern Arizona, and tolerates frost very well, but it needs to be protected from damp in winter. It suffers from early spring temperature fluctuations and frequent rainfall, which can completely destroy it. As an alternative to placing it permanently in a very well-drained rockery with an adequate drainage layer, there is the option of wintering the plant in an unheated greenhouse, where success is almost 100 % certain. The species is propagated by seed, but in the past, grafting was common, using offsets from parent plants.

Opuntia phaeacantha

Pediocactus paradinei

Pediocactus paradinei ☐ ○

FLATTENED-GLOBOSE

The flattened-globose stem grows to a maximum of 3in in diameter and 2in in height, and its lower part merges smoothly into a bulky, beet-like root. There are about 20 white radial spines which are about 3/4in long, longer in older plants. The central spines form mainly on older plants, and may be up to 2 3/4in long. The elegant, whitish yellow flowers appear near the growing point and are about 1in across. The berry contains a relatively small number of large seeds, up to 3/16in long. There are very few localities where it has been found; perhaps the best-known is Coconino County in Arizona, where it grows partly in juniper-pine wood (6,500ft above sea level), and also on grassy plains at lower altitudes of about 5,000ft. Like other members of the genus, it is usually grown in collections only as a graft, preferably on *Eriocereus jusbertii* or *Trichocereus pasacana*. Growing plants on their own roots is extremely difficult and, in view of the poor availability of seeds, very risky. Wintering is possible in a very cold environment; during active growth the plant needs full sun, and marked temperature differences between day and night suit it very well.

Pediocactus peeblesianus var. *fickeiseniae*

Pediocactus peeblesianus var. *fickeiseniae* ☐ ○

GLOBOSE-COLUMNAR

This relatively small, columnar plant grows to a height of 2 3/4–3in and a diameter of roughly 1 1/2in. Its prominent spination is made up of soft, corky spines. There is only one central spine, which may vary in length, but the maximum is 2 1/4in. There are 5–7 radial spines, about 1/4in long. The plant blooms from the upper areoles with yellow flowers up to 1in across. The fruit is a greenish spherical berry containing a few irregular, obovate, black or black-gray seeds.

The area of distribution of this cactus is not very wide; it extends along the Little Colorado River in the northern part of the Grand Canyon in Arizona. It favors sandy soils in grassland, in which it is very well camouflaged. This is another difficult plant for growers, which usually appears in collections as a graft. The seeds are reluctant to germinate, and it is therefore advisable to make small incisions in them with the tip of a scalpel (scarification). After germination, immediate grafting onto *Pereskiopsis* is recommended and, as soon as the plants reach a size of about 1/2in, it is advisable to re-graft them onto a slow-growing permanent rootstock. Another option is to try and rooting the grafts, but this calls for a certain amount of cactus-growing experience and practice. Otherwise the entire *P. peeblesianus* range is frost-resistant in cool climates, and if the plant is grafted onto an equally resistant type of *Opuntia* or *Echinocereus*, it can be wintered in an unheated greenhouse.

Pediocactus simpsonii ☐ ○

GLOBOSE-COLUMNAR

A slightly columnar cactus, which may reach up to 8in high, with a stem diameter of about 4 3/4in. The spirally arranged ribs, of which there are usually 12, are divided into pyramid-like tubercles, each bearing an elliptical areole. Growing from this, there are whitish radial and darker, brownish or red-brown central spines. This species shows great variability in spination and flower color, which is to be expected with such a huge area of distribution. The flowers are 5/8–1 1/4in across, and their color may range from light mauve through pink to white, as in the plant in the photograph.

This is a typical representative of the cactus flora of the USA. The center of distribution of the species lies in the states of Utah and Colorado, but it also grows in southern Oregon, northern Arizona, and, among other places, the northern regions of New Mexico, and eastern Nevada. The arid regi-

Pediocactus simpsonii

ons of the southwestern USA consist of varied terrain, and this *Pediocactus* found in the most varied localities from level prairie to rocky valleys. Under suitable conditions this cactus can survive cold winters unharmed. However, the plant must be sufficiently dried out before the frosts come; during wintering, damp and a rise in temperature are more harmful to it than severe frosts. It is therefore advisable to winter the plant in an unheated greenhouse, or try to grow it in a rockery with a drainage layer. In terms of cultivation, it is one of the difficult cacti, because it has poor tolerance for high temperatures, and its growth cycle is rather distinct, with growth occurring mainly in early spring and in fall.

Toumeya papyracantha □ ○

COLUMNAR

Many taxonomists are now inclined to classify this plant in the genus *Pediocactus*, but most cactus growers know the plant by the name used here. In the wild, it forms individual stems; under cultivation, grafted individuals form offsets. This is a columnar cactus, which grows about 4in high, with a stem diameter of 1 1/4in. The areoles bear 8–9 radial spines, arranged in a radiating pattern, and up to 4 soft, flexible, papery central spines, over 1 1/4in long. Hence the species name *papyracantha*, which means "with papery spines." The whitish yellow flowers grow from the crown, and are up to 1 1/4in long.

This is a typical representative of the cactus flora of the USA, growing on the grassy plains of the southern states (New Mexico and Arizona). A challenge for the grower, especially in the case of self-rooted cultivation. In order to obtain a large number of plants, the best option is seed, followed by early grafting of the germinated plants onto *Pereskiopsis*. The young plants can then be re-grafted, or severed from the rootstock and then grown on as self-rooted plants. However, this calls for a very well-drained and, ideally, mineral-high soil mix, a position in full sun, and very low temperatures during wintering.

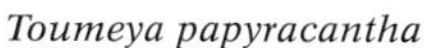

Toumeya papyracantha

3. Peru

The coastal lowlands rise steeply along the length of the whole coast. The Peruvian Andes mountain range extends from north to south across the country (area 500,000 square miles). The highest mountain in this range is 22,000ft high (Huascarán). The range's escarpment falls gradually eastward from mountains and uplands to regions covered in grassland savannah.
The coastal areas of southern Peru have a similar climate to northern Chile – a hot desert climate with an average annual temperature of 65 °F. Temperatures in the warmest month reach 80 °F and range from 50–72 °F in the coolest months.
Even though Peru is fairly close to the equator, cacti found in these areas are able to withstand cold winters, because most of them are found at fairly high altitudes. Only a few lowland species need overwintering at higher temperatures (e.g. *Melocactus*).
The cacti which grow in Peru are very colorful and there are two distinct main groups. The first grows on the coast or the western slopes of the Cordillera (*Islaya*, *Eriosyce*, *Neoraimondia*) and the second grows on the eastern slopes of the Cordillera or in eastern Peru (*Cleistocactus*, *Espostoa*, *Oroya*).
They thrive in cultivation, and Peruvian cacti are an essential part of any fairly large collection. There are a number of interesting high-altitude species and various columnar cacti, which can be used to create a very impressive collection. Peru is also home to a few endemic genera (*Neobinghamia*, *Mila*, and *Morawetzia*), which definitely make an interesting ornament to any collection. Recently a number of cactus collectors have headed off for Peru to investigate hitherto unexplored areas.

Left: *Espostoa lanata*

Acanthocalycium violaceum ▣ ⊙

GLOBOSE

The stem is usually globose or slightly columnar and about 8in tall. The thin radial (12–15) and thicker central spines (3–5) are straw yellow in color and form a magnificent contrast with the pale violet of the flowers, which bloom in late spring or at the start of summer. In the wild this species occurs in the Peruvian province of Cordoba. It is very popular among cactus growers owing to its ease of cultivation. You have to wait a fairly long time for flowering and it can take as much as ten years. Overwintering in cool, light conditions is also required for flowering.

Acanthocalycium violaceum

Akersia roseiflora

Akersia roseiflora ▣ ○

COLUMNAR

This is a columnar cactus which produces stems about 3ft tall and 2in in diameter. It is thickly covered in oval areoles from which sprout straw yellow spines. At the points where the flowers are borne, the spines are longer than on other parts of the stem. The beautiful pink-red flowers are bent slightly into an S-shape. These flowers, which are about 2 1/4in long, are what are known as zygomorphic (symmetrical about a single plane).
This species occurs in a number of places in northern Peru, where it forms dense colonies. It should become more popular in collections in cool climates, because it requires little upkeep. It grows fairly slowly, so is usually grafted; grafting is not essential for successful cultivation, however, because it blooms at a stem height of 16in. It can be propagated from seed of cuttings, which should be left in a warm shady place for about three weeks. Only plant after the wound has completely dried out.

Arequipa erectrocylindrica

Armatocereus cartwrightianus

Arequipa erectrocylindrica

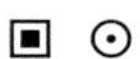

COLUMNAR

Like other members of this small genus, *A. erectrocylindrica* is not particularly well-known among cactus growers. It is extremely rare to come across it in collections. It has a columnar stem, which can grow up to 26in tall, with attractive spines, particularly at points where flowers bloom. These zygomorphic flowers are up to 4in long and are scarlet in color, adapted for pollination by hummingbirds.
It grows in high-altitude areas of southern Peru and northern Chile, like other members of the genus forming dense colonies. In collections it should be placed in a sunny spot and ideally should be stood outside during the summer, provided there is a roof to protect the plants from prolonged rainfall. It should be overwintered in cool, dry conditions.

Armatocereus cartwrightianus

COLUMNAR

This cactus branches irregularly and forms a shrub up to 15ft high. The individual stems are divided into 7 or 8 ribs. The newly formed annual shoots have few spines and can be distinguished from the previous year's growth by the segmentation, a characteristic of the whole genus. Older annual shoots have a central spine up to 4 3/4in long. The flower is white, 2 3/4–3 1/2in long, and is narrowly funnel-shaped. The round fruit is covered in yellow-brown spines and conceals black shiny seeds within the pulp. The species is not only found in northern areas of Peru but also extends to southern Ecuador. One of the places it grows there is in the Catamayo valley, near the administrative town of the same name. It grows on relatively steep, south-facing, southwest-facing and southeast-facing slopes. It is relatively rare to find this cactus in collections, partly because the seeds are hard to come by, but also because it requires adequate space. Cultivation itself is relatively simple: this species of cactus only needs fairly warm wintering at temperatures of around 60 °F. This is especially so for specimens from Ecuador.

Armatocereus laetus ▣ ○

COLUMNAR

This tall columnar cactus forms tree-like plants, which can grow up to 20ft tall. The individual branches with their green-gray epidermis can be up to 4in in diameter and are split into 6–8 ribs. As with other members of the genus, annual shoots for this cactus are also segmented, thus clearly showing the length of growth for that season. Initially, the spines are only 3/4in long and 12 or so can grow from each areole. The flowers open at night. The petals are white and the sepals are greenish-red. The flowers measure about 2in across. There is little reliable information about their place of origin and so only the best-known location, where they have been gathered frequently, is given here. This is near the river Rio Huancabamba in Peru, between Pucara and Jaen. Here this cactus grows at altitudes of 3,250–4,000ft.

Armatocereus laetus

Armatocereus matucanensis

Few growers can boast a specimen of this species in their collection, because it is one of those cacti which requires a relatively large amount of space. Cultivation is simple, but in cool climates it can take many years before plants reach flowering size. Essential factors for successful cultivation include a fertile soil mix, a sufficiently large container, occasional applications of fertilizer, and cold wintering, preferably in the light. Shade the plant when in active growth.

Armatocereus matucanensis 

COLUMNAR

This widespread, shrubby cactus is interesting because the individual columnar annual shoots separate into distinct segments. The stems themselves have 5–8 ribs, which have an epidermis ranging from dark green to gray-green. There are usually 8 spines growing from each areole, but sometimes more. The longest spines can reach up to 4in in length. White flowers, which are a narrow funnel shape, bloom toward the top of the stems. After fertilization they turn into a greenish-white fruit with a thick covering of spines.

Their location is specified as central Peru, near the town of Matucana, where they grow at altitudes of 7,000–9,000ft. Few cactus growers have enough space for this species and therefore it is very rare to come across this it in specialist collections or in exhibitions of succulents in botanical gardens. It is not difficult to grow, however. This species can be kept outdoors in summer and to maintain it in good condition it must be provided with a large container and occasional applications of a balanced fertilizer.

Armatocereus oligogonus

Armatocereus oligogonus ▣ ○

COLUMNAR

This cactus is very similar to *A. laetus*, with the only general difference being that there are fewer ribs, usually 5. They are very prominent and fairly deep and have sharp edges where areoles are situated. Like other members of the genus, it has annual shoots separated into segments. There are 8–12 relatively short spines, 1 of which can reach up to 4in in length. The white flowers of this cactus can also reach the same length and after pollination and fertilization change into round fruit, covered with thick brown spines.

The species is to be found in the northern regions of Peru, near Olmos in the Huancabamba valley, where it can grow on steep hillsides. This particular species has been studied by many travelers and is sometimes found in catalogs under field collection number KK306. Few growers can boast this cactus in their collection and therefore it is generally only found in specialized collections in botanical gardens or in the private collections of cactus experts. Cultivation is fairly simple, but it must have a fairly large container or be planted directly in open ground. It takes a number of years for it to flower.

Browningia candelaris ▣ ○

COLUMNAR

This tree-like cactus can reach heights of up to 15ft. The trunk can be up to 20in in diameter. The stem branches about 6ft above the ground and branches often bend toward the ground, the terminal shoots growing upward again, giving them an S-shape. The distinctive stem spine covering is interesting: the spines on the trunk can be up to 6in long, whereas the spines on the branches from the crown are short. The pinkish white flowers of this cactus can reach 4 3/4in in length. They open in the evening and then wither in the morning.

One of the typical locations where this species is found is at an altitude of 9,000ft between the towns of Tacna and Arequipa. They can also be found, however, in many other places in southwest Peru and into northern areas of Chile. This cactus is not really suitable for a small porch because of its size and is not particularly well known in cultivation. It never reaches the same sizes as in the wild when grown in a collection, however. Another reason as to why it is so rare in collections is that seeds are very scarce. They are the easiest way of propagating it.

Cereus peruvianus ▣ ○

COLUMNAR

This columnar species has stems which can reach up to 10ft in height. The plant spreads out over a wide area and can be up to 15ft across. It produces large, white, funnel-shaped flowers and the indigenous people are very fond of its fruit.

This is a very widespread and highly variable cactus and so it is almost impossible to deter-

Browningia candelaris

Cereus peruvianus

mine where it originates. It can be found today across large tracts of South America but it has also found its way to places such as Madagascar. Cactus growers use it as a stock for grafting more delicate cacti. Various monstrous forms are grown, more for show, or clones with spiraling ribs.

Corryocactus apiciflorus 

CLUSTERING

This species is usually distributed under the genus name *Erdisia* or under the older genus name *Cereus*. The erect or clambering stems can grow to a length of 20in without excee ding a diameter of 1 1/4in. The funnel-shaped flowers are scarlet and are carried near the crown.
The species comes from the Huari region in Peru, where it grows at altitudes of approximately 8,000ft. It is not actually widespread among growers, but some specialists in Peruvian cacti have it in their collections. It is not particularly demanding, but must be overwintered in cold, light conditions. The plants flower after just six or seven years.

Corryocactus apiciflorus

Corryocactus ayacuchoensis

Corryocactus ayacuchoensis 

COLUMNAR

Nowadays this cactus is generally included within Erdisia, but for this book the original name proposed by W. Rauh and C. Backeberg has been retained. It produces dense bushes more than a yard tall with shoots twisted in all directions. They are light green in color and 9 or 10 radial and 3 central spines grow out of the areole. The latter can be up to 11/2in long. The beautiful orange-red flowers are 1 1/4–1 1/2in cross and are diurnal. The fruit is a round berry.
This cactus comes from southern Peru where it grows on stony hillsides where there is little associated vegetation. It has been distributed in Europe in the past under field collection number KK 1072. This refers to Karel Kníže's collection from the region near Ayacucho. It can be found in very few collections and can only be seen in specialized amateur collections or botanical gardens. There is little experience in cultivation of this cactus, but it does not require any special conditions and can be grown in the same way as other, less demanding South American cacti.

Corryocactus brevistylus

Corryocactus brevistylus 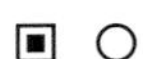

CLUSTERING

This is a bushy cactus which can reach heights of up to 10ft. Some specimens have reached an average of up to 13ft. Each stem has 6 or 7 ribs. The areoles are conspicuous, up to 1 1/4in apart and are densely woolly. A unique feature of this cactus is its long brown spines, which can reach up to 10in in length (usually, though, they do not exceed 2in). The yellow flowers grow toward the tops of the stems. After pollination and fertilization these change into round, juicy berries full of tiny black seeds.
C. brevistylus grows in southern areas of Peru at altitudes of about 6,500ft. Cultivation poses no problems.

Corryocactus puquiensis ▣ ○

CLUSTERING-COLUMNAR

There is a fair amount of dispute about this little known cactus. It is reputed to reach the height of 16ft, but we have never managed to find evidence of this. As a rule it is a shrubby, columnar species which reaches a maximum height of 8ft. One of its characteristic features is its long central spines, which can be up to 8in long in certain cases. The large, pure yellow flower is also elegant and can reach a diameter of up to 2 1/4in when fully open. The fruit is an oval berry covered in short spines.
Anyone wanting to see this cactus in the wild must cope with the demanding climb up the Peruvian volcano Volcan Chachani, to an altitude of 10,000ft above sea level. It is not the type of cactus to be found in many collections. It is not demanding to grow but has certain specific requirements, has certain specific requirements, primarily because the plant is intolerant of excessive heat or overwatering in summer as growth slows down.

Espostoa lanata 

COLUMNAR

The columnar stems of this species form an freely branching shrub, which can be up to 13ft high. The ribs and areoles are covered with a thick blanket, of short, white or reddish radial spines, and long, silky hairs cover the youngest stem parts. Its white flowers open at dusk and grow from the lateral cephalium. This cactus also boasts large red fruit.
It can be found in locations throughout southern Ecuador and in northern regions of Peru, where it forms relatively dense bushes. Every collection contains plants of this species because of their striking spine pattern. Young plants are almost obscured by their delicate covering of hair-like spines, the reason for their popularity among cactus growers. Cultivation is simple – they can withstand normal porch conditions but do not react well to watering on a hot day.

Corryocactus puquiensis

Espostoa lanata

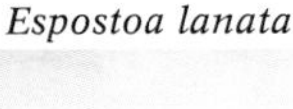

Espostoa lanata var. *sericata*

Espostoa melanostele

Espostoa lanata var. *sericata* ▣ ○

COLUMNAR

Because of the considerable variability of the typical species, some authorities consider this to be just a local variant, the difference being that it does not have striking central spines. It is a columnar cactus, which reaches heights of up to 16ft, and individual branches can be up to 6in in diameter. The radial spines growing out of the areoles are very short and the central spines are only a fraction of an inch long and are almost covered in thick white hair. The yellow-white flowers can reach 2 3/4in in length and can also have a pink tinge. After fertilization they change into pulpy, crimson-red fruit. The woolly lateral cephalium is yellow-white and usually 18in long.

The author of the description gives a relatively precise location for this varietas in the wild: Huancabamba in northern Peru. Other information, however, also exists about where it can be found, for instance the collection item found at Olmos at an altitude of 3,250ft, published by Karel Kníže under field collection number KK 293. Cultivation is the same as for the typespecies. Here too, young plants are much more beautiful than older ones, which do not respond well to watering from the domestic supply or to atmospheric pollution.

Espostoa melanostele ▣ ○

COLUMNAR

Some cactus specialists list this species under *Pseudoespostoa*, while others feel that the original classification is correct. It is a columnar cactus with few branches, which can reach a height of approximately 6ft. The individual stems can be about 4in in diameter. There are usually about 25 ribs and, particularly in the case of seedlings, they are completely covered in white hair. The spines are up to 1 1/2in long. Creamy white flowers, occasionally with a hint of pink, grow from the lateral cephalium, which is very woolly, fairly broad, and compact. The fruit is a fleshy, yellow-white berry containing shiny black seeds.

In the wild *E. melanostele* can be found in the central areas of Peru, where one of the places it grows is near Chosica, at Huinco in the Eulalia valley. It can be found at altitudes of 3,250–6,500ft above sea level. It is easy to grow in collections and grow rapidy initially. Older plants lose their roots sometimes, however, which causes an interruption in growth and even the death of the cactus. Ground water should be used when watering, so that the beautiful, luxuriant white hair is retained as much as possible. During the summer this cactus can withstand full sun but the first rays of spring sunlight can cause unsightly scorching. If you have an older specimen in your collection, then it is a good idea to provide it with a fairly large container, which is not too deep, and occasional applications of fertilizer.

Epostoa melanostele var. *nana* ▣ ○

COLUMNAR

In the wild this cactus usually reaches heights of 6 1/2ft and forms clumps with a small number of fairly strong, lateral offshoots, branching from

Espostoa melanostele var. *nana*

Espostoa mirabilis

ground level. The whole plant is also covered in thick, woolly spines. The flowers grow from a lateral cephalium and open at night. This varietas is also found in Peru. Found frequently in collections as the typical species and it also has similar cultivation demands.

Epostoa mirabilis

COLUMNAR

This is an tree-like, columnar cactus, which differs from other members of the genus in having a reduced quantity of white hair. This is replaced, especially in seedlings, by coarse, hairy spines. It also produces woody central spines protruding from the stem, which sting.

The author of the description gives a general location for *E. mirabilis*: northeastern Peru. We know, however, of places on the Rio Marañon at Balsas, where they grow at altitudes of 4,000–5,000ft and where they were collected by Karel Kníže (number KK 295). Cultivation is the same as for other members of the genus, bat the seedlings do not grow as quickly.

Eulychnia ritteri

COLUMNAR

This is a shrubby cactus, which can reach a maximum height of 10ft. The maximum diameter of the individual stems is 2 1/4–3in. There are usually 12 radial spines but only 4 central spines, which are black and can be up to 2 1/4in long. The pinkish red flower blooms toward the top of the stem. It is about 3/4in long and only stays open for a few hours.
The species comes from the province of Arequipa in Peru. It is extremely rare to come across it in collections and it is mostly only owned by specialists in South American cacti.

Haageocereus acranthus 

COLUMNAR

This robust cactus forms offsets from the base and produces a bush about 3ft high. A thick cover of radial spines and 2 central spines clothes the stem. On closer scrutiny this can be seen to be made up of 14 ribs with areoles. The white, tubular flower grows toward the tip of the stem. The flower tube is about 2 3/4in long and greenish white in color, as are the inner petals. The flower is full of yellow-white anthers, which produce a huge amount of pollen. This Peruvian cactus can be found near the settlement of Santa Clara at altitudes of 1,300–2,000ft. It grows here in very dry and sunny places, conditions necessary for successful cultivation. It should be placed in direct sun with good ventilation. To develop properly it needs a standard cactus soil mix and regular potting on into larger containers. Cactus growers only grow a limited number of species from this genus.

Eulychnia ritteri

Haageocereus aureispinus 

SHRUBBY

This is a bushy cactus with individual stems reaching about 32in in height and 2–3in in diameter. The yellow radial spines measure 1/2–3/4in and 1 central spine can reach up to 1 1/2in in length. The white flowers are a narrow tube-shape and open at night. They can be up to 2 3/4in long and 1 in across. The fruit is a round red berry, full of tiny black seeds, about 2in in diameter.
One of the places this species is found is near the Rio Chillon in Peru, where it grows at altitudes of 4,000–4,5000ft. It is rare to find it in collections and you are more likely to come across it in larger succulent houses in botanical gardens. A standard soil mix is suitable for cultivation, and the cactus should have cold wintering and be placed in a fairly large container or the greenhouse bed, where it can reach a fairly large size and thus display its full elegance.

Haageocereus chosicensis 

COLUMNAR

This columnar species forms offsets from the base. It can reach heights around 6ft with a stem diameter of almost 4in. There are usually 20 ribs. The areoles are small and have over 30 delicate radial spines and 3 or 4 central spines 3/4in in length,

Haageocereus acranthus

Haageocereus aureispinus

which are yellow-gray in color and needle-shaped. The flowers are found close to the growing point. The sepals and tube are green and the petals are maroon, contrasting vividly with the yellowish white of the anthers and stigma. The color of the flowers is very variable, however, and in places these cacti can be found with pink or pinkish white flowers.

The small town of Chosica, after which this cactus was named, is situated along the road from the Peruvian capital to the town of La Oroya. It is primarily specialists who are interested in this species or cactus growers with enough room in their porch. It responds particularly well to being placed outdoors over the summer, however, and does not mind cold wintering in low light.

The large greenish red, round fruit is usually about 1 1/2in in diameter.

This species can be found to the north of the Peruvian capital, Lima, 166 miles along the Pan-American Highway. It grows on desolate, stony plains where it is not overshadowed by any taller vegetation. Thanks to its hardy nature in the wild, this species of *Haageocereus* is very simple to grow in cultivation. The plants look elegant even when when young and you do not need to wait years for them to mature.

Haageocereus chrysacanthus ▣ ○

COLUMNAR

This is a very elegant member of the genus, because of its striking gold spines (*chrysacanthus*). It grows to about 3ft in height and the plants produce offsets from the base. The thick radial spines and the longer central spines toward the top of the stems form an impressive gold "head." The flowers measure up to 2in across and 2 1/4in in length.

Haageocereus chosicensis

Haageocereus chrysacanthus

Haageocereus repens

Haageocereus repens ▣ ○

TRAILING

The procumbent stem of *Haageocereus* repens produces a trailer, which is able to "travel." The stem grows horizontally and sometimes the connection with the original parent plant can be broken over time. The young part of the cactus, however, once it has taken root by means of lateral adventitious buds and crept "further away" from the parent plant, itself clonally produces further offshoots over time. The longest stems reach lengths of about 6 1/2ft and measure 3in in diameter. The long, tubular flowers are about 2 3/4in long and 1 1/4–1 1/2in in diamter and open at night. They are pure white in color. The fruit is a round, fleshy berry, full of tiny black seeds.Peru's northern coastal areas are very barren and the sandy landscape looks almost lifeless at first sight. It is precisely here that this species grows; it is found, to be specific, to the south of the town of Trujillo. It is actually relatively rare to come across this cactus in collections, but it is found most often in specialized collections or very occasionally in botanical gardens. It must be grown in a mineral-high, well-drained soil mix in full sun. It should be wintered at a mean temperature of about 50 °F.

Islaya grandiflorens ▣ ○

GLOBOSE

The present extent of the whole genus is somewhat uncertain and some taxonomists feel that it is just a northern branch of the genus *Neoporteria*. For clarity, *Islaya* is treated here as a separate genus. The columnar stem can grow to a height of 8in with a stem diameter of about 3in. The spine pattern is variable which is why two further variants have been recorded. (*I. grandiflorens* var. *tenuispina* and *I. grandiflorens* var. *spinosior*). The funnel shaped and richly yellow flower, as the epithet grandiflowers indicates, is large and can be to zin across.
I. grandiflorens is a Peruvian cactus. Its locality is given as 435 miles along the Trans-American Highway, south of the town of Atico. It grows in coastal desert areas at low altitudes between 325 - 650 ft. It is found on low knolls in drift send,

Islaya grandiflorens

Islaya islayensis

where rainfall is rare and most water is absorbed in the form of thick mist. In view of its natural habitat, there are certain specific requirements that have to be observed in cultivation as well. The very long, wiry spines are adapted to absorbing minimal precipitation, and as a result watering must be performed little and often and with great care. For less experienced growers grafting the species onto *Eriocereus jusbertii*, for instance, is recommended. Overwinter in full light at temperatures around 50 °F.

Islaya islayensis

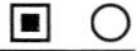

GLOBOSE

The stem is usually solitary with no offsets. In the wild it is globose and in collections almost columnar. It can be up to 4in tall and 2–2 1/2in across. There are oval, densely woolly areoles on the edges of the 19–25 ribs, at intervals of 1/12-1/6in. Out of them grow 8–22 radial spines and 4–7 central spines, which are 5/8–3/4in long. The bright yellow flowers are quite small (about 1in across). Sometimes the sepals are reddish in color.
Like other members of the genus, they are found at lower altitudes as 300 – 1300 ft in dry areas on the coast of southern Peru. This species has been often collected in the Peruvian province of Islay, near Matarani, under field collection number KK 1078 for example. The same cultivation conditions apply as for other members of the genus. This cactus is not recommended for beginners.

Islaya maritima

GLOBOSE –COLUMNAR

Because of ongoing confusion regarding the genus *Islaya*, there are slight difficulties in classifying thie this species. Some consider it to be the same as *I. grandiflorens*, not a distinct species. The almost columnar stem reaches a height of 10in with a diameter of about 5in. In the wild the light brown spines completely cover the epidermis, which is gray-green in cultivation. The yellow flower, up to 1 1/4 in across, changes into the cylindrical fruit with a red pericap after pollination. It grows along the coast, south of the Peruvian town of Atico and north of the town of Chala to be precise. Cultivation is as for *I. grandiflorens*. These cacti do not respond well to growing outdoors in summer, but they are suited to greenhouse cultivation in full sun.

Islaya maritima

Lobivia aurea

Lobivia aurea

GLOBOSE-COLUMNAR

This is a very variable species, sometimes classified within *Echinopsis*. The stem of the typical species is mostly solitary, producing offsets only in exceptional cases. It does not grow above 6in tall and the stem is generally about 4in in diameter. The stem is formed of 11–16 ribs with round areoles on the edges. 8–16 radial spines grow from these areoles, as well as 4 centrally. Theseare thicker and protrude from the stem. Beautiful yellow flowers, almost 3in across, bloom from the side areoles.
Because of its wide distribution, many variants of this species that are only slightly similar have been recorded. Among the best-known are *L. aurea* var. *callochrysea*, *L. aurea* var. *fallax*, or *L. aurea* var. *albiflora* with its white flowers. All the forms mentioned, including the type, are found in two ranges of hills in Peru: the Sierra Chica de Cordoba and the Sierra San Luis. Cultivation is easy. Seeds germinate freely and like most high-altitude cacti, this species grows better in the open during the summer than in a greenhouse.

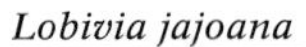

Lobivia jajoana

Lobivia jajoana

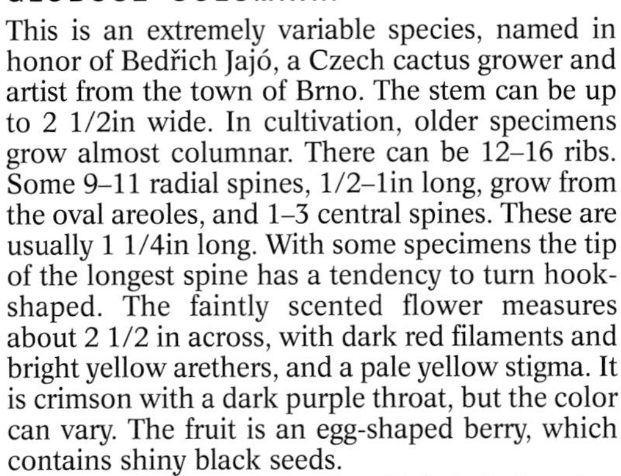

GLOBOSE-COLUMNAR

This is an extremely variable species, named in honor of Bedřich Jajó, a Czech cactus grower and artist from the town of Brno. The stem can be up to 2 1/2in wide. In cultivation, older specimens grow almost columnar. There can be 12–16 ribs. Some 9–11 radial spines, 1/2–1in long, grow from the oval areoles, and 1–3 central spines. These are usually 1 1/4in long. With some specimens the tip of the longest spine has a tendency to turn hook-shaped. The faintly scented flower measures about 2 1/2 in across, with dark red filaments and bright yellow arethers, and a pale yellow stigma. It is crimson with a dark purple throat, but the color can vary. The fruit is an egg-shaped berry, which contains shiny black seeds.
Because of the vast area in which it is found, a number of forms have been recorded. These have been classified as separate subspecies in the past and no doubt they will continue to be so in the future. Mention could be made, for instance, of *L. jajoana* var. *fleischeriana* with its tomato orange flower and long hook-like central spines, or *L. jajoana* var. *nigrostoma* with its black-throated, yellow flowers. The type species is reported as occurring on Volcan Chani in the Quebrada de Humahuaca valley in Peru. Every collection boasts this cactus in some form or other. It has attracted a great following among collectors, from beginners to connoisseurs. because it is easy to grow and has beautiful flowers with a range of colors. As with other high-altitude *Lobivia*, basic requirements are sufficient light, ventilation, and cold wintering. If winter temperatures are too high, the flowers are produced prematurely, leading to stem distortion.

Lobivia pampana

GLOBOSE

The clustering, globose stem of this cactus usually reaches diameters of about 2–3in and is formed of 17–21 slightly undulating ribs. The white felting gradually disappears from the areoles. It is difficult to distinguish between radial and central spines and about 15–20 of them grow from each areole. They are brown and bent toward the stem. The flower is about 2 1/2in long and the petals have a yellowish base, but otherwise they are a very bright red. The round fruit is covered in fine white hair.
The species was named after the town of Pampa de Arrieros in southern Peru, at about 13,000ft. The type locality of the species is near the town. This cactus generally grows between the stones on rocky outcrops with very little associated vegetation. Because this is one of the high-altitude mem-

Lobivia pampana

bers of the genus, the same conditions apply as for other specimens from similar locations – in the summer it may be stood in the open with shelter from prolonged rain. Cold wintering and early emergence from dormancy in the spring are essential to ensure that growth is not distorted by the effect of higher temperatures and low light intensity over winter.

Lobivia wrightiana

Lobivia wrightiana

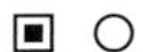

GLOBOSE–COLUMNAR

The stem of this cactus is solitary. Initially globose, it then extends into an almost columnar shape and is formed of 13–19 ribs. The number and length of the radial spines are variable. The central spine can be up to 2 1/4in long and is sometimes hooked at the tip. The pale pink-violet flower blooms from the side of the cactus, and is about 2 in long with a long, narrow flower tubs. La Mejo rada and La Esmaralda in the Peruvian department of Huansavelica are where most findings have been reported. They are usually found at altitudes of 8,200–9,200ft. This is another species which is found relatively often in collections, partly because of its ease of cultivation, and partly because of the beauty of its flowers. In the summer it prefers being out in the open to the overheated conditions in a greenhouse.

Loxanthocereus clavispinus

Loxanthocereus clavispinus ▣ ○

COLUMNAR

The stems of this cactus cluster from the base. Initially solitary, they reach heights of about 20in- and diameters of up to 4in. The stem is formed of about 14 ribs. About 30 radial spines grow from each areole and these are very stiff and about 1/2in long. There are about 2 or 3 central spines which are needle-shaped and grow to 1 1/2in long. The virtually zygomorphic flower is up to 2 1/2in long and bright red. This species is found in central Peru, in the Nazca Valley, where it grows at altitudes of between 1,650 and 2,300ft. It can only be found in a small number of collections and you are more likely to see it in botanical gardens. It is not particularly difficult to cultivate, but flowering occurs only after a number of years. The reason why it is only found seldom in collections is primarily because of the shortage of seeds.

Loxanthocereus eriotrichus 

COLUMNAR-TRAILING

The stems of this cactus are straight, columnar, and sometimes even slightly trailing. They are formed of approximately 16 ribs. The crown is covered in fine, hair-like spines. There are 12–15 radial spines, which are 1/2in long, and 3–6 central spines, which are up to 1 1/4in long, growing from the lower areoles. The flowers are fiery red, virtually zygomorphic, and bloom toward the top of the cactus. The fruit is about the same size as a cherry and contains tiny black seeds.
This species is cited as originating in Peru, specifically from the town of Matucana, and also near the river Rio Rimac. It grows there at altitudes of about 5,250ft. It is very rare to find it in collections and therefore there is very little practical experience of growing it. It is important to place it in full sun, use a nutrient-high soil mix, and overwinter it at temperatures generally no lower than 50 °F.

Loxanthocereus lanatus 

COLUMNAR

Most cactus growers seem to have never heard of this cactus, because the name is a provisional one for the plant identified by Karel Kníže during his expeditions to which he gave field collection number KK 1897. The stems cluster from the base, are tufted, and grow only to 16in long and about 2in in diameter. The species is clearly related to *L. eriotrichus*. The virtually zygomorphic flowers are a luminous red and bloom toward the top of the stem.
It is recorded as being from near Rio Lurin in Peru, where it grows at altitudes of about 7,200ft. There is as yet little experience of cultivation of this cactus, but it can be assumed that this will be as demanding as for other members of the genus.

Loxanthocereus eriotrichus

Loxanthocereus seniloides ▣ ○

COLUMNAR

This name is a provisional one for a species of interesting, fairly robust cacti, which can reach a maximum height of 3ft. The upper part of the stem is covered in fine white hair. The beautiful, fiery red, zygomorphic flowers are carried near the top of the stem and can be up to 2 3/4in long.

So far there is little information about where this cactus grows, and were it not for collections from near Rio Lurin in Peru, probably practically nothing would be known about it. It is generally familiar among specialists under field collection number KK 1896 and is almost never found in collections. However, the same cultivation principles apply as for other members of the genus.

Loxanthocereus sulcifer 

TRAILING

The trailing, slightly arching stem of this cactus can reach a length of up to 6ft. The stem is usually 3in in diameter and has 8 ribs, formed of tubercles. The radial spines, of which about 9 grow from each areole, are fairly short, approximately 1/2in long. There are usually 4 central spines, arranged in the formof a cross. The longest of these can measure up to 1 3/4in. The zygomorphic red flowers can reach a length of about 2in.

The species is found near the river Rio Fortaleza at altitudes of 7,800–9,850ft. Its habit allows it to spread over a large area, and the long stems can clamber over nearby vegetation as well. It is relatively rare to find this plant in collections, although it is definitely an interesting if, unfortunately, rather unattractive cactus. With regard to its cultivation, summering is best in the open, and overwintering should be cold. It needs a sufficiently large container to accommodate its growth.

Loxanthocereus lanatus

Loxanthocereus seniloides

Loxanthocereus sulcifer

Matucana aurantiaca

Matucana aurantiaca ▣ ○

GLOBOSE

This is a somewhat controversial and also very variable species, which is referred to in older literature as a species of the genus *Submatucana*. The globose stem can reach a diameter of up to 6in and usually forms 15–18 ribs. The spines are fairly variable; they can be brown or yellow. In the case of certain specimens they jut out from the stem and with others they are flattened against it. The flowers bloom at the start of the summer and are orange-yellow. The flower tube is covered with prominent scales. This species is found in northern Peru, in a number of departments including Cajamarca and Huancabamba. It grows at altitudes of 7,200–11,800ft. K. Kníže collected it at Hualgayoc (KK 455) 7,200 ft above sea level, and others have found it between Chota and Hualgayoc. Cultivation is not difficult, and its requirements are the same as the usual species cultivated. It has beautiful flowers, however, with eye-catching colors.

Matucana aureiflora 

FLATTENED-GLOBOSE

In the wild the flattened-globose stem of this cactus grows to about 8in in diameter and a height of slightly less. The stem is formed of about 18 flat ribs, which are made up of tubercles, ending in an areole with 8–10 radial spines and 1–4 central spines growing out of it. Generally these are darker at the base and lighter toward the tip. The large yellow flower is adapted to pollination by insects, whereas other *Matucana* are generally pollinated by hummingbirds. Because of the structure of the short flowers, F. Ritter classified this species within Incaia. The green-brown or purple fruits, which can grow up to 5/8in in diameter, contain black seeds.

M. aureiflora is found in northern areas of Peru and grows near the town of Cajamarca. The type locality is Baños del Inca, at altitudes of 8,800–10,000ft, where it grows in association with grasses, fully exposed to the sun. It is vital that there is sufficient sun and ventilation for successful cultivation. This species also flourishes outdoors during the summer. Beware, however, of the first rays of spring sunlight, which can cause ugly scorch marks to the cactus. Summering should be in a light position, at temperatures of 50 °F. Propagation is by seed and the emerging seedlings are best lightly shaded.

Matucana formosa 

COLUMNAR

Initially globose, this cactus becomes columnar as it gets older. Generally it can grow to up to 6in in diameter and about twice this in height. It is formed of undefined ribs, which are made up of spiraling tubercles, at the tip of which is a circular areole, from which emerge 5–8 spines, 3/4–1 1/4in long. Some experts consider that there is a long-spined varietas: *M. formosa* var. *longispina*. However, others argue that because of the great

Matucana aureiflora

Matucana formosa

Matucana formosa var. *longispina*

variability in spine length from one location, there are no grounds for this distinction. This can be seen from the photograph of two cacti from the same location. The flower of the cactus is about 2in long, red, and virtually zygomorphic.
M. formosa is found on hillsides near Rio Marañon, at altitudes of 4,000–5,000 ft, near Baqua, in places where *Matucana madisoniorum* also grows. Cultivation is not demanding and it requires the same level of care as other members of the genus. The only consideration which should be borne in mind is that this is not a particularly high-altitude cactus. The need for good ventilation and respect for the period of summer dormancy apply for this species as well.

Matucana haynei var. *erectipetala*

Matucana haynei var. *erectipetala*

GLOBOSE–COLUMNAR

The stem of this cactus is initially globose and later becomes columnar. It can reach a height of 20in and a diameter of approximately 6in. There are 25–35 radial spines, about 3/4in long; 2 or 3 of the stronger and more prickly central spines can be up to 2in long. The zygomorphic, bright red flowers can be up to 2 3/4in long. This varietas differs from the type in having finer spines and flowers with erect inner petals.
This variant is found in the same places as the type species, i.e. near the town of Matucana, to the east of Lima, at altitudes of 6,500–8,850ft. This cactus will in as much sunlight and fresh air as possible flourish or in plunge beds and they grow well in the open in warmer areas of low rainfall. They must have cold wintering in good light. Propagation is almost exclusively by seed.

Matucana herzogiana

Matucana herzogiana ▣ ○

GLOBOSE

This is a relatively complex taxon, which has undergone several changes in nomenclature. Even today it is not entirely clear what typical specimens of this species are supposed to look like. The plant in the photograph perhaps has the typical spines, if not the flowers, since those who have observed them in the wild say that they should be smaller. It has even been reported that there are cacti with various different flower shades in one location.

K. Kníže recorded observing this species in Peru's Cordillera Negra, at altitudes of approximately 10,500ft. Little experience of cultivation has so far been collected, but it can be assumed that these cacti will be as demanding as the other high-altitude species belonging to this genus.

Matucana intertexta 

GLOBOSE–COLUMNAR

The stem of this cactus is initially globose but becomes almost columnar with age. The stem can reach a diameter of 2 3/4–7 3/4in and can grow to twice this in height. The radial spines, of which there are usually about 20, grow from elliptical, densely woolly areoles. Young plants have short spines and only when the specimens are older do the spines lengthen. They have a tendency to intertwine. The central spines, 1 to 4 in number, are firm and can be up to 1 1/4in long. The flowers bloom near the crown and are 3–4in long and 2–3in across. They range in color from orange-yellow to orange-red. The flower tube is usually hairier than appears illustrated here, which is why the cactus is usually classified within *Submatucana*.

F. Ritter discovered this species at Puente Crisnejas, which is situated to the north of the Peruvian town of Cajamarca. He designated his collection FR 693 and the seed was shipped to Europe under this number. K. Kníže found another location where he came across related cacti, which are not yet recorded (KK 1153, KK 1316, KK 1054). Like many other species of South American cacti, *M. intertexta* needs adequate ventilation, full sun, and a slightly acidic, free-draining soil mix to maintain it in good condition. It is easy to propagate the cactus by seed, but seedlings need to be given a certain amount of shade over the first few years. They reach flowering size after 7 to 10 years.

Matucana krahnii ▣ ○

GLOBOSE–COLUMNAR

The globose stem of this cactus, initially solitary, can grow into a column and produce offsets when older. The tallest specimens can grow to 6in in height and a maximum of 4in in diameter. 8–15 radial spines and usually 1–4 central spines grow from the circular, white-felted areoles. The remarkably zygomorphic, fiery red flower emerges near the growing point and is strikingly long at up to 3 1/2in.

Its type locality has been specified as an area approximately 10 miles from the settlement of Balsas in the Peruvian province of Chachapoyas. It is usually found in the dappled shade provided by associated vegetation among rocks near the river Marañon. *M. krahnii* is a very popular cactus, mainly cultivated by less experienced cactus growers. The cacti should be provided with sufficient light and relatively large amounts of water during the summer. It should not have to put up with

Matucana intertexta

temperatures that are too low during the winter – the ideal temperature is about 50 °F. The seed germinates freely and seedlings grow quickly; can bloom from the third year.

Matucana madisoniorum ▣ ○

GLOBOSE

The stem of this cactus is initially globose and starts to extend almost into a column when adult. It is an eye-catcher, because 1 long, black-gray slightly curved spine often protrudes from some areoles on what is mainly a completely glabrous, gray-green stem. The flowers appear in summer and grow from the youngest areoles. These flowers are long and tubular and the flower tube is covered with gray-white hairs. The whole flower is virtually zygomorphic and the color of the petals is a deep red.
To find this species in the wild, you must visit the department of Ancash in the Peruvian province of Huari, where you can come across it at altitudes of about 6,500ft. It is not particularly difficult to cultivate this species in collections: these plants welcome slightly dappled shade and a slightly acidic soil mix, which requires regular watering during the growing season.

Matucana madisoniorum

Matucana myriacantha ▣ ○

GLOBOSE

This is a lesser-known member of the genus. It used to be classified within either *Borzicactus* or *Submatucana*. The globose, solitary stem grows to a height and diameter of about 4in and is formed of about 25 ribs. It is striking because of its distinctive, yellow, hair-like spines. It is difficult to differentiate between the radial and central spines. 25–30 emerge from each areole and they can be up to 1in long. The beautiful, virtually zygomorphic flowers bloom near the crown and are orange-yellow in color, often with a pinkish tinge. They are up to 2 1/4in long and 1 1/2–2in across. The location of this species is given as the Amazonas region of Peru. The best-known location, as specified by K. Kníže, is Balsas, where it grows at an altitude of 5,000 ft. Collections of this *Matucana* were accorded field collection number KK 457. Cultivation is the same as for other mem-

Matucana krahnii

Matucana myriacantha

Matucana paucicostata

bers of the genus. Great care should be taken, however, with watering when dormant in summer. The species should be found more often in collections, because it is a cactus with very impressive spines and flowers. Wintering should be at temperatures of about 60 °F.

Matucana paucicostata ▣ ○

GLOBOSE-COLUMNAR

The globose or almost columnar stem of this cactus is initially solitary, but often clusters as it gets older. The name *paucicostata* or "with few ribs" derives from its modest number of ribs (7–11).

Matucana variabilis

These are broad, with 4–8 radial spines growing from the areoles on the tubercles and usually 1 central spine as well. The zygomorphic, red flower can be up to 2 1/4in long and creates a beautiful contrast with the yellow anthers. The fruit is a greenish berry with several side openings.
M. paucicostata has been collected several times in the wild and is therefore found under several field collection numbers, including KK 791 and FR 597. It grows in the province of Huari in Peru. The type locality of the species is near Rahuapampa, at an altitude of 6,500–8,200ft above sea level. For successful cultivation these cacti have to have enough sunlight, but they react badly to excessive summer heat and it is a good idea to provide them with at least some shade when the weather gets really hot. The seedlings grow very quickly and flower after just 4 to 5 years. You can propagate them using offsets, which you have to separate carefully to avoid damaging the parent plant and the other offsets.

Matucana variabilis ▣ ○

COLUMNAR

When fully grown, the columnar stem of this cactus reach about 6in high and about 3in in diameter. It is completely covered in white spines. The numerous radial spines are about 1/4in long. There are 1–3 central spines, which can be up to 3/4in long and are also white but with a brownish tip. The flower is clearly zygomorphic and its fiery red color contrasts sharply with the white of the spines.
This species is recorded as being found in areas of central Peru in the wild, where it has been collected several times. The exact location specified is 6 miles to the north of the town of Churin at altitudes of about 27,000ft above sea level.
Cultivation is fairly simple, it responds better to well-ventilated conditions than high summer temperatures in an overheated greenhouse. It needs a standard cactus soil mix, occasional watering during the summer, and to be sited in full sun.

Melocactus bellavistensis 

COLUMNAR

The short stem can reach 16in high and a width of 10in. Most of the spines hook back, claw-like, toward the stem wide. The terminal cephalium takes a number of years to appear and with the oldest specimens can grow to up to 4in high. The pink-violet flower is only 1/2in wide; all *Melocactus* also have red, club-shaped fruit which emerge from the cephalium on maturity.
The species grows in very hot areas of southern Ecuador and northern Peru, where temperatures do not fall below 68 °F. Wintering at temperatures

Melocactus bellavistensis

Melocactus peruvianus

of around 60 °F. Both seedlings and adults are reluctant to put on growth. Grafting onto a slow-growing stock is recommended. The cephalium starts to form after approximately 15 years.

Melocactus peruvianus ■ ○

COLUMNAR

Adult specimens have a short, pyramidal stem, maximum 8 ft in height, with thick, intertwimd, stiff spines. There are 1 or 2 central spines protruding straight out from the cactus. The cephalium is formed after a number of years and is usually about 2 1/4in across and a maximum of 3in high. The flowers are violet-red in color and measure about 1/2in across.
The species belongs to a complex, disorganized family, due to its large area of hundreds of miles of coast line along the Pacific Ocean, between the northern and southern borders of Peru. *M. peruvianus* is one of the most demanding of the genus to cultivate. This cactus must be provided with warmth ad light over winter. Propagation is by seed.

Melocactus peruvianus var. *lurinensis* ■ ○

GLOBOSE

This cactus is a varietas, though there is doubt, and it is sometimes considered a synonym for the type species. Along with the fact that it is found in different locations, it also differs from the species in being smaller (the globose stem reaches a height and diameter of only 4in) and in having smaller flowers and shorter, flattened spines. This species is found at altitudes of approximately 3,300ft among rocks on stony terraces from the Lurin valley to the Eulalia valley in Peru. Cultivation is as for the type.

Melocactus peruvianus var. *lurinensis*

Mila caespitosa

Mila caespitosa ▣ ○

COLUMNAR

This tufted cactus has short, cylindrical stems, which can be up to 6in long and 1 1/4–3in in diameter. Some 20 radial spines and 1–3 central spines grow from the densely spaced areoles. Flowers emerge mainly from the top third of the stem. These are yellow and sometimes reddish. After pollination yellow-green, fleshy berries develop from them, as can be seen from the cactus in the photograph. The seeds are a fraction of an inch long.
These cacti are found in central Peru, near Chosica, where many cactus growers have collected them in the past. The altitude at which it is found is given as 2,600–4,000ft. This species is normally found in collections belonging to experts in South American cacti, but generally they are not particularly demanding. It is important that they are always watered carefully, allowing the soil mix to dry out completely between waterings, that they are planted in full sun and in a shallow pan with sufficient soil mix, and that applications of fertilizer are given a number of times through the growing season. Wintering should be cool and in the light if possible.

Morawetzia doelziana 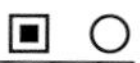

COLUMNAR

This is a relatively unknown species which many classify within *Oreocereus*. It is indeed closely related to this genus, not only in terms of habit, but also in terms of its reproductive parts and fruit. The main difference is that the flowers grow from the small terminal cephalium. The species forms shoots about 3ft in height and 3in in diameter, which cluster from the base, with 10–11 ribs. About 20 radial and 4 central spines, about 1 1/2in long, grow from the elliptical areoles, along with long hair-like spines, as is found in *Oreocereus*. The funnel-shaped flower grows from the cephalium on top of the cactus. It is about 4in long and crimson with a stigma ranging in color from yellow to green.
This cactus is found in the mountains of central Peru, where it grows near to Ayacucho and Huanta at altitudes of 8,200ft. In collections it is sometimes found under field collection number KK 342. You usually only come across it in collections belonging to experts or in botanical gardens. Cactus growers do not cultivate it much, mainly because of the lack of seeds. Cultivation is relatively simple and the requirements are similar to those for species of *Oreocereus*.

Neobinghamia climaxantha 

COLUMNAR

The stems of this columnar cactus reach over 3ft in height. They can be up to 3in wide and are formed of 19–27 ribs. The elliptical areoles have 50–70 radial spines and 1–3 central spines, which are more than 3/4in long. The species epithet *climaxantha* indicates the graded arrangement of the flowers on the stem. They emerge from false cephalia, which develop at various heights on the stem, so the flowers grow in floral areas at different levels. The tubular flowers open at night, are white to pink in color, and are about 1 1/2in long.
They are found in the Chosica valley in Peru, where they form columnar bushes at altitudes of 3,300ft. The species epithet *climaxantha* has been altered in catalogs and some publications to *climaxacantha*, which is incorrect. This species is not found particularly often in collections, but even small seedlings, when just 4–6in tall, are very impressive because of

Morawetzia doelziana

Neobinghamia climaxantha

Neoraimondia roseiflora, detail

their thick, yellow-brown spines. Winter temperatures should not be allowed to fall below 54 °F for long.

Neoraimondia roseiflora 

COLUMNAR

This cactus reaches heights of over 6ft. Individual branches are formed of 5 prominent ribs, on the edge of which are flower bearing areoles with wartli protubereranus, carrying bristles and white hair. They have deep pink flowers and spines at up to 4 in long growing from them. Its elegant habit means that it virtually dominates the landscape. It is only cultivated very rarely. The same conditions apply for this cactus as for the preceding species.

N. roseiflora is found in Peru, where it forms fairly large bushes.

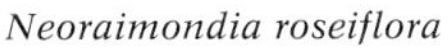

Neoraimondia roseiflora

Opuntia pachypus

Opuntia pachypus ▣ ○

COLUMNAR

This prickly pear is usually classified within *Austrocylindropuntia*, which a few cactus growers now have in their collections. Its stem can reach a height of up to 3ft and a diameter of 2–3in. The areoles are arranged in a spiral. They have spines a fraction of an inch long growing out of them and also a large number of tiny yellow glochids. The scarlet flowers measure 2 1/4–2 3/4in across when fully open. The fruit is easy to break off and contains a smaller quantity of seeds than most other *Opuntia*. This relatively rare species occurs in a few familiar localities above Chosica in the Santa Eulalia valley. It is very rare to come across it in collections and it is only found in those belonging to specialists. New plants are best raised from seed rather than vegetative methods.Winter temperatures should drop no lower than 50 °F.

Oroya borchersii ▣ ○

GLOBOSE

This cactus was named after Dr. Borchers, a cactus grower who discovered it back in 1932. The globose stem usually grows to a diameter of 8in and is formed of about 30 indistinct ribs, which are made up of tubercles. There are up to 25 radial spines growing from the areoles and usually 3 central spines, which are relatively difficult to distinguish from the radial spines, however. Lemon yellow flowers grow from the youngest areoles on the crown. These are 3/4in long and 1/2in across. This is a typical high-altitude species, which can be found in the Cordillera Blanca and Cordillera Negra hills in northern Peru, where it grows in inhospitable surroundings at altitudes of 11,000–13,000ft.

Cultivation is as for other high-altitude species. It was usually grafted in the past, but plants that are grown hard appear much more impressive than grafted ones, which grow to unnatural sizes. It must have cold wintering, however, and sufficient ventilation when in active growth. This cactus also responds very well to summering in the open.

Oroya laxiareolata ▣ ○

GLOBOSE

This species has beautiful spines and a globose stem, which can be up to 6in in diameter. The ribs are not pronounced; these and the light green epidermis are almost covered in a tangle of spines, which range in color from straw yellow to rusty or red-brown. There are usually up to 30 radial spines and either 1 central spine or none at all. The flowers grow near the crown and the petals show two colors. The top two-thirds are red-violet and the bottom third is creamy white or yellowish.

This Peruvian cactus is found near the town of Oroya in central Peru. According to observers who have seen it in the wild, it is found on low limestone outcrops high up in the mountains at altitudes of 11,500ft above sea level. Because of the extreme conditions in which it grows in the wild, it need not be handled with kid gloves in collections. It should be planted in a sunny spot with good air circulation, and it can be observed how these high-altitude species flourish during

Oroya borchersii

the summer outside the greenhouse, even in cool climates. It must be provided with some overhead cover, however, to protect the cactus against prolonged rain during cold days in spring and fall. Propagation is by seed.

Oroya neoperuviana ▣ ○

GLOBOSE-COLUMNAR

This cactus, closest relative to *O. peruviana*, is considered by some to be simply a varietas of this species. Its stem is globose or almost columnar (mainly in collections) and it can be up to 16in tall and 10in across. Its thicker spines differentiate it from the type species, and are more pressed against the stem. The spines are generally straw yellow with a brownish tinge. There are usually 20–30 radial spines and 5 or more centrals spines of 3/4–1 1/4 in long, which are generally straw yellow with a brownish ting. The flower's beauty is thanks to the variable colors of its petals, which are light yellow at the base and pinkish scarlet toward the top. This is a high-altitude species (14,000 ft), which withstands very harsh conditions of extremely cold winters and general dampness. Its precise location is near the mountain pass along the road from the Peruvian town of Oroya to Tarma. These cacti are found in open areas, with no shade from other vegetation. Cultivation is the same as for other *Oroya*. They seem to prefer being outside with some overhead shelter to protect against ongoing rain. Some cactus growers also like to plant it directly into the greenhouse bed, where this species displays beautiful spines and forms more flattened stems.

Oroya laxiareolata

Oroya neoperuviana

Oroya peruviana

Oroya peruviana ▣ ○

GLOBOSE

The habit is fairly similar to that of the preceeding species, but it has smaller stems and fewer spines. Also, the spines generally stick out from the stem more. A maximum of 20 spines grow from 1 areole (at least for cacti in the wild), but specimens in cultivation usually have a lot fewer spines. The flower has coloring is as beautiful as the species above.

It can be found in the same areas as *O. neoperuviana*. These locations are spread around the Peruvian town of Oroya. Cultivation is the same as for other *Oroya*, and it prefers spending summers outdoors to the overheated environment of a greenhouse. It does not need grafting because the plants grow well with their own roots. Older specimens can become corky at the base, but this phenomenon is difficult to influence, unfortunately, and is primarily an indication of the age of the plant.

Pygmaeocereus rowleyanus ▣ ○

COLUMNAR

Some growers refer to this cactus under the generic name *Arthocereus*, but because it is so distinct, it possibly deserves the status of an independent genus. It is clump-forming and the stems can be up to 4in high and 1 1/4in across. The radial spines are gray and the single central spine

Pygmaeocereus rowleyanus

Tephrocactus crispicrinitus

is usually red-brown. The white flower can be up to 2 1/4in long and is narrowly funnel-shaped. It flowers at night during the summer.
The author of the description, C. Backeberg, stated very generally that it could be found in Peru. Even today there is no information available about where it can be found exactly and it is only known that it grows at altitudes of about 1,300ft in the south of the country. From the point of view of cultivation, it can be classified under the category of cacti that are difficult; as a result, it is generally only encountered as specimens grafted onto strong, slow-growing stocks. It requires full sun, good ventilation, and cold wintering at temperatures of about 50 °F.

Tephrocactus crispicrinitus ▣ ○

CUSHION-FORMING

This species forms large, cushion-like mounds made up of a large number of egg-shaped sections, which are about 2 3/4in tall and 1 1/2–2in in diameter. A large number of long, hair-like spines grow from the areoles, which completely cover the stem. They grow up to 1 1/4in long. Needle-like spines show various colors, from straw yellow to brown and red-brown. The flowers are broadly funnel-shaped and are usually red in color.
This high-altitude species can be found in many locations in the Peruvian mountains. The best-known places where it grows are at Punta Caillan in the Cordillera Negra, at an altitude of about 13,800ft, and in the Cordillera Blanca at Quebrada Queshque at an altitude of 13,000ft. (also the home of *T. crispicrinitus* subv. *flavicomus*). Cultivation of this cactus is definitely not simple. The same principles apply as for other *Tephrocactus*, the only difference being that this cactus benefits from being place outdoors in summer. It responds very badly to the overheated environment of a greenhouse during the summer. Cacti in collections are never as beautiful as in the wild and they seldom flower.

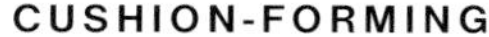

Tephrocactus dimorphus ▣ ○

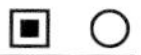

CUSHION-FORMING

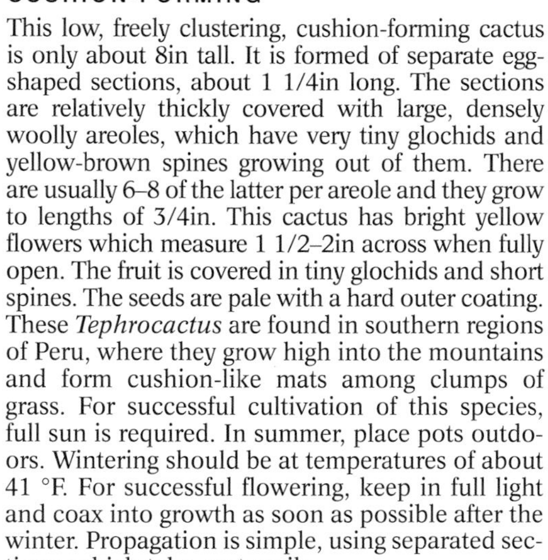

This low, freely clustering, cushion-forming cactus is only about 8in tall. It is formed of separate egg-shaped sections, about 1 1/4in long. The sections are relatively thickly covered with large, densely woolly areoles, which have very tiny glochids and yellow-brown spines growing out of them. There are usually 6–8 of the latter per areole and they grow to lengths of 3/4in. This cactus has bright yellow flowers which measure 1 1/2–2in across when fully open. The fruit is covered in tiny glochids and short spines. The seeds are pale with a hard outer coating. These *Tephrocactus* are found in southern regions of Peru, where they grow high into the mountains and form cushion-like mats among clumps of grass. For successful cultivation of this species, full sun is required. In summer, place pots outdoors. Wintering should be at temperatures of about 41 °F. For successful flowering, keep in full light and coax into growth as soon as possible after the winter. Propagation is simple, using separated sections, which take root easily.

Tephrocactus dimorphus

Tephrocactus floccosus

Tephrocactus floccosus □ ○

CUSHION-FORMING

This cushion-like species, which forms mats in the wild, can grow up to 6ft across. The individual cylindrical sections are about 4in across and are covered in white, hair-like spines. The flowers grow at the top of the sections. They are usually yellow or orange in color and are 1 1/4–1 1/2in across.

T. floccosus is a beautiful example of high-altitude flora in Peru and Bolivia. It is found at altitudes of 11,500–15,000ft. Snow and ice can also be found at the very highest levels. Despite the fact that seeds from this species have found their way into commerce in recent years, few people have so far had much success with germinating them. The large seeds with their hard outer coating are very reluctant to germinate, even in the face of diverse methods; for instance heat-treatment of the seed (warm stratification) or abrasion of the coating (scarification). However, there are not enough parent plants from which offsets can be taken. Despite the fact that this beautiful cactus is relatively widespread in the wild, it is particularly rare in collections belonging to cactus growers. It takes a number of years to flower (at least 10) and only does so provided there is cold wintering. During the growing season it responds best when planted in the open.

Tephrocactus ignescens ▣ ○

CUSHION-FORMING

This cactus forms cushion-like or semi-globose mounds, a maximum of 8–10in tall. Often they have as many as a hundred very fleshy sections, up to 4in long. The long, yellow-brown spines, which can reach a length of more than 2 1/4in, create a striking effect. The species epithet igne-

Tephrocactus ignescens

scens, which translates as flaming red, clearly relates to the color of the flowers, which really are fiery red and relatively large. The fruit is a berry, covered in tiny glochids. The seeds are pale and only a fraction of an inch long.
It is found in the mountains on the border between Peru and Chile, where it grows among tussocks of grass. Its place of occurrence is most often given as Sumbay in southern Peru. It is not often cultivated in collections. Although its spines are very attractive, specimens grown in temperate zones are considerably less beautiful than those in the wild. It is very shy to flower in cultivation.

Tephrocactus kuehnrichianus ▣ ○

BUSHY

The low mounds this cactus creates are formed by sections clustering on top of one other. One of its defining characteristics is the gray-green color of the epidermis. The color becomes particularly pronounced in sunny spots. The glochids growing from the woolly areoles are only a fraction of an inch long and the spines grow to a maximum of 1 1/4–1 1/2in in length. They are gray, pointed, and very prickly. The yellow of the flower indicates that the genus is a close relative of Opuntia.
The species is found not far from the Peruvian capital, Lima, near the town of Chosica, where it grows at altitudes of about 3,300ft. In cultivation it needs to be placed in the sunniest spot in the greenhouse. Even better is out in the open, in a sufficiently large container, and with cold wintering in the light to trigger flowering. They are propagated by breaking off sections, which should then be left in a warm, shady place for approximately 1 month. The wounds callus over during that time, and the sections can then be planted in an appropriate rooting medium.

Tephrocactus kuehnrichianus

Tephrocactus sphaericus ▣ ○

CUSHION-FORMING

This low, spreading, bushy cactus is formed by a large quantity of cylindrical to globose sections, about 1 1/2in across. This taxon varies greatly in spin number and length, but they are usually 1 1/4 in. long and gray. The glochids are short and very numerous. The yellow to yellow-orange flowers are carried at the top of the oldest sections and change into a fruit, covered in a huge number of glochids. The seeds are relatively large and less than 1/4in long.
As a result of the enormous area over which this cactus is found, other forms have been recorded (e.g. *T. s.* var. *unguispinus* or *T. s.* var. *rauppianus*), distinguished by their spines. The type species is typically found near Arequipa in Peru, where it grows at altitudes of 6,500–9,200ft. Cultivation of this species is not particularly complicated, provided the container is of adequate size and that it is placed in the open during the growing season. Persuading the cactus to flower is a major problem. Propagation is as for *T. kuehnrichianus*.

Tephrocactus sphaericus

Trixanthocereus blossfeldiorum

Trixanthocereus blossfeldiorum ▣ ○

COLUMNAR

Because of its spines, the considerable number of hair-like spines, and the shape of the flowers and fruit, this cactus used to be classified within the genus *Espostoa*. Generally it grows as a solitary, non-flowering stem, which can reach a height of 13ft and a diameter of more than 4in. The thickly dotted, woolly areoles have about 25 radial spines, which are soft and white in color. There are about 6 central spines, which are prickly, red-brown in color, and usually up to 1 1/4in long. The lateral cephalium develops on plants when they have reached a height of 3ft, and it produces creamy white flowers, often with a tinge of pink.
In the wild they are found in various locations and, according to observations made in the field, certain specimens are more conspicuous and with few spines. They are generally said to grow in the hilly terrain of northern Peru, at Huancabamba (KK 1569), and at Pucara, where a less spiny variety grows (KK 1218). It is a beautiful columnar species, n ornament to collections of globose cacti. It is made even more attractive by its relatively early flowering. It requires winter temperatures of about 54 °F in full sun.

Weberbauerocereus albus ▣ ○

COLUMNAR

This massive cactus can grow up to 16ft tall, forming a magnificent group of columns with white spines. It clusters toward the base. The individual stems have 16–20 ribs, with some 20 soft or hair-like radial spines and 4–7 stronger central spines growing from the brown areoles. Both types of spine are white. In the flowering zone they are up to 1 1/2in long and yellowish. The flowers are up to 4in long and almost the same across. They stay open for a few days and nights. They are white or pale pink in color.
The species is said to be distributed in the Peruvian department of Ancash, where it grows in central areas around San Marcos (at an altitude of approximately 8,200ft). In collections it is sometimes wrongly classified as *Thrixanthocereus senilis*, but there are also collections where it is currently only recorded under field collection number KK 1524. Few cactus growers own it. Cultivation is very simple but the main problem is the space and large container required. It is propagated from seed, which germinate freely but are seldom available.

Weberbauerocereus horridispinus ▣ ○

COLUMNAR–BUSHY

This cactus clusters from the base and grows to a height of 6ft. Its strongest shoots can grow to a diameter of up to 6in. The stems are formed of about 18 ribs. Some 5–7 strong spines, which point in all directions, grow from the large, woolly areoles, along with a number of tiny spines, which surround the areole on all sides. The flowers bloom toward the top of the stem. They are green and the sepals are often brownish, as are the fine hairs which cover the buds and later the flower tube. The fruit is an olive green berry which measures about 3/4in across.
The species grows in southern Peru in the same locations as members of *Browningia* and *Corryocactus*, in very dry desert areas with minimal associated vegetation. The Chala valley, where it is found, is about 2,500ft above sea level. In collections it has also also been recorded under field collection number KK 545. Although an elegant and interesting cactus, it is not found very often in collections. For it to reach a larger size, it needs a sufficiently large cultivation container, full sun, cold wintering, and a free-draining soil mix. It be-

Trixanthocereus blossfeldiorum, detail

nefits from applications of a balanced fertilizer two or three times during the growing season.

Weberbauerocereus rauhii ▣ ○

COLUMNAR

These high large cacti grow to a up to 16ft and cluster from near ground level. At the base the individual shoots measure up to 6in in diameter and at the tip only about 3in. The spines are gray and yellowish on younger plants. The radial spines are short (1/2in) but the central spines can reach lengths of up to 2 1/4in. The flowers are a narrow funnel shape and about 4in long. The petals are creamy brown and the sepals are violet. The mature fruit is red-brown in color.
The species, found in the southern regions of Peru near Nazca, grows at altitudes of 3,300 – 6,500 ft. Another varietas, *w. rauhii* var. *laticornus*, is a synonym for the type species, because plants do not, because plants do not display sufficiently distinct characteristics to gain the status of a subspecies. It is rarely found in collections due to a lack of interest among cactus growers, and poor seed availability, which is the best which is the best method of propagating it. Smaller plants in collections do not initially form enough shoots for intensive vegetative propagation. This is only possible by removing the tip of the parent plant, which then produces a number of offsets on the wound.

Weberbauerocereus albus

Weberbauerocereus horridispinus

Weberbauerocereus rauhii

Weberbauerocereus seyboldianus

Weberbauerocereus seyboldianus ▣ ○

COLUMNAR

This species can be classified as a close relative of *W. weberbaueri*. The stems and spines are relatively similar. The only difference is in the structure of the flower, which has a narrow flower tube only 1/2in long. The whole flower can grow up to 3in long and is light scarlet.
Even the location given is relatively close to where *W. weberbaueri* is found. This species is said to occur on the Chachani volcano near Arequipa in Peru. With regard to cultivation, the same applies as for other members of the genus, but it could be argued that this species is more a product of the work of C. Backeberg and W. Rauh than a species in its own right.

Weberbauerocereus weberbaueri

Weberbauerocereus weberbaueri ▣ ○

COLUMNAR

This bushy cactus grows to a maximum height of about 13ft, with the individual stems 2 1/4–4in in diameter. They are formed of 15–22 sharp ribs. The stems have an eye-catching covering of spines, which are reddish initially, turning yellow-brown. The 6–8 central spines reach a length of up to 2 1/4in and the radial spines, of which there are approximately 20, grow to about 1 1/4in. The large, funnel-shaped flowers are covered in scales and dark hair. The petals are a unique white-brown color. The fruit, a yellow-orange berry with green scales, is 1 1/2in in diameter.
In the wild this cactus can be found in southern Peru, at altitudes of 2,400–10,000ft above sea level, not far from the Misti volcano near the town of Arequipa. Because of its size, it is not a cactus that is often seen in cultivation. All the same, cultivation is relatively simple and it requires the same treatment as other high-altitude species from South America. It flourishes particularly well in a fairly large container or planted directly into a greenhouse bed. Even with this treatment, it takes many years before flowering.

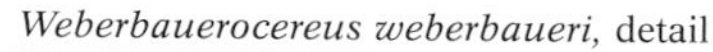
Weberbauerocereus weberbaueri, detail

Wittia amazonica ■ ⊙

EPIPHYTIC

This epiphytic species is freely branching, with leaf-like lateral stems often overhanging, and up to 20 in long and 2 – 3 in across with wavy edges.

The pink-violet flowers at the stem tips are produced throughout summer and fall, are 1/3 in long, and stay open all day and night. This rare species is found in Peru's tropical rainforest, growing in the shade of treetops and clinging to tree bank or in clifts. There are few cactus growers who can boast this elegant and unusual species in their collection, which is a pity cactus. In cultivation it needs conditions similar to those in which it grows in the wild. Therefore it is best suited to a slightly acidic soil mix and a rather shady location. Temperatures during the winter must not fall below 60 °F.

Wittia amazonica

4. Bolivia

The diversity of Bolivian cacti species bears comparison with Mexico from various aspects. Bolivia may be only half the area of Mexico, but it is unusually diverse in terms of cacti. Bolivia is about 424,000 square miles in area, whereas Mexico is about 761,000 square miles in area. It is high in altitude because of the Cordillera Real mountain range, with the highest peak Illimany (22,600ft above sea level). The altitude falls gradually to the east and flattens out into the region of Gran Chaco. The cacti growing in Bolivia are unbelievably diverse and variable in terms of species or groups in individual locations. This phenomenon is characteristic for many genera from South America, but the Bolivian genus *Sulcorebutia* is a typical example. On just one hill you can find long-spined cacti, short-spined cacti, red-flowered cacti, orange-flowered cacti, and even yellow-flowered cacti – and all these are members of the same species. It is therefore not surprising that over recent years there has been a whole series of unsubstantiated records whose authors were unaware of the conditions on site and could only compose the report from material sent to Europe or the USA. In addition to *Sulcorebutia*, there are a number of other interesting genera typical for Bolivia, which have a number of species in Bolivia. These include the following: *Echinopsis*, *Lobivia*, *Parodia*, and *Weingartia*. Bolivia also boasts beautiful columnar cacti from the following genera: *Cleistocactus*, *Corryocactus*, and *Oreocereus*.

Bolivian cacti are also found at altitudes of about 10,000ft and are therefore typical high-altitude species (this must also be taken into account when growing in cultivation). Most grow at these points with very little associated vegetation and are exposed to intense sunshine and fairly low temperatures, above all during the dormant period. Culture of these cacti in the northern hemisphere is relatively well mastered and they are the typical kinds of cacti that withstand summer outdoors. Cacti from the Altiplano plateau are adapted to shade from grass or other associated vegetation and the temperature differences in these regions are not as high as up in the mountains. Cacti species from Bolivia are an integral part of every large collection. The unusual diversity of their spines, habit, and also the range of color of their flowers are one of the main reasons why growers are still so interested in them. The relative ease of cultivation and propagation is also a reason for their popularity in collections.

Left: *Neocardenasia herzogiana*

Cintia knizei ▣ ○

GLOBOSE

Growers have known about this species for a relatively long time, but it was only recorded in 1996 when the completely new genus Cintia was created. So far this consists of only one species. They have a small, globose stem, only 1 1/4–2in wide, which is made up of prominent warty tubercles. Underground these stems change into a long, tuberous root. Adult specimens are completely spineless and the epidermis changes color to reddish or bronze in full sunlight. The flowers are 1/2–3/4in wide and are carried on the crown of the plant. Their narrow petals are a deep yellow. The fruit is a small dried-out berry, which matures within a few weeks. It contains shiny black seeds that are 1/25in long.

This cactus comes from the Bolivian province of Nor Cinti, which gives it its generic name. The author of the description, Jan Říha, chose the species epithet in honor of K. Kníže, a Czech cactus expert living in Peru. It is found in a number of locations near the town of Lecori at altitudes of 10,000–13,000ft above sea level. Usually these cacti are mainly restrictedto stony ground, and sometimes they are covered in deposits of dust and clay particles, so they are not at all easy to find. Because the species has not been in cultivation for long, most seedlings are grafted onto a variety of stocks. In recent years these plants have started being grown on their own roots. Because of their fleshy roots, a free-draining compost is particularly important. It is a high-altitude species and therefore requires a sunny location with good ventilation. During the hottest summer days growth slows down significantly. It can also be propagated by seed and by rooting of offsets, which produce roots within two weeks after splitting from the parent plant.

Cintia knizei

Echinopsis arachnacantha

Echinopsis arachnacantha

GLOBOSE

This cactus is sometimes referred to under the generic name *Lobivia*. These clustering cacti are columnar until the individual stems are about 1 1/2in in diameter; the epidermis is usually dark green and sometimes almost violet. The spines are flattened and spread out like a spider (the reason for the species epithet *arachnacantha*, meaning "with spines in the shape of a spider"). The flower is a narrow tubular shape and about 2in long. The color of the flowers varies with some cacti from light yellow to a dark yellow-orange.
In the wild this cactus can be found at Samaipata in the department of Santa Cruz in Bolivia, where it grows on rocky mountainsides at altitudes of about 8,000ft. It is easy to cultivate, flowers as a young plant, and has a highly variable appearance. This has made it highly popular among cactus growers. The numerous offsets can be used for propagation, but it grows just as easily from seed.

Echinopsis subdenudata 

GLOBOSE

The stem of this cactus is solitary and barrel-shaped. It grows to about 3in tall and up to 4 3/4in across. The prominent ribs have white, woolly areoles with spines growing out of them, especially during the juvenile stage. Adult specimens do not produce any spines. The flower is large and opens at night. It is fragrant and white-green in color. The flower tube is covered in fine dark hairs.
This species occurs in the wild in the Bolivian department of Tarija. It grows at the relatively low altitude of 2,000ft. It is becoming more common in cultivation, above all as an outstanding stock which can be used for very good grafting. It is also very popular incollections because of its unique, distinctive habit and also because of its beautiful, fragrant flowers.

Frailea chiquitana

GLOBOSE

This species usually grows solitarily, but it occasionally has a clustering stem, which usually does not grow above 1 1/4in. It is made up of 24 ribs with densely woolly, dark brown, elliptical areoles on the edges. These have 8–10 radial spines and usually 3 central spines growing out of them. The crown of the plant is depressed and flowers 1in in diameter grow inside it. The outside of the whole flower is covered in white hair and the petals are bright yellow. The dried perinath clings to the tip of the fruit.
The originally specified location is the mountain Divi Miserato and it was not until later, in 1962, that other places were published, such as Roboré and Santiago de Chiquitos, south of San José in southeastern Bolivia. According to information from the site, the cactus grows out of cracks in sandstone and red ocher rocks. Because the species is not completely cleistogamous, it only forms

Echinopsis subdenudata

Fraileа chiquitana

a limited quantity of seed, which is why it is found so rarely in collections. It is by no means easy to cultivate. It needs a well-drained, slightly acidic soil mix and shade when it is really hot in the summer and at the start of the growing season. Cold wintering in absolutely dry conditions is another requirement for successful cultivation.

Gymnocalycium cardenasianum ▣ ○

GLOBOSE-COLUMNAR

This is a magnificent member of the genus, which is perhaps at its most beautiful when young. Even large adult cacti have an exquisite, wild spine covering. It usually forms columns about 8in high. The species is extremely variable in terms of number of ribs and spine covering and that is why there are many interesting extremes, both in collections and in the wild. Most of the central and radial spines bend toward the stem and the longest central spines can grow to up to 3in. The pink-white flowers grow near the top and are up to 2in long. Sometimes they have trouble forcing their way through the thick spine covering. After pollination and fertilization a round fruit appears, covered in tiny scales, which is full of seeds about 1/25in inch long. In the wild this is an extremely variable species and that is why so many variants have been recorded. It is found in many locations in the Bolivian province of Mendez, near the town of Carrizal. It grows on mountainsides at altitudes of about 4,000ft above sea level. Like most other *Gymnocalycium* it is a very obliging cactus in culture. Seedlings are slow to develop the first year after sowing.They take more than 10 years to reach flowering size. They can withstand cold and dark wintering.

Gymnocalycium cardenasianum

Gymnocalycium pflanzii ▣ ⊙

GLOBOSE

The barrel-shaped stem of this species grows to approximately a foot across and has a dark green epidermis. The flat ribs are formed of tubercles and on each one there is a large areole with 8 radial spines and 1 central spine. Most of the central spines are gray in color, but they are darker at the end. The flower is about 1 1/2in long and the same across. It is white in color with a reddish throat. The flower is full of violet filaments and yellow anthers with a large quantity of pollen.
It is found in many locations in the wild, and the banks of the Rio Pilcomayo at Pala Marcedo in Bolivia are considered the type locality. It was here that Karl Pflanz discovered the first specimens. This man, the German consul in Bolivia, was an amateur cactus collector. Today, though, locations are known in both the lowlands and the mountains, and not only in Bolivia but also in Argentina and Paraguay.

Helianthocereus tarijensis ▣ ○

COLUMNAR

This columnar cactus generally reaches heights or more than 5ft and its stems are up to 10in in diameter. There are about 15 ribs with woolly areoles from which grow 10–17 spines, 4 central the rest radial. The longest central spines can grow to up to 2 3/4in in length. The funnel-shaped flowers are about 4in long, the flower tube is covered in brownish hair, and the petals are bright red. The fruit is a round berry, up to 1 1/2in across, the pulp of which is prized by the indigenous people.
This cactus is recorded as being found in the Bolivian department of Tarija (from where it has acquired its species epithet), where it grows near Escayachi at altitudes of about 10,000ft. Germination of the seeds is not difficult and the seedlings are quick to grow in the early stages. Larger plants do well outdoors in summer and should be grown in a suf-

Gymnocalycium pflanzii

Helianthocereus tarijensis

ficiently large container. For the best results, apply a balanced fertilizer when in active growth.

Hildewintera aureispina 

TRAILING

This cactus clusters at the base and has trailing stems. These can be up to 5ft long but have a diameter of only 1in. The golden yellow spines are very thick, especially around the flower buds, so much so that they almost cover the light green epidermis of the 16 ribs. The flowers grow from the youngest parts of the stem and are almost zygomorphic. The petals are a beautiful pink-violet color, as are the stamens, from which a yellow stigma protrudes.
They were first discovered relatively recently in the wild (1958). They grow on steep hillsides and rocky ledges at Agua Clara in the Bolivian province of Florida. They have become very popular among growers not only for their distinctive habit but also because of their beautiful spines, which form a splendid contrast with the color of the flowers. Cultivation is very simple. The plants just need to be given enough space to trail and can be grown in a basket hanging froma shelf in the greenhouse or outside during the summer. Propagation is by seed or cuttings.

Hildewintera aureispina

Lobivia backebergii ▣ ○

GLOBOSE

This beautiful and interesting species usually has a clustering stem, but it can occasionally be solitary as well. It is usually glubose, up to 2 in across, with a light green epidermis, and elongates slightly towards a column shape.
There are 13-15 prominent ribs with 3-7 radial spines growing out of the areoles, occasionally with 1 central spine up to 1/2 in long. The pink to bright scarlet flower is about 1 3/4 in across and after fertilization it changes into a round fruit about 1/3in in diameter.
According to Dr. Erich Werderman, it is found in low areas near the Bolivian capital, La Paz, which are now part of the town Challapampa. This cactus can be recommended to all growers. Growers with little experience are surprised by how easy it is to cultivate and experienced cactus growers appreciate the beauty of its flowers. It needs cold wintering at temperatures below 50 °F. If temperatures rise above this limit, some distortion can occur as a result of low light levels, especially in the early spring. These cacti have a tendency to emerge from dormancy very early, which applies generally for the whole genus.

Lobivia backebergii

Lobivia ferox ▣ ⊙

GLOBOSE

This is an extremely variable taxon, appearing in collections under many of names, including *Lobivia ducis-pauli.* The stem is relatively large: 12–20in tall and about 10in in diameter. Large, adult specimens have 25-30 ribs, and 10-14 radial spines grow from each areole, as to 2-5 central spines. On some individuals, these can reach the unbelievable length of as much as 7 1/4in! The flower grows from the side of the plant. It is 3 1/2–4 1/4in long and when fully open can be up to 3in across. It can be pure white in color, but there is generally a tinge of pink or pale pink. The fruit is a round berry about 3/4in across.
The variability of this species is influenced by the huge area in which it is found, stretching from the Bolivian province of Oruro to the town of Tupiza in the neighboring province of Potosi. It prefers partial shade to full sun, and is better placed outdoors in summer than kept in the overheated greenhouse. Germinating the seed is not difficult, but seedlings can take a relatively long time, 10 years roughly, to reach flowering size.

Lobivia ferox

Lobivia tiegeliana

Lobivia tiegeliana ▣ ⊙

GLOBOSE

The globose stem of this species is usually solitarily, but some specimens form clusters. The maximum height is usually about 2 3/4in and offsets are usually smaller than the parent plant. There are generally up to 15 flattened, radial spines and 1–4 central ones. These are usually darker than the radial spines. The narrow, funnel-shaped flower has a long tube and is about 1 1/2in across. It varies in color from purple to violet-red; white-flowered forms are known to occur. This species can be found near the town of Tarija in southern Bolivia. It grows here at altitudes of 6,500–8,000ft. Cultivation is very simple. This species flourishes on its own roots and it can be propagated by offses from the parent plant (assuming these are present), and by seed. Seedlings grow quickly and bloom after just 3–5 years. Adult plants prefer partial shade to the scorching heat of the sun.

Neocardenasia herzogiana

Neocardenasia herzogiana 

COLUMNAR

This columnar cactus reaches a height of around 30ft and forms a strong woody trunk when adult. There are large areoles on the edges of its 6 or 7 ribs with firm spines up to 7in long protruding from them. The flower-bearing areoles are like the woolly, spineless areoles of Neoraimondia, but according to the author of the description they differ in producing a narrower flower tube with long spines. The flower is about 2 3/4in long. The petals are red and the cluster of stamens are a creamy white color. The fruit is an egg-shaped, fleshy berry, up to 2 1/4in long.

The species is found in the wild in two Bolivian provinces: Cochabamba and Chuquisaca, where it grows on hillsides at altitudes of about 6,500ft. It appears in collections only rarely, because of its size. The young seedlings are appealing and can be accommodated by most greenhouses until about 20 years old. They need fairly cold wintering and a container of adequate size.

Neocardenasia herzogiana, young plant

Neowerdermannia vorwerkii 

GLOBOSE

The genus was created for this species, which is the only one known so far. Some authorities classify it under *Weingartia*. The round stem is usually up to 3in in diameter and is generally made up of 16 ribs, formed of tubercles. The areoles are located in the grooves and there are 10 radial spines and 1 hooked central spine growing out of them. The flowers grow toward the top and are white or a pale pink-violet color. The fruit only contains a small number of seeds.

This is a typical high-altitude species from the mountains of Bolivia, where it grows at a height of just below 13,000ft. It is found on rocky ground without the cover of any associated vegetation. It is not found in collections very often for some reason, although it is relatively undemanding. It needs adequate light and ventilation for successful cultivation and development, and, where grown outdoors, should be sheltered from prolonged rainfall towrd the end of the growing season. Seed is the only means of propagation. Seed trays should be protected against too much heat, however.

Neowerdermannia vorwerkii

Oreocereus celsianus  

COLUMNAR

This columnar species has stems around 6ft tall, and the individual branches are 3–4 3/4in in diameter. It does not form a main stem and clusters from the base. Some 7–9 radial spines, 1–4 central spines, and also long, white hairs, which almost cover the plant, grow from the woolly areoles. Flowers bloom near the top and are a pink-red color. The fruit is a dried-out berry with seeds randomly spaced inside.

It is found in the south of Bolivia and the also spreads into Argentina. It grows relatively high up in the mountains and its closest relative is clearly *O. trollii*, which it resembles, not only in terms of habit, but also in terms of its reproductive organs. Propagation and cultivation are very simple and are the same as for other South American Cereus. Because of their long white hairs, seedlings are attractive by the second year after sowing. It is relucatant to flower in cultivation.

Oreocereus celsianus

Oreocereus neocelsianus

Oreocereus neocelsianus 

COLUMNAR

This cactus clusters from the base and reaches a height of 3ft. Its individual branches can reach a diameter of 3 – 4 3/4in. The epidermis is light green initially and becomes darker green later. There are 10–17 ribs with protruding, elliptical areoles with 9 radial spines and 1–4 strong central spines and a huge quantity of fine hair-like spines growing out of them. The scarlet flowers are narrow, tubular, and 2 3/4–3 1/2in long. One striking feature of this cactus is its long style and yellow stigma. The fruit is a round berry, which splits at the base.

There are a number of locations where this cactus can be found, from southern Bolivia to northern Argentina. Cultivation is not demanding: because this is a high-altitude species, it can be stood outdoors in summer, with some protection against prolonged rain. Sow seed in early spring under growing lamps to ensure a long first growing season before the first winter.

Parodia gracilis

Parodia gracilis 

COLUMNAR

The species epithet gracilis translates as fine or delicate and relates to the interesting spine covering and clearly to the beautiful flowers as well. The non-clustering stem is globose initially and later grows into a fairly low column, 2–4in diameter and 10in tall. At the tip, which is covered in white hair, there are 13–19 spiraling ribs. A variable amount of spines grow from the areoles – there are 14–22 radial spines, which are 1/5–3/4in long, thin, and often hair-like. The central spines, of which there are usually 4–10, are often fairly firm and 1/4–1/2in long. The flowers are 1 1/4–1 1/2in long and are orange or orange-yellow in color. The fruit is a round berry containing a large number of small, black seeds, 1/50in across.

The Bolivian department of Tarija is currently the only area where this species is known to occur. The specific area it is found is the Condor Pass near the Alto de España wilderness. It has been collected here by F. Ritter (FR 740) and A. B. Lau (L 935), for example. It is probably best to use the Fleischer method for germinating seed, using jars to providethe right conditions for the seedlings to reach the right size for pricking out. Adults provide no cultivation problems. The same principles apply as for other members of the genus.

Parodia maassii 

GLOBOSE-COLUMNAR

It would be possible to compose an impressive and very extensive collection from the many different forms of this *Parodia* found in cultivation. The stem grows into a column, about 8in high and 4in in diameter. There are 10–15 radial spines and 3–4 central spines growing out of the prominent areoles, which are up to 1/6in in diameter and covered in large quantities of white hair. The lower central spines are up to 2 3/4in long and bent; they are sometimes hooked at the tip. The flowers are about 1 1/4in wide and are formed of narrow petals, which are orange-red in color. The very fine seeds are only 1/33in across.

Parodia maassii

P. maassii is a typical high-altitude species, which grows in Bolivia and Argentina at altitudes of about 11,500ft. A large number of cactus growers have collected it in the past and seeds or young plants can currently be found in catalogs under field collection numbers FR 46, KK 957, P 237, etc. Like the majority of Parodia, it has to be propagated by sowing the tiny seed. The seed germinates very well, but the seedlings are very slow developers. This cactus is vulnerable to scorch by the spring sunshine (it prefers a certain amount of shade in the summer as well). It takes at least 10 years to flower and prefers cold wintering, preferably in light conditions.

Parodia schwebsiana

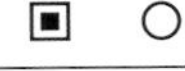

GLOBOSE–COLUMNAR

As a young plant, this species is globose initially and only starts to grow into a columnar form after about 10 years in cultivation. It is usually 2 1/2in in diameter and 4 3/4–6in tall. Some 10 radial spines grow from the areoles and 1 central spine, which points downward and usually has a hooked tip. The deep red flowers are 1in across and are carried on the crown of the plant.

This species can be found in many locations in the wild between the Bolivian towns of Sucre and Cochabamba, where it grows at altitudes of 6,500–10,000ft. It can be found on rocky slopes with gravel outcrops, where it usually grows along with grasses and other drought-tolerant plants. It is particularly popular among cactus growers for a number of reasons: it has attractive flowers, which are large enough to bloom after only about 4 years, and in contrast to other members of the genus, germination is simple and the seedlings grow relatively quickly. Like other high-altitude species, it prefers to spend summers outdoors rather than being in a greenhouse.

Parodia schwebsiana

Parodia slabaiana

Parodia slabaiana

GLOBOSE

This species is very similar to *P. occulta*, the only difference being that it has a smaller number of flowers and a yellow or pale pink perianth. The barrel-shaped stem is only 1 1/4–2 3/4in in diameter and is made up of 12–15 indistinct ribs, which are formed of prominent tubercles. There are 8–14 short, gray, radial spines and 1–4 central spines, up to 1/2in long. The flowers are about 1/2in across with a strong fragrance of bitter almonds. The specimen illustrated has extremely short spines.

The species was first recorded recently and its status as a destinct species is no longer in dispute. It is a variable taxon, which grows near Cieneguillas in Bolivia. The plants grow on a shingle substrate with *Weingartia fidaiana* the only associated vegetation. It is not found in many collections, but cultivation is as for other *Parodia* species.

Quiabentia pflanzii

Quiabentia pflanzii 

BUSHY

This species belongs to a genus that is very closely related to *Pereskia*, with which it shares certain similarities. In terms of the evolution of the *Cactaceae* family, it is one of the most primitive. It is a bushy species with fleshy leaves about 1 1/2in long and there are 2 1/4in long, gray-white spines growing out of the areoles. The pink flowers are up to 2in across.
Q. pflanzii is found in shrubland in Bolivia. The authors give the type locality as 30 miles downstream from Villamontes. It is rare in collections. Cultivation is very simple, provided it can be overwintered in warmth and given occasional watering, even during the winter months.

Rebutia albiareolata

Rebutia albiareolata 

GLOBOSE

This is a relatively new *Rebutia* species, which was named for the white, densely woolly areoles, typical for these plants. It usually grows as a solitary stem, but can form clusters in cultivation. The radial spines, which grow from the areoles covered in short white hair, are 1/4–1/2in long and are usually 10–14 in number. The central spine is usually stiffer and 1/3–2/3in long. The flowers grow from the lower part of the cactus, have a long flower tube, and are up to 1 1/4in across when fully open. The fruit is a dried-out berry, which later completely breaks down and releases the tiny black seeds.
This species was discovered in Bolivia, between Arque and Patcaya, and it can be found in European collections under field collection number FR 761. Cultivation is as simple as for other Rebutia. It can tolerate full sun, but is also not averse to some shade. It needs a well-drained, slightly acidic soil mix. Propagation by seed is simple and seedlings flower three years after sowing.

Rebutia heliosa 

COLUMNAR

This is a beautiful cactus, partly because of its spines but also because of its wonderful flowers. It forms columnar, slightly clustering stems with a beet-like root. The stems are about 1in in diameter and 1 1/2– 2in high (sometimes taller if grafted). The indistinct ribs are made up of small tubercles, which end in an elongated areole with brown dense felt. These cacti only form fine, radial, comblike spines, 1/25in long, which are pressed toward the stem (described as "pectinate"). The orange flowers are about 1 1/2in wide and the author of the description, Werner Rausch, chose the name *heliosa* because of the color of the flowers which are the same color as the rising sun (Helios being the Greek god of the sun).This species was discovered in 1968. It grows between the Bolivian towns of Tarija and Narvaez, at altitudes of about 8,000ft above sea level. Two other varietiants of the typical species from isolated locations have been recorded: *R. heliosa* var. *condorensis* and *R. heliosa* var. *cajasensis*. Plants on their own roots do not grow particularly quickly, but their habit is more similar to cacti in the wild. Grafted plants form sizeable, highly clustering tufts, which are somewhat atypical. Seed-raised plants or divisions are best grown in a free-draining soil mix, overwintered in cool, bright conditions, and coaxed into growth early in the season. They reach flowering size afer 3–5 years.

Rebutia heliosa

Rebutia mixticolor

Rebutia heliosa var. *condorensis* ▣ ○

COLUMNAR

This taxon is similar to the type species and forms cushion-like tufts in the wild. It also clusters in cultivation and the individual stems are 1 1/4–1 1/2in tall and the same in diameter. It has longer and thicker spines than the basic species and the flowers generally have a shorter flower tube and are more reddish in color.
This varietas was discovered near the Abra Condor pass, which is situated in the Bolivian province of Tarija, at an altitude of approximately 8,000ft. It acquired the name condorensis from where it was found. Because the species forms beet-like, fleshy roots, it is prone to rotting, especially when dormant in summer. Propagation is by seed and also by detaching offses, which take root easily in perlite, after being dried out for about a week in the shade. Grafted plants grow to unnatural sizes. The most beautiful plants are grown hard on their own roots, and these most closely resemble specimens in the wild.

Rebutia heliosa var. *condorensis*

Rebutia mixticolor 

GLOBOSE

Some growers classify this species within *Mediolobivia.* The barrel-shaped stem is solitary when young and only develops offsets later. It is formed of 11–13 indistinct ribs, made up of tubercles with an areole at the end. There are usually 11 central spines, 1/4–1/2in long, growing out of the areoles. The flower forms in the side areoles and is of interest because the edge of the petals is usually slightly lighter than the center. The flower tube is as long (1 1/4–1 1/2in) as the flower is wide when fully open.
This species is found in the Bolivian province of Tarija between Mendez and San Antonio, where it grows among grasses on rocky outcrops. There are no problems with cultivation, but seed needs to come from non-hybrid plants and from verified sources if the collection is to have botanical value. It is currently available under field collection number FR 1108.

Rebutia muscula in culture

Rebutia perplexa

Rebutia muscula

GLOBOSE-COLUMNAR

Cactus growers still sometimes classify this species under the old generic classification *Aylostera* muscula (*Aylostera* is now considered a subgenus of *Rebutia*). It is a very beautiful cactus, partly because of its spines, but also because of its flowers. It clusters to a certain extent. Its individual stems, which are 1 1/4–1 1/2in in diameter, are globose initially and then become slightly columnar later. It has 25–40 indistinct ribs, formed of tiny mammillae with woolly oval areoles at the tip, from which grow 30–50 spines. It is difficult to distinguish between central and radial spines, because they are all the same length (1/12–1/6in), white in color, and not prickly. They have beautiful bright orange flowers growing from the side, which are about 1 1/3in long and 1 1/4in wide.
This species was found in Bolivia, near Tarija, Arque, and Padcaya. K. Kníže collected it at Piedra Larga at an altitude of about 9,000ft. It is usually available in lists under field collection number KK 842. It is suitable for cultivation by all beginners because plants are unlikely to fail. After cold and dry wintering, in early spring beautiful flowers bloom which contrast with the glassy white thorns.

Rebutia perplexa

CUSHION-FORMING

This is a very beautiful *Rebutia*, though its growth is rather dense, which accounts for the species epithet perplexa, meaning complicated and intricate. The clustering stem forms small cushions, and the individual plants are generally 3/4in in diameter. The ribs are formed of indistinct tubercles. These have areoles about 1/12in across with 10–16 rust yellow spines, but it is impossible to differentiate between central and radial spines. The beautiful flowers are about 1 1/4in across and are pinkish violet in color. The fruit is a dried-out berry with black seeds.
A. B. Lau discovered this species in canyons leading off the tributaries of the Rio Pilaya river in the Bolivian province of Tarija. It grows here in the cracks between rocks, but also on rocky outcrops

Rebutia muscula in the wild

Rebutia pygmea „elegantula“

Rebutia pygmea „haagei“

and flat raised ground among grass and moss. It is a heterogamous species, which is easy to cross with other *Rebutia*. For successful pollination of the species, at least two or preferably more plants are required. The seed germinates freely, and seedlings grow well and produce beautiful blooms by the third year. Propagation by detaching offsets is also possible. Grafting is not required. Specimens should be brought into growth early, because they flower in the early months of spring.

Rebutia pygmea

GLOBOSE-COLUMNAR

This is an extremely variable and diverse group of cacti, which a number of botanists and taxonomists have tried to organize, but nature has won out here for the time being. It is not easy to slot individual examples into the "pigeon-holes" of the botanical system. They are cacti with an almost columnar stem mostly, which can grow to 3in tall with a diameter usually of 3/4in. There are also smaller and more compact specimens, however. The spine covering is also very diverse, as is the range of colors of the flowers, which vary from pale pink to scarlet and bright yellow, the throat of the flower often being a different color to the upper sections of the petals.

All these *Rebutia* are easy to cultivate and because propagation by offsets guarantess plants identical to the parent, collections can easily be built up. Every cactus grower with an interesting specimen would certainly be glad to share an offset. There are three different forms of this species found in collections, listed here for the purposes of information. They have even been recorded separately, but there is justified doubt as to their taxonomic classification: *Rebutia pygmea* 'Eos', *Rebutia pygmea* 'Elegantula', and *Rebutia pygmea* 'Haagei'.

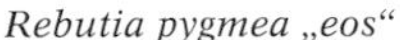

Rebutia pygmea „eos“

Rebutia steinmannii

Rebutia steinmannii

COLUMNAR

This is an extremely variable taxon, which has very different extreme forms. The specimen illustrated corresponds fairly closely to the description of the type species. The stems are columnar and grow to a height of 1 1/4–2in and a diameter of 1/2–3/4in. There are 8–10 ribs. It only has radial spines, which number 8–11, and grow to about 1/2in long. The orange-red flower measures about 3/4in across.
It is found in Bolivia between Oruro and Cochabamba at altitudes of about 13,000ft. It is found relatively rarely in collections, although it is very easy to cultivate. Cacti classified as *R. eucaliptana* (FR 340 and KK 971) are currently found among cactus growers, but these are just a local form of *R. steinmannii.*

Rebutia steinmannii f. *costata* 

COLUMNAR

This taxon was originally classified as an independent genus, *R. costata*, but we feel that it is a closely related plant, which differs only in having more pronounced ribs, a squatter stem, and flowers with petals rounded at the tip. The stems are about 3/4in tall and clustering, and after a while they can form a small, cushion-like mound. Radial spines alone, which are thin and sometimes curved as well, grow from the areoles. The red flower has a relatively long tube (3/4in) and is up to 1 1/4in across. The fruit is a dried out berry, which breaks down after a time and releases the tiny brown-black seeds.

The location is given by Werner Rausch, who specifies the Bolivian department of Potosi, between the towns of Potosi and Cucho Ingenio.
It is a simple, undemanding taxon to cultivate, which prefers partial shade to full sun, but responds well to placing outdoors during summer. Propagation can be by seed but also offsets, which sometimes take root on the parent plant.

Rebutia torquata

COLUMNAR

This is a small, elegant, columnar species. Its individual stems usually grow to a height of 1 1/4–1 1/2in (more in cultivation) and a diameter of about 5/8in. It forms small cushions and each stem consists of 8–10 indistinct ribs. There are 6–10 tiny spines, only 1/12in long, growing from the thickly dotted areoles. The beautiful orange-yellow flower is up to 1 1/4in across.
This cactus, which F. Ritter introduced into cultivation, was distributed under field collection number FR 1117 and is found in the Bolivian province of Potosi at Sud Chicos and Mal Paso. It is not particularly widespread among cactus growers, which is a great shame. It can be propagated by seed and by offsets. Keep it cool in winter and encourage it back into growth in early spring.

Stetsonia coryne 

COLUMNAR

This is another large, tree-like cactus, which grows to up to 26ft in height in its native environment. It clusters from the base and the woody trunk can be up to 16in in diameter. The blue-green or gray-green stems are about 4in across and consist of about 9 ribs with large tubercles.

Rebutia steinmannii f. costata

Rebutia torquata

6–9 radial spines, about 1 1/4in long, grow from each areole, along with a single central spine, which can reach lengths of up to 3in. It produces a long flower with a scaly tube, which blooms nocturnally. It then changes into a fruit, full of tiny black seed.
The species is cited as occurring on the border between Argentina and Bolivia, at relatively low altitudes of 4,000–5,000ft. Yacuiba in northern Argentina or Palos Blancos in Bolivia are given as locations. It grows on rocky mountainsides with little associated vegetation. This is a particularly well-known columnar cactus, because both its seedlings and older specimens are very attractive. It is also one of the limited range of plants grown extensively for supply to the general market. It is found more than other, much more interesting columnar cacti in collections, because of its undemanding cultivation, fast growth, and elegant appearance. In cool climates, very old specimens can flower in exceptional cases.

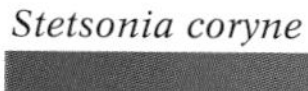

Stetsonia coryne

Sulcorebutia alba

Sulcorebutia alba ▣ ○

GLOBOSE

The stem of this beautiful cactus grows to about 1 1/3in in diameter. The indistinct ribs and the gray-green or violet-red epidermis are usually covered in elegant white spines. This is the reason for the species epithet (alba = white). There are only radial spines, flattened close to the stem, growing from the elongated areoles. They are 20–25 in number and are about 1/10in long. The flower grows from the side of the stem. It is a deep red-violet color and is about 1 1/4in wide. The fruit matures early and contains a relatively small amount of tiny black seeds.

This *Sulcorebutia* has been found very little in recent years and that is why it has such considerable variability. The type locality is near the highway from Sucre to Los Alamos in the Bolivian province of Chuquisaca. It has the same requirements as other members of the genus. This is a high-altitude plant which does not respond well to the conditions in overheated greenhouses on hot summer days. Because of its beet-like root, it is very sensitive to overwatering, particularly when dormant. It is best placed outdoors during summer, with some overhead shelter from prolonged rain, or can be planted directly in the greenhouse bed. Keep cool in winter, preferably in light conditions, and bring into growth as quickly as possible in spring.

Sulcorebutia breviflora 

GLOBOSE

Initially this species is solitary, and only older specimens form a few small offsets. The globose stem is about 2 1/4in in diameter and the same in height, although there have been reports of plants up to 4in tall, or, at the other extreme, only 3/4in tall, as described by Cárdenas. Adult specimens have fleshy or beet-like roots, which can be up to 6in long. There are 10–16 radial spines, which vary in length from 1/12in to 5/8in. Sometimes there is no central spine, but there can be up to 4, about 1/2in long. The flowers grow from the side and are 3/4–1 1/2in across. The external petals often have a thin reddish or greenish brown central stripe. The other petals are a vivid dark or light yellow.

This is another Bolivian cactus which grows in the department of Cochabamba in the hills near Rio Caine, about 6 miles southeast of the town of Capinota at an altitude of about 6,500ft. The type collection from Cárdenas was classified as Cárd. 6140 and it also found its way into collections under this number. This species is not particularly widespread among cactus growers, although it is not at all difficult to grow, cultivation

Sulcorebutia breviflora

Sulcorebutia candidae

being basically the same as for other members of the genus.

Sulcorebutia candidae 

GLOBOSE

This is a barrel-shaped species, which produces relatively few clusters. The individual stems are up to 2in in diameter and the offsets are usually smaller than the parent plant. The stem, with its dark green, shiny epidermis, has tubercles which end in an elongated areole. Radial spines (15–20) sprout from these areoles, which are flattened spider-like against the stem. The funnel-shaped flowers are about 3/4in across and generally emerge from the side of the plant in fairly large quantities. This species is spread across eastern parts of Bolivia in the province of Ayopaya, where it grows at altitudes of 8,000–9,000ft on rocky hillsides. There is practically no taller associated vegetation, and it is usually found among shorter clumps of grass. It is one of the more rarely cultivated members of the genus. It has the same requirements as other species. On hot summer days, the greenhouse should be well ventilated and watering should be restricted to prevent rotting when the plant is dormant. This species can also be cultivated as a grafted plant, but the resulting cacti grow to sizes that are too large and atypical for the species.

Sulcorebutia gerosenilis 

GLOBOSE

This species, known for a relatively long time, was only fully classified in 2001.

In the wild it forms beautiful, cushion-like mounds, and has fleshly to beet-like roots under the ground. It has a covering of line, hair-like, white spines up to 1 1/3 in in length.

A violet-red flower emerges from the side of the plant, and can reach about 1/2 in across.

This cactus can be found in the Bolivian province Zudafez, on rocky flat, raised, ground at an altitudes of 8,500 ft. This species is unusually beautiful, but it is not easy to cultivate. Because of its sizeable roots, it can easily rot if overwatered, particularly when dormant in summer. If the temperature is allowed to climb too high, excess water will evaporate and create a steamy atmosphere. It prefers a site outdoors, with some overhead protection against persistent rain. It is usually propagated by grafting, though some growers have had some success growing it on its own roots.

Sulcorebutia gerosenilis

Sulcorebutia krahnii

Sulcorebutia krahnii 

FLATTENED-GLOBOSE

This species was first classified in 1970 and is a very beautiful member of the genus. The stem is usually solitary, barrel-shaped, and about 1 1/4in tall and up to 3in across. It is made up of 32 spiraling ribs, with areoles 1/6in high and 1/8in across. There are approximately 24 radial and central spines which cannot be differentiated from one another and they are about 1/2in long. They are fairly variable in color, ranging from yellow-white to yellow-brown. The flower tube is covered in greenish red scales and the petals are deep yellow. Flowers about 1 1/4in cross emerge from the side of the plant.
The species is found in the Bolivian province of Caballero, near the small town of Comarapa, where it grows in the northern areas of Cerro Tukiphalla at altitudes of 7,500–8,000ft. It has the same cultivation requirements as other *Sulcorebutia*. It is perhaps one of the most difficult, but is best grown as a self-rooted plant, because grafting results in distortion of its characteristic features, such as a flattened crown.

Sulcorebutia rauschii

Sulcorebutia rauschii 

GLOBOSE

When a description of the species was published in 1969, it unleashed a chase for this unconventional *Sulcorebutia* and everyone wanted to have it in their collection. It is an interesting plant which does not grow very large: its stem is usually only 1 1/4in in diameter and the same in height, and it is often clustering. Some 10 radial spines, 1/25–1/12in long, sprout from the elliptical areoles, spread out spider-like and flattened against the stem. The dark pink-violet flower is about 1 1/4in across and the same in length. It blooms during the day.
This species was discovered high up in the mountains of Bolivia by W. Rausch, a famous Austrian expert in South American cacti. The species was also named after him. It grows at altitudes of about 8,000ft in the hills around the town of Zudañez in the Bolivian province of Chuiquisaca, among grasses and dwarf shrubs. In the past this plant was only available grafted because it was relatively rare, but today most cactus growers try to cultivate it on its own roots. They grow slowly, but they retain their natural appearance and do not cluster as much as grafted specimens. They like to be placed outdoors in summer, a well-drained soil mix, and cold wintering in the light.

Sulcorebutia steinbachii 

GLOBOSE

This globose plant, which can sometimes be clustering, is only 1 1/4–1 1/2in in diameter. The radial spines are arranged comb-like on the ellipsoidal areoles and are red-brown in color. There are a maximum of 2 central spines, which point straight out from the stem. The flowers emerge from the side of the cactus and are funnel-shaped and approximately 1in across. They are scarlet to violet in color. Cacti producing these flowers have even been classified as *S. steinbachii* f. *violaciflora*, but in view of how variable the species is and the fact that it grows in the same location as the type species, there seems to be no reason for this distinction.
This Bolivian cactus grows in the department of Cochabamba, near the town of Arani, at an altitude of about 10,000ft. Cultivation is the same as for other high-altitude *Sulcorebutia*, i.e. full sun, with adequate ventilation, and summers spent outdoors. Propagation is either by seed or by rooting offsets.

Sulcorebutia steinbachii

Sulcorebutia tuberculata-chrysantha

Sulcorebutia swobodae 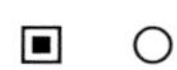

GLOBOSE

The barrel-shaped stem of this species usually grows to about 1 1/2in in diameter and is divided into 20 spiraling ribs. The areoles are covered with yellow-brown dense wool and have spines growing out of them, which cannot be distinguished either as central or radial spines. There are about 30 of them and they range in length from 1/2in to 3/4in. The pink or pink-violet flower is 1 1/4–2in long and blooms from the side areoles.
This species is found in the Bolivian department of Cochabamba in the provinces of Mizque and Campero, where it grows at altitudes of 9,000ft between the towns of Aiquile and Mizque. The same cultivation needs apply as for other high-altitude species of *Sulcorebutia*. It needs a sunny spot and adequate ventilation, and is ideal for growing in the greenhouse bed. Summering in the open is also possible, but it needs a glass or polycarbon roof to protect it

Sulcorebutia swobodae

against prolonged rain. The soil mix should be free-draining, mineral-rich, and neutral or slightly acidic. Cold and absolutely dry wintering, preferably in the light, guarantees free flowering the next season. Propagation is by seed.

Sulcorebutia tuberculata-chrysantha 

GLOBOSE

The plant illustrated is actually an extreme form of *Sulcorebutia steinbachii*, an extremely variable taxon which so far has eluded precise taxonomic classification. These cacti are not only variable in terms of morphology, but they also have fairly variable reproductive parts. The cactus in the photograph is distinguished by its sparse spine covering and, above all, because it has yellow flowers. In the past this type was created from a certain number of groups and was classified as the separate species *Sulcorebutia tuberculata-chrysantha*. This does not reflect the real situation in individual locations, where these cacti can bloom in a whole range of colors. We have classified the species separately in our book, because it has been displayed in some collections under this name.
This *Sulcorebutia* can be found about 30 miles east of the town of Cochabamba in Bolivia and its area of distribution stretches approximately 90 miles to the south-east from there. It is relatively widespread in collections. The same cultivation needs apply for this species as for other members of the same genus. Collections are now starting to appear primarily specializing in *Sulcorebutia* with an authorized source. The place of occurrence is often more important for these taxa than the name dictated by botanical science.

Sulcorebutia verticillacantha

Sulcorebutia verticillacantha ▣ ○

GLOBOSE

This is a very variable taxon and a very diverse collection of miniature cacti could be composed from its various local forms. The stem is globose in the wild and extends into an almost columnar shape in collections. It is small and only about 1 1/4in across. It has a dark green epidermis and forms a number of offsets. 12–14 radial spines, flattened against the stem, grow from the extended areoles, which are about 1/6in long. There are no central spines. Olive green or brown buds grow from the side areoles. The flowers are 1 1/2in long and the same across and their inner petals are red, violet, and orange. The fruit is an egg-shaped berry, 1/6–1/4in across.
The type species is recorded as occurring in the Bolivian department of Cochabamba, in the province of Arque, where it grows between Estación de Bombeo and Sayari on rocky slopes with very little associated vegetation at altitudes of 12,000–13,000ft. This *Sulcorebutia* has been recorded many times in the wild but type specimens come under field collection number FR 725a. It is found very often in collections, and as with other *Sulcorebutia*, it is best to include plants of known origin in a collection. Only then does the collection have proper botanical value, because plants are sold under various names that do not necessarily match their botanical classification and origin. Cultivation is the same as for other high-altitude members of the genus.

Tephrocactus bolivianus

Tephrocactus bolivianus ▣ ○

CUSHION-FORMING

This used to be considered a species but is now classified as just a synonym for *T. pentlandii*. It is an extreme, compact variant with beautiful, golden orange flowers. There is no doubt that it belongs to the above species. It is also found in identical locations to *T. pentlandii*.
We are listing this name in our book because a number of cactus growers now have this species classified under this title.

Tephrocactus pentlandii 

CUSHION-FORMING

This cactus forms mounds of densely grouped stems, formed of individual, minute, rounded sections, only about 1 1/4in long. The glochids are insignificant, but the spines can be up to 3in long. Generally, however, they are shorter. The short, funnel-shaped flowers are yellow and are flattened, so they hardly emerge from the cluster of sections. Some travelers have even reported specimens in certain locations with red flowers.
They are found high up in the Bolivian mountains, near Tupiza for instance, at altitudes of about 13,000ft, although they are also found much lower, e.g. collections classified under KK 1556 Tupiza – Villazon 9,000ft. This is the most widespread *Tephrocactus* in cultivation. Cultivation and vegetative propagation do not pose major problems, but it is fairly difficult to force these cacti to flower. It seems as though the only way to achieve this is to provide the cactus with the maximum direct sunshine out in the open during the summer, very cold wintering, and a sufficiently large container to develop an extensive root system.

Trichocereus tacaquirensis 

COLUMNAR

The tallest stems of this columnar cactus can reach a height of 8ft. The radial spines are shorter than the central ones, which grow to up to 3in long. The white flowers are about 8in long and open during the day.
It is found in Bolivia not far from Tacaquira, where it was also collected by K. Kníže and distributed among growers under field collection

Tephrocactus pentlandii

number KK 1092. His collections come from altitudes of about 10,000ft. It is cultivated only rarely, and you are more likely to see it in botanical garden collections than in collections belonging to amateur growers. Propagation by seed is simple and rooting offsets is also a possibility. Cold wintering is required and low light levels are tolerated.

Vatricania guentheri 

COLUMNAR

Some authorities classify this cactus under the *Espostoa*, but most growers refer to it under the generic name of Vatricania. It is a columnar species which clusters from the base. The largest specimens can grow to a height of over 6ft with a stem diameter of about 4in. It is interesting because of its spine covering, composed of a fairly large quantity of fine, yellowish brown spines which grow from each areole. In the flower-producing section of the stem, it forms a brown lateral cephalium of fine rust-colored bristles, up to 16in long. The flowers, which open at night, are a creamy white color and are about 2 1/4in across. There is a certain amount of discussion as to where this species grows, but it looks as though the information published by C. Backeberg is correct. He said that *V. Guentheri* occurs in a relatively small area in the Rio Grande valley, not far from the settlement of El Oro in Bolivia (Chuquisaca province). It is not cultivated very often, but it is very beautiful by the time it is a three-year-old seedling. It needs adequate room, a nutrient-rich soil mix, and to be placed in full sun. It withstands cold wintering, even in low light. In cool climates, flowers can be expected only on old plants, after some 20 years.

Trichocereus tacaquirensis

Vatricania guentheri

Weingartia knizei

Weingartia knizei ▣ ○ ⊙

GLOBOSE

This species was named in honor of the Czech cactus expert based in Peru, Karel Kníže, a specialist in Peruvian cacti, who also discovered it. The globose plant is a very close relative of *W. westii*. The stem can be up to 6in in diameter and consists of circular tubercles. There are 10–20 radial spines growing from the elliptical mammillae and a maximum of 3 central spines, but it is difficult to distinguish between the two.

This species is recorded as being found between Tiraque and Comarapa in the Bolivian department of Cochabamba, where it grows at altitudes of 7,000–8,000 ft. It grows among clumps of grass or in patches of moss and the total average annual rainfall in this region is 32in. Karel Kníže also mentions a location in Bolivia between Aiquile and Saipina at an altitude of about 9,000ft. He classified his collection as KK 1756 and it is found as this in collections. Cultivation is the same as for other high-altitude South American species. Beware of letting this cactus be scorched by spring sunshine: it should be placed in shade at this time of year. Later, though, it can withstand full sun. Generally it responds very well to summering outside or growing in the greenhouse bed.

Weingartia mairanana

Weingartia mairanana 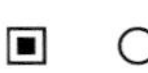

GLOBOSE

Systematic classification of this species is not easy, but it definitely belongs to the group of plants related to *W. pulquinensis*. The stem is globose and there are 12–15 spines growing out of the densely woolly areoles. The bright yellow flowers bloom near the crown. This group of cacti is very variable: the type locality is near Pulquina in Bolivia. The information about the plant in the picture is fairly contentious. It was found by the Czech cactus expert Karel Kníže and it has proved impossible to determine any more information about the plant. In his catalog Kníže refers to it as *W. Mairanana* nom. nud. KK 1521. Cultivation is the same as for other *Weingartia*.

Weingartia neocumingii 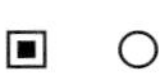

GLOBOSE

This is an extremely variable species, particularly as regards morphology. It is usually globose or barrel-shaped and some plants in the wild can reach up to 1ft in diameter (generally less in collections). The prickly yellow spines stick out from the stem. There are usually about 20 radial spines and the number of central spines fluctuates considerably. Some plants have been encountered without any central spines, while others have up to 12 central spines growing out of each areole. The yellow flowers appear near the crown and mostly grow in a ring in greater numbers than can be seen on the plant in the photograph.

The location where the species was found and after which it was named is situated just a few miles southwest of the Bolivian town of Sucre, at altitudes of 7,500–10,500ft. The cacti grow here in stony ground with very little surrounding vegetation. In cultivation they do best planted directly into the greenhouse bed or placed outdoors during the hottest months of the year. They respond poorly to an overheated greenhouse with the full heat of the sun. Sowing of seed is generally simple, but small seedlings should be kept lightly shaded.

Weingartia neocumingii

Weingartia neumanniana ssp. *kargliana*

Weingartia neocumingii ssp. *kargliana* ▣ ○

GLOBOSE

In taxonomic terms this is a very complex group of plants. They are barrel-shaped, the epidermis is a striking color, and they have a different spine covering to other members of the genus. The beet-like root is much more extensive than the part of the plant above ground. The spines stick out from the stem and there is huge variety in their quantity and length. The same applies for the flowers. The type species has yellow flowers, orange flowers, and even red flowers, and the subspecies mentioned has yellow flowers.
The whole extent of the basic species is found in southern Bolivia and northern Argentina. They grow at high altitudes in places where there is little associated vegetation. Few collections can boast adult specimens of this taxon. It is only recently that the availability of seed has increased and these plants are starting to occur in collections. From the point of view of cultivation technology, it is one of the most troublesome members of the genus, mainly because of its beet-like roots. It requires fairly deep pots with a very free-draining soil mix, regular watering in the summer, and placing outdoors when in active growth. Propagation is only by seed and the seedlings should be kept lightly shaded.

Weingartia riograndensis ▣ ○

GLOBOSE

This is a globose or slightly columnar species, which forms offsets in the wild. Older plants also produce offsets in cultivation. The individual stems are about 4in across when adult and 4–6in tall. The stem consists of prominent tubercles with very woolly, circular areoles. There are 10–16 radial spines, about 1 1/4in long, and 3–6 central spines, about 1 3/4in long. The flowers bloom both near the crown and also from areoles further away from it. They are deep yellow and about 1 1/4in across. The fruit is glabrous and covered in scales.
The species occurs in a relatively small area in the lowlands near the Rio Chico river in Bolivia. Cultivation is the same as for other members of the genus, with the only difference being that they cannot withstand such cold wintering as plants from high-altitude areas.

Weingartia riograndensis

5. Argentina

Argentina is the second largest country in South America (1,100,000 square miles) and has a very wide range of terrain, from high mountains (Aconcagua 23,000ft) to upland pampas and llanos to the hot prairies across which the river Paraná wends its way.
The regions of northern Argentina, which form the border with Bolivia and Paraguay, are very interesting from a cactus grower's point of view. A whole series of cacti grow in the province of Jujuy and the eastern and western slopes of the Andes are very rich in cactus flora. Cacti in lower areas often grow among grasses. A number of species from the genus *Gymnocalycium* grow here, which spread into Uruguay and Paraguay. These lowland areas have a unique climate which is known as a virgin climate. It is typical for the Argentinian provinces of Misiones, Corrientas, Entre Rios, and Buenos Aires. Summer in these provinces is hot, with temperatures above 72 °F, and the winter is relatively cold, with the temperature even falling below 32 °F. There are also high summer temperatures in the subtropical prairies of the western part of Patagonia, which includes the foothills of the Andes. These can reach as high as 95 °F, but during the cold part of the year, temperatures fluctuate between just 36 °F and 60 °F. These areas usually boast a relatively high number of different species of Opuntia and plants from the genus *Pterocactus* are also to be found here. These are spread from southernmost Patagonia to Salta in northwestern Argentina. One interesting Argentinian genus is *Tephrocactus*, which can be found from the province of Salta to the province of Mendoza in central Argentina.
Argentina's cacti are a very interesting group, extremely rewarding to cultivation. The most popular genus is rightly *Gymnocalycium*. Currently all sorts of Opuntia, and its subgenera, and *Tephrocactusare* at the peak of their popularity with growers.

Left: *Collection of assorted Parodia*

Acanthocalycium klimpelianum ▣ ○

GLOBOSE

White flowers differentiate this species from every close relative. The stem is globose, up to 4 in across, and made up of 19 sharp ribs with round areoles, from which 6-8 radial spines and 2-3 central spines. These are stiff and prickly, and can be upto 1/2 in long.
The 2 in wide white flowers grow from areoles the crown and the flower tube is covered in hairs and brown brisths.
This species is found on steep hillsides near the Argentinian town of Cordoba in the province of the same name. They grow there at altitudes of about 3,000ft. Cultivation in collections poses no problems and if you abide by the general principles then they should flower after 8–10 years. They require full sun and very cold wintering; experience has shown that they do well outdoors in summer.

Acanthocalycium klimpelianum

Blossfeldia liliputana

Blossfeldia liliputana ▣ ⊙

GLOBOSE

This whole genus is unique because its stem is shorter than any other. Adult specimens start to flower when the stem diameter is about 1/2in. *B. liliputana* is no exception. In some places it starts to bloom when the stem is about 1/4in high and the tiny yellow flowers are about the same across. The areoles produce fine white hair and there are no spines at all.

In the wild it grows on vertical rock faces with a clay substrate and forms tiny cushions made up of a large number of offsets. *B. liliputana* grows in the north of Argentina in the province of Jujuy, but it is not easy to find specimens in the wild, because the tiny stems are perfectly disguised, especially during dry periods, blending into the background. Cactus growers also cultivate *B. minima*. Both taxa are more or less only grown as grafted plants. Although the plants lose their characteristic appearance somewhat, self-rooted culture is so difficult that only the most experienced growers undertake it. Where possible, grafts should be made onto a slow-growing stock, so that the grafted plants are not too unnaturally inflated.

Cereus forbesii

Chamaecereus silvestrii

Trichocereus pasacana seedlings are suitable for this purpose, for instance.

Cereus forbesii 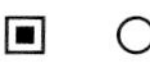

COLUMNAR

This columnar cactus has a number of straight branches which can grow to up to 13 ft high. The individual stems are usually split into 6 prominent ribs, with round, densely woolly areoles. The epidermis is blue-green and is a very deep shade, particularly in the case of young growths. The radial spines, of which 5–7 grow out of each areole, are usually 1/2–3/4in long. There are a maximum of 2 central spines per areole and they can reach a length of 2in. The white, tubular flowers grow to 10in long and open at night. The fruit is a red fleshy berry, which splits laterally when ripe.
The species occurs in many locations in Argentina, where it grows at altitudes ranging from 2,500–5,000ft. It is very rare to find this species in collections, because of the space it requires. Otherwise cultivation is very undemanding and it is often found on terraces as an interesting, portable cactus, or it is planted in gardens in the summer. It requires cold wintering in the light and for successful cultivation it needs a large container with a nutrient-rich soil mix.

Chamaecereus silvestrii 

CUSHION-FORMING

Although now classified *Lobivia*, we are listing this species here as *Chamaecereus silvestrii*, because it is one of the most familiar and cultivated cacti. Its trailing stems usually grow to a length of about 6in and a diameter of about 1/2in. Covered in tiny spines, it produces elegant flowers which are characteristically red.
Little is known about where this cactus is found in the wild, but it was first discovered in the northern regions of Argentina in the province of Salta. It is one of the most frequently cultivated cacti in collections, however, and it is not only a regular in collections belonging to cactus growers, but can also be spotted in the windows of flats and houses and wherever plant lovers are to be found. It is undemanding because it grows easily and propagates very well, and often forms roots on the parent plant. That is why such a relatively large quantity of cultivars has been produced, grown for the varied colors of their flowers, and their stronger and squatter stems, and because they are so undemanding in cultivation. They require cold wintering to promote good flowering the following year. Perhaps the only drawback is that they are a popular prey for spider mites.

Cleistocactus jujuyensis 

COLUMNAR

Often listed under the name *C. strausii* var. *jujuyensis*, it is quite similar to the type species and it is distinguished by the variable coloring of its spines. It produces a bright red, zygomorphic flower, about 1 1/3in long. As its name suggests, it is found in the northern Argentina province Jujuy. With these variable plants, you should above all ensure that any seed sown is from sources with a stated origin. This is the only way of being certain of the botanical value of the specimens in the collection. Cultivation is the same as for *C. strausii.*

Cleistocactus jujuyensis

Cleistocactus smaragdiflorus  

COLUMNAR

The stem of this clustering cactus, which is made up of 12–14 ribs, is initially erect and later becomes arching. It has a vivid green epidermis and small, densely woolly areoles on the edges of the ribs. The radial spines are usually light to rust brown in color. The central spines stick out from the stem and are longer and stiffer. The flower can be up to 2in long and has interesting coloring: the flower tube is reddish purple and the scaly petals, which are not particularly striking, are green in color (the origin of the species epithet *smaragdiflorus* – meaning with emerald green flowers). The red, fleshy berry is about 5/8in across and contains brown seeds, 1/25in long.
This species is to be found in a relatively large area in northern Argentina, in the provinces of Jujuy, Catamarca, Salta, and La Rioja. It also extends into Paraguay. It grows at altitudes of about 5,000ft. In cultivation it is undemanding. It is important to grow it in a fairly large container or plant directly in the ground, where it forms offsets with a strong and beautiful spine covering and flowers freely. Propagation is either by seed or by detaching offsets or stem cuttings. They take root relatively easily after drying out for about two weeks in the shade.

Cleistocactus strausii ▣ ○

COLUMNAR

This columnar species clusters from the base and grows to about 3ft tall in the wild, but usually less than this in collections. The individual stems are covered in a thick web of spines, with thin, hair-like spines and straight, prickly ones growing from the areoles. A stigma and stamens protrude from the red, zygomorphic flowers.
It grows in northern Argentina and also in southern areas of Bolivia, where it favors rocky slopes with sparse vegetation. This is one of the cactus species that are often produced in plant nurseries around the world. It is popular because it is easy to cultivate and because of its beautiful spines. It is to be found in every larger collection. It even flowers and fruits well in cool climates. Propagation is best by seed, but older plants can also be propagated by stem cuttings. These take root easily and bloom early.

Cleistocactus smaragdiflorus

Cleistocactus strausii

Denmoza rhodacantha 

COLUMNAR

This species has a striking, columnar stem, which can grow to up to 8in in diameter with a maximum height of 5ft. The new spines which grow out of the adolescent areoles are more colorful than the old ones, while the color intensity and length of spine differs from plant to plant. Most of these cacti have 8 radial spines and 1 central one, and all of them are about 1 1/4in long. The plant produces tubular flowers near the growing point. They are red and can be up to 2 3/4in long, and the stigma and stamens protrude from the flower before it opens fully.

Denmoza rhodacantha

Areas near the town of Mendoza in Argentina are the type locality of the species, but it can be found as far away as San Juan and La Rioja. This has become one of the commonest South American cacti in cultivation, particularly in recent years, since the seed from original plants has become available among cactus growers. The species does not have any specific cultivation requirements, it needs maximum light and sowing early in large containers. Unfortunately only older plants produce flowers, about 20 years after germination.

Echinopsis mamillosa var. *kermesina* ▣ ○

GLOBOSE

The stem of this species is globose initially and extends into an almost columnar shape as it gets older. It can grow to about 6in tall. The radial and central spines are spiky and stick out from the cactus. It has beautiful, pinkish red flowers, which can grow to up to 8in long. These flowers open in the daytime and never during the evening, which is one of the main reasons why some authorities have wanted to classify this group of plants under the separate genus *Pseudolobivia*. It is found in the mountainous regions of northern Argentina and is often seen in collections. Cultivation is very simple; placing plants outdoors during the summer suits this high-altitude species, provided there is overhead shelter against prolonged rain during cool weather. It requires cold wintering at temperatures not exceeding 50 °F.

Echinopsis mamillosa var. *kermesina*

Gymnocalycium andreae

GLOBOSE

This is one of the few *Gymnocalycium* with an atypically eye-catching flower color, which does not occur particularly often within the genus. It usually forms cushion-like clumps, formed of individual stems, generally only 2in wide. The dark green epidermis contrasts with the light, flattened spines, which are up to 1/2in long. The canary yellow flower is relatively rare among *Gymnocalycium* and so a *G. andreae* in full bloom can brighten up any collection specializing in this genus.

This is a typical meadow-growing cactus, where it forms dense mats of stems. It grows, shaded slightly by grasses, in the Sierra Cordoba mountains near Cerro Los Gigantes at altitudes of 6,500ft. *G. andreae* makes most impact in collections if cultivated in pots which allow it to form a fairly large unit. It also requires partial shade and occasional watering, but only when the soil mix has completely dried out. Propagation is simple by offsets or by seed, which always produces forms with an interesting spine covering.

Gymnocalycium andreae

Gymnocalycium bruchii

Gymnocalycium bruchii ▣ ⊙

CLUMP-FORMING

Cactus growers are familiar with this species under the name *G. lafandense*. The slightly columnar stem is about 2 1/4in tall and freely clustering. Offsets do not generally reach the same sizes as the original parent plant. This species only has pale, soft radial spines, but some ecotypes can also have 1 straight central spine. It has beautiful pink flowers with pale yellow anthers.

This Argentinian species is found in the La Falda mountains, which form part of the massive Sierra de Cordoba range, at an altitude of about 6,500ft. These cacti favor rocky fissures, which they completely fill with their cushion-like mounds. It is one of the easiest members of *Gymnocalycium* to cultivate. Propagation by offsets, which form roots on the parent plant, is simple and is not beyond even a complete beginner.

Gymnocalycium calochlorum  ⊙

GLOBOSE

The clustering stem of this species is usually barrel-shaped, about 2 1/4in in diameter and 1 1/2in tall, and is formed of 10–12 flat ribs. Up to 9 radial spines grow from the oval areoles, which are flattened against the stem and can be various lengths. The specimen in the photograph a long-spined form; usually the spines are shorter and finer. The flower tube is green and the scales have a pink edge. The petals are white to pale pink. When fully open the flowers are about 2in across. The egg-shaped fruit is about 1/2in long and contains a large quantity of seed 1/25in long.

The author did not specify the type locality, but a number of specimens have been collected by travelers and it has been possible to determine where the species occurs from them. It is found in locations in the Argentinian province of Cordoba, at altitudes of 2,000–4,000 ft. This *Gymnocalycium* is often cultivated in collections and poses no

Gymnocalycium calochlorum

problems. Basic requirements for success include a slightly acidic soil mix and partial shade. The temperature during winter can fall to 41 °F. Propagation is either by seed or by offsets, which form roots on the parent plant.

Gymnocalycium carminanthum 

FLATTENED-GLOBOSE–GLOBOSE

The barrel-shaped stem of this cactus usually grows to a maximum of 4in in diameter and a height of about 2 3/4in. It is made up of about 10 indistinct ribs, which are formed of prominent tubercles. There are usually 5–9 radial spines growing from each areole, while there is either no central spine, or they grow from the top edge of the areole and point upward. The flower blooms on the crown of the plant and, as the species epithet *carminanthum* suggests, it is a beautiful scarlet color.

In the wild this cactus is found in the Sierra Ambato hills in Argentina in the province of Catamarca, where it grows in flat clearings in deciduous forests at altitudes of about 5,000ft. The tiny seeds might cause a problem for cultivation to less

Gymnocalycium carminanthum

Gymnocalycium horridispinum

experienced growers. Usually they germinate freely and if densely sown need pricking out early. The tiny seedlings are very difficult to handle during this process. That is why it is a good idea to plant all species of *Gymnocalycium* with small seeds more sparsely than for other species. Otherwise cultivation is not difficult: the plants respond best to partial shade shade at temperatures not exceeding 95 °F in the summer. It requires cold wintering and does not have to be in full light.

Gymnocalycium horridispinum 

GLOBOSE

This is an interesting member of the genus, distinguished by its barrel-shaped stem. This can grow up to 3in in diameter and forms 10–13 ribs, which are made up of prominent tubercles. It has spines growing from the elongated areoles and they can be divided into radial spines and central spines according to their position. All of them are relatively hard and prickly. The longest central spines can grow to up to 1 1/2in long. There are beautiful, broadly funnel-shaped flowers growing from the youngest areoles near the crown and they are a deep pink color. When fully open they can reach up to 2 1/4in across. The fleshy, elongated berries covered in scales are full of black seed.

The species is reported as being found in the Argentinian province of Cordoba where it grows at altitudes of about 3,000ft. It favors gently sloping, south-facing or southwest-facing terrain, covered with associated grasses and low, whippy shrubs.

Like most *Gymnocalycium*, it requires shade when young, but older specimens can withstand direct sunlight. It also needs a free-draining soil mix with a slightly acid content, which you can ensure by adding a small amount of peat. Wintering must be in a cold place at temperatures of about 50 °F, and light levels need not be high. It flowers when the stem is 1 1/2–2in in diameter.

Gymnocalycium kurtzianum  ○

FLATTENED-GLOBOSE

This is an interesting and relatively variable taxon, which is a close relative of *G. mostii*, of which it used to be classified as a varietas. It has barrel-shaped, solitary stems which can grow to 6in in diameter and about 3in tall. They are made up of about 18 ribs. There are 8–10 strong radial spines and usually 1 central spine growing out of the elliptical, densely woolly areoles. The flowers are up to 3in across and are formed of white petals with a red base, whereas the outer petals are greenish, like the scales on the flower tube.
This species is found in the Argentinian province of Cordoba. It grows on rocky slopes among grasses and relatively rich associated vegetation. In collections it is a relatively common member of the genus. There are no problems involved in its cultivation and the same principles apply for this species as for other *Gymnocalycium*. It takes a fairly long time, about 10 years, to reach flowering size, however.

Gymnocalycium ochoterenai  ⊙

FLATTENED-GLOBOSE

The short, barrel-shaped stem of this species grows to 3–4in in diameter. It has a dark green epidermis, which sometimes has a brownish tinge. Its 16 flat ribs are formed of tubercles, separated by a transversal groove. There are usually 3–5 spines growing from each areole, which are only a fraction of an inch long. The flower is about 1 1/3in long, the flower tube is green, and the petals are white with a pinkish throat.
The only thing known about where this cactus occurs is that it is in Argentina, where it grows amont grasses. Cultivation poses no problems. Like other *Gymnocalycium* it requires a slightly acidic soil mix with added peat, and it prefers partial shade to scorching direct sunlight. Propagation is by seed, which germinates freely. The seedlings should be kept shaded initially.

Gymnocalycium oenanthemum 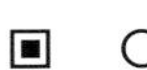

GLOBOSE

The slightly depressed stem of this species grows to a diameter of 6in and can reach a maximum height of 4in. The indistinct ribs consist of tubercles with a large oval areole. This has radial spines growing out of it, of which there are usually more than in the plant in the photograph, which illustrates a specimen with extremely sparse spines. There are no central spines. The flower can show varying shades of pink, which not only vary from plant to plant, but also alter significantly according to the age of the plant. Flowers which have just opened display the brightest colors, and the colors fade as the flowers continue blossoming. This species grows in the mountains near the Argentinian town of Cordoba, where it is found most frequently in meadowland, shaded to a certain extent by shrubby vegetation. Because it has tiny seeds, specialists have classified it under the subgenus *Microsemineum*. It can be propagated successfully by seed and this is the only effective method of growing new plants. It responds best to partial shade in collections, a slightly acidic, well-drained soil mix, and ample watering in the summer. It can also withstand wintering at low light levels. It matures after about 10 years.

Gymnocalycium ragonesei ▣ ⊙

FLATTENED-GLOBOSE

The smallest of all miniature members of the genus, its flat stem grows to a max. of 2in in diameter and 1in in height. The red-brown color of its epidermis is interesting, as are its minute, delicate radial spines, which are flattened against the stem. The flower is narrow and funnel-shaped and, at 2in in long, is fairly large for the stem. The flower is white and the outer scales are gray-green.
The original known locality of this species is on the boundary between the provinces of Catamarca and Cordoba, at altitudes of about 1,300ft. According to reports from travelers, it grows in soil rich in sodium chloride, and the stems are completely sunk into the ground. It is cultivated frequently because it looks so distinct, and is completely unique within *Gymnocalycium*. It does not respond well if the soil mix tends to retain water and fails to dry out.

Gymnocalycium oenanthemum

The only effective method of propagation is by seed. Well-cultivated seedlings can flower by the second season, once they have grown to just over 1/2in tall.

Gymnocalycium ragonesei

Gymnocalycium saglionis 

FLATTENED-GLOBOSE

The non-clustering stem of this species, which is globose initially, grows to more than 1ft across and finally starts to extend when older. Some specimens then grow to truly remarkable sizes. The flat ribs are made up of flattened tubercles, with spines growing out of the large, densely woolly areoles at the tip. These spines are of varying lengths and are usually curved toward the stem. After watering they turn dark red. The flower is very wide from the base (up to 1 1/2in when fully open) and almost stalkless. It is pale pink and produces a huge quantity of pale yellow pollen. Cacti with darker flowers are often thought of as an independent variety *G. saglionis* var. *roseiflorum*, but we feel that there are no grounds for this taxonomical distinction.

This cactus is found across a large area of northwestern Argentina, where it grows on stony ground with low associated vegetation. Because this area is so extensive, it is an extremely variable species. This was shown in the past when new formas, variants, and even species were recorded. These are now considered as synonyms. After sowing seed and its subsequent germination, seedlings appear as tiny balls on the soil mix, which can fall victim to a variety of molds, particularly when densely sown. After pricking out, cultivation becomes simple, but a slightly acidic soil mix needs to be prepared.

Gymnocalycium schuetzianum 

FLATTENED-GLOBOSE

The flat or barrel-shaped stem of this cactus can grow to about 6in in diameter, and when it is mature it occasionally forms a few clusters. Older specimens have up to 17 ribs and these consist of flat tubercles, which end in a large ellipsoidal areole. Older specimens have 1 central spine, but otherwise there are usually 7 light radial spines growing out of each areole. There is considerable variety in the color of the flower, which ranges from pale to dark pink.

The species is found in the Argentinian province of Cordoba, and in the literature the specific place of occurrence is given as Cruz del Eje. It was named in honor of B. Schütz, a cactus expert from Brno in the Czech Republic, but this is a somewhat contentious species. Cultivation, however, causes no problems. The seed should be sown in late winter under growing lamps, to ensure a long growing season for the emerging seedlings. The other requirements are the same as for other *Gymnocalycium.*

Gymnocalycium saglionis

Gymnocalycium schuetzianum

Gymnocalycium spegazzinii 

FLATTENED-GLOBOSE

This is a beautiful and fairly variable taxon, with a barrel-shaped stem, which can reach up to 5 1/2in in diameter. The epidermis is gray-green in color and on some specimens it has a brownish tinge. There are usually 10–15 low flat ribs, with areoles about 1/2in long, from which radial spines grow, but no central spines. Mostly there are 5–7, but we have come across plants with 3 or 11 spines. The spines are usually flattened against the stem or slightly twisted. White flowers with a pink throat grow from the youngest areoles. The outer petals have a green central strip. The long round fruit contains brown-black seeds just 1/25in across.

Over recent years a huge number of observers have visited the localities where these cacti are found in Argentina. The consensus is that this species is found over a large area stretching north to south for 180 miles. It is found on mountainous, stony ground at fairly high altitudes with very sparse associated vegetation. Dr. Carlos Spegazzini, after whom the species was named, was the director of a biological institute and museum in La Plata in Argentina. He also classified the species as *Echinocactus loricatus* in 1905, after

Gymnocalycium spegazzinii

which Briton and Rose listed it under the *Gymnocalycium* in 1922 and renamed it *G. spegazzinii.* A beautiful collection can be built up from the extreme forms of the species. Seed sown should be from a known source. This cactus grows in full sun or partial shade, but you have to watch out for root rot during the summer dormant period, when these cacti can easily fail if watered excessively or at the wrong time.

Gymnocalycium valnicekianum var. *polycentralis* ▣ ⊙

GLOBOSE

The type species was described from a specimen with 1 central spine, but it was shown by subsequent local study that most specimens where this cactus is recorded as occurring have more central spines and correspond more closely to the description published as *G. valnicekianum* var. *polycentralis*. These cacti are usually globose, solitary initially, and later start to produce a very small number of offsets. There are about 12 ribs, made up of flattened tubercles, which end in a large, elliptical, densely woolly areole, up to 1/2in long. There are usually 9–15 radial spines, with up to 20 in exceptional cases, and 4–6 central spines; however, there are specimens with as many as 11 central spines. They do not usually grow to more than 1 1/2in long. This species produces flowers which are white on the inside with a pink tinge. They are about 2in long and the same across.
This cactus can be found in the wild in many famous localities near the town of Capilla del Monte in the Argentinian province of Cordoba. It grows here on flat granite hills in fissures full of humus. This is a very popular taxon among cactus growers and can also be recommended to growers starting out. It needs partial shade, abundant watering when in active growth, a soil mix with added peat, and a shallow pan. Wintering should be cold, and it withstands low light levels without any problems. Seedlings flower after just 5–7 years.

Gymnocalycium vatteri ▣ ○

FLATTENED-GLOBOSE

This species has a flat or barrel-shaped stem, which can grow to up to 4in across. Its 11 ribs are divided by transverse grooves and the areoles are situated in slight depressions on the tips of the tubercles. Each areole has 1 spine growing out of it, but quite often there are plants in collections with 3 or even 5 spines per areole. The flower is carried near the growing tip and its olive green tube is covered in scales. The petals are white and often pinkish at the base.
This species grows in northern Argentina near the town of Cordoba in a number of separate localities in the Sierra Grande mountains. It grows here on grassy slopes at an altitude of about 3,000ft. The type plant,which A. F. H. Buining used to compose the description in 1950 was collected near the settlement of Nono in these mountains at an altitude of 2,600ft. It is a slow-growing *Gymnocalycium*, but it has minimal requirements in cultivation. It withstands full sunshine, but needs a slightly acidic soil mix and cold wintering. Small seedlings should be provided with partial shade. When young these cacti respond well to abundant watering and flower after about 8 years.

Gymnocalycium valnicekianum var. *polycentralis*

Gymnocalycium vatteri

Helianthocereus grandiflorus

Lobivia chrysantha

Helianthocereus grandiflorus ▣ ○

COLUMNAR

This is a columnar cactus with individual stems about 16in tall and 2 1/4in in diameter, bright green, and formed of about 14 prominent ribs. There are 12–14 radial spines growing out of each areole and usually 1 central spine as well, which is about 1/2in long, like the other spines. The beautiful, deep crimson flowers bloom near the crown and are about 4in long.

These cacti are found in the Argentinian province of Catamarca, where they grow in stony ground, usually without any other vegetation. It is a very hardy species, which can survive all manner of blunders in cultivation. It can withstand very cold wintering, even at low light levels. When in active growth it prefers full sun and adequate water. It does best in the greenhouse bed or in a sheltered spot out in the open. Offsets can be used for propagation but seed is an alternative. When in active growth, applications of a low-nitrogen fertilizer can be beneficial.

Lobivia chrysantha 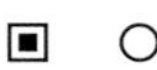

COLUMNAR

This is another variable taxon, which has spread to many locations in forms which usually have only a little in common. They grow to up to 8in tall with a stem diameter of about 2in. There are usually 8–10 radial spines and 2 or 3 prickly central spines, about 5/8in long. The widely funnel-shaped flower is about 2 1/4in long and 2in across. It is deep yellow in color, as are the stamens, style, and stigma.

It grows in northern areas of Argentina at high altitude in rocky ground with little associated vegetation. Cultivation is as simple as for other high-altitude Lobivia. It requires very cold wintering, in light conditions if possible, and temperatures before the start of the growing period must not rise above 50 °F, or else the plant may emerge from dormancy too early, leading to distorted growth because of lack of light. Beware also of overwatering when dormant in summer.

Lobivia ferox var. *longispina* 

GLOBOSE

This cactus was originally listed as a separate species and was only reclassified as a varietas in 1975. The globose stem can grow to up to 10in in diameter and usually only a little less in height. The epidermis has a gray-blue tinge and there are relatively large areoles on the prominent ribs, with up to 15 radial spines, which sometimes give the impression of being central spines. The longest spines can grow up to 3in long, hence the name of the varietas– *longispina* or long-spined. The funnel-shaped flowers, which have a flower tube covered in gray hair, are up to 4in long and 2 3/4in across when fully open.

Lobivia ferox var. *longispina*

This species grows at relatively high altitudes of 8,000–13,000ft. It grows in northern Argentina between Tilcara and La Quiaca. So that the plant can grow the longest spines possible (which is its main feature), it needs adequate light and good ventilation. Summering in the open is also possible: outdoor conditions suit it better than the stuffy conditions in the greenhouse. It is not demanding in terms of soil mix or wintering, but must be overwintered in cool, light conditions so that a premature emergence from dormancy does not result in distorted growth.

Opuntia clavaroides 

SHRUBBY

The freely clustering stem forms a low shrub, made up of cylindrical stems of various lengths. These are narrower at the base and wider at the tip and thus give the impression of a small club. It is from this that the cactus derives the species epithet *clavaroides*, which translates as club-shaped. The sections have a particular tendency to become crest-like or comb-like at the tips. There is a large quantity of areoles on the brown epidermis, mainly at the crown of the sections, from which about 10 fine spines grow, flattened against the stem. The yellow flowers are up to 2 1/4in across and after fertilization change into a conical fruit, about 1 1/4in long. There have not been many authenticated reports about where this Opuntia grows in the wild, because it grows in high, inaccessible places near the Argentinian–Chilean border in the province of Mendoza (Argentina). It is extremely popular among cactus growers, even though it seems to be disappearing from collections over re-cent years. Cultivation, however, is not all that simple, because it has strong, beet-like roots, which tend to rot in the event of excessive watering. Many cactus growers recommend grafting this species onto a verified Opuntia stock (such as *O. tomentosa*). The basic requirements for successful cultivation are: cold wintering, sufficient light during the summer, and good ventilation. It is very reluctant to germinate, even if you adhere to all the recommendations and principles.

Opuntia clavaroides

Opuntia subulata

Opuntia subulata ▣ ○

SHRUBBY

The stem of this species has prominent clusters and forms an extensive bush, up to 10ft tall. It is formed of cylindrical sections about 4in long and 1–1 1/4in in diameter. The long central spines, which grow out of the areoles with a number of glochids, are very prickly and easy to break off, often along with the whole section. Orange-red flowers grow from the young sections at the tips, and they soon change into fruit, covered in tiny glochids. This species grows over a very extensive area, covering a number of South American countries (Argentina, Peru, and Chile), where it can be found in mountains in very exposed locations. It is relatively widespread among cactus growers as a variation in their collections of columnar cacti. This *Opuntia* needs to be given a sufficient amount of space, not only for the part of the cactus aboveground, but also for its root system. Propagation is very simple to perform, through rooting detached sections.

Opuntia subulata, detail

Parodia nivosa ▣ ○

GLOBOSE–COLUMNAR

When adult, the non-clustering stems of this species become almost columnar and reach heights of up to 6in with a diameter of 3in. The youngest areoles have a striking covering of white hair, but on older areoles the hair disappears. There are usually 20 or more radial spines, which are glassy white and needle-shaped, and 4 thin, fragile central spines of the same color. This *Parodia* acquired the species *epithet nivosas* (snow-covered) because of its spines and the dense white wool on its areoles. Deep red flowers usually grow from the crown, but forms have been encountered with orange flowers.

Parodia nivosa

The type locality is Quebrada del Toro, which translates as the Valley of the Bull, situated near the Argentinian town of Salta, where it grows at altitudes of about 8,000ft in gravelly ground. For these cacti to achieve their full beauty with their thick, snow white spine covering, they should not be grafted but shoud be grown hard, on their own roots. Avoid watering the plants from above, which soon makes it lose the white hair from the areoles. Otherwise cultivation poses no problems and is as for other *Parodia*.

Parodia sanguiniflora ▣ ○

GLOBOSE

This is a very variable species of cactus. Usually the globose stem is 3in tall and almost the same in diameter, and is almost completely covered in spines, which grow from the areoles on the mammil-

Parodia sanguiniflora

Parodia schuetziana

lae. There are usually 20 white spines and 4 red central spines, the longest of which is about 1in long and often hooked. Blood red flowers (the derivation of the species epithet *sanguiniflora*) grow from the youngest areoles. They are up to 1 1/2in across and mostly several bloom at the same time. A.V. Frič, the famous Czech cactus expert, discovered this species in 1928 between the towns of Tucmán and Catamarca in northern Argentina. They are found in many other locations, however, and they have a very wide area of distribution. This *Parodia* can be found in just about every collection. Because of its enormous blood red flowers and its ease of cultivation it has become one of the most popular of all cacti. The only problem is sowing the tiny seeds, but the young seedlings grow without any problems.

Parodia schuetziana

GLOBOSE

This is a globose or slightly columnar cactus with a rather flattened stem. It is completely covered in white, bristle-like, tangled spines. The longest radial spines can grow to up to 3/4in long, as can the single central spine, which can also be hooked at the tip. A large number of red flowers, often with a hint of violet, grow from the crown, which is covered in wool. This is a very variable species and variants with brown spines have also been encountered.
The author of the discovery, H. Blossfeld, gave the type locality of this Parodia as the province of Jujuy in Argentina, but travelers have tied the location down to places such as Volcan or Quebrada de Humahuaca. Like most Parodia, *P. schuetziana* is most delicate when a seedling. Although its seeds are relatively large (more than 1/4in in diameter), the seedlings make slow progress initially. Beware of scorch by the spring sun, particularly if the cactus is overwintered at low light levels.

Pterocactus australis

Pterocactus australis

SHRUBBY

This cactus has a large, beet-like root, which can be up to 4in long and 1 1/4in in diameter. Because it is related to *Opuntia*, it has a segmented stem and the individual sections are cylindrical. The radial spines are very short, at only 1/4in, while the central spines can be up to 3/4in long (on older sections). The flower is yellowish white with a large number of deep yellow anthers. In the wild it grows in southern Argentina between Rio Santa Cruz and Magellan. It is a very rare species in collections and its cultivation needs are relatively complex. It is very rare for these plants to flower in cool climates. Propagation by cuttings, which take a relatively long time to take root, is possible, and by seed, but the latter are very reluctant to germinate.

Pterocactus tuberosus

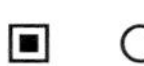

SHRUBBY

The narrow, cylindrical stems of this cactus are divided into sections of varying length. Some are only 2in long, whereas others grow to almost 20in long, but they do not usually grow to more than 5/8in in diameter. The epidermis is dark green, often with a hint of brown. The spines are white, hair-like, and only fractions of an inch long. The structure of the root system, which forms fairly large, tubers, is also interesting. Yellow flowers about 1 1/3in across open during the day in summer and their structure suggests a close relationship with *Opuntia*.

P. tuberosus grows at high altitudes in the Argentinian province of Mendoza, where it is found among rocks and on rocky outcrops in the hills. Like the preceding species, it is not particularly widespread in collections and is usually only found in those belonging to specialists in the specific area or in the *Opuntioideae* subfamily.

Pyrrhocactus bulbocalyx

GLOBOSE

Taxonomists are currently trying to incorporate a number of South American genera into what used to be the oldest genus, *Eriosyce*. This is the case with *Pyrrhocactus*. *P. bulbocalyx* forms a globose stem, which can be almost columnar in collections and reaches 8in tall. The oval areoles on the round tubercles can be more than 3/4in long and have about 12 yellow-gray spines growing out of them, sticking straight up. The lemon yellow flowers, with orange-red throats, usually grow in a ring near the crown and when fully open can reach up to 2in across.

This cactus grows in the Argentinian province of Jujuy, at altitudes of less than 3,000ft. The type locality is near the town of Marayes. It grows on gentle stony slopes with sparse xerophytic vegetation. Few growers cultivate this slow-growing cactus on its own roots. It is generally only encountered grafted onto stocks of *Trichocereus*, on which they grow slowly and produce beautiful spines. Practically the only method of propagation possible is by seed, but the seeds are not particularly willing to germinate. The species requires full sun when in active growth, along with good ventilation, and occasional, sparing doses of water.

Pterocactus tuberosus

Pyrrhocactus bulbocalyx

Pyrrhocactus villicumensis

Pyrrhocactus villicumensis 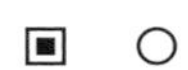

GLOBOSE

Recently taxonomists have reclassified this cactus within *Neoporteria*, but to keep classification clear, we have kept the original generic designation, which we feel is correct at present. It is a small species and grows to about 4in in size. It has an interesting gray or gray-green epidermis and on the short round ribs there are oval, densely woolly areoles, with 8 dark gray or black-gray radial spines and usually 1 or 2 central spines. The flower color is fairly variable, usually a lighter or darker shade of pinkish brown.

We do not know much about the locality as yet, apart from the fact that it grows in Argentina, in the Sierra Villicum, which gives it its species epithet. It has also been collected at Baños la Laja at an altitude of 3,000ft. It is not found too often in collections, and usually it is only encountered in specialists' collections. Recently seeds have been on offer in catalogs, so it is possibly becoming more widespread among cactus growers. Cultivation is fairly demanding and seedlings grow quite slowly. That is why it is generally grafted, a method that will produce flowers after about 5 years.

Rebutia aureiflora 

GLOBOSE

This species has been successively classified under various genera, such as *Lobivia* and *Mediolobivia*, but recently taxonomists have placed it within *Rebutia*. The stem is usually solitary, but can sometimes be clustering. The striking spine covering consists of fairly soft and tiny radial spines, of which some 15–20 grow from a single areole, and central spines, which are firmer and darker than the radial spines and over 1/2in long. In the case of older plants they can be significantly longer. Flowers emerge from the side of the plant and on plants of the type species they are orange-yellow in color. The varietas *R. aureiflora* var. *kesselringiana* is recorded as having light, pink-violet flowers and *R. aureiflora* var. *sarothroides* has golden yellow flowers.

The type species occurs in the Quebrada del Toro valley, near Chorillos and Yacones in the province of Salta in northern Argentina. It grows here among tracts of grasses, slightly shaded by associated vegetation. It has come into collections under field collection numbers FR 407, WR 158, and also WR 680. Cultivation poses no problems and its requirements are the same as for other members of the genus. It requires a well-drained soil mix, cold wintering in the light if possible, and an early start into growth.

Rebutia aureiflora

Rebutia huasiensis

Rebutia marsoneri

Rebutia huasiensis ▣ ○

GLOBOSE–COLUMNAR

This is a columnar *Rebutia*, which is initially solitary and only starts to form clusters at a more advanced age. The stem is about 1 1/4in in diameter and about 2in tall (more in the case of grafted plants). The color of the epidermis changes in intense sunlight from dark green to violet-red. There are 3–7 fairly short, dark spines growing out of each areole. Funnel-shaped flowers emerge from the side of the cactus. They are pale yellow and the outer petals have a darker, pinkish brown stripe. The fruit is a brown-black berry with green scales. This cactus acquired its species epithet from the settlement of Huasi, in northern Argentina, which is near where the species is found. It grows on dry hills with relatively sparse associated vegetation at an altitude of about 8,500ft. It is not found too often in collections and is almost unknown among cactus growers. *R. huasiensis* KK 1922 is occasionaly listed in catalogs, incorrectly named by Karel Kníže. The only thing the latter has in common with *R. huasiensis* is the name.

Rebutia marsoneri 

FLATTENED-GLOBOSE

This barrel-shaped cactus clusters only a little or not at all and grows to a diameter of 1 1/2–2in. There are small areoles on the tips of the tiny mammillae, from which about 30 soft, light spines grow. The yellow flower blooms from the side of the plant in early spring.
This species can be found in many locations in the province of Jujuy in northern Argentina, where it grows among tracts of grasses and low vegetation. It is a very undemanding species in terms of cultivation, and so can be recommended to those starting out growing cacti, because every spring, after cold wintering, large numbers of beautiful flowers bud from the side of the plant. The species is heterogamous and for seed to set two separate specimens must be grown in proximity. Beware of allowing early spring sunshine to scorch the plant (this applies for all members of the genus). Like all *Rebutia*, they are often attacked by spider mites.

Soehrensia bruchii var. *nivalis* ▣ ○

GLOBOSE–COLUMNAR

A.V. Frič classified this varietas, but today it is not certain whether it is justified. It is included here because many cactus growers have it listed in their collections. It is clearly just a white-spined variant of *S. bruchii*, of which specimens with spines in different colors can be found locally. It reaches up to 20in in height and can be almost the same in diameter. The numerous ribs have densely spaced areoles, with 9–15 white spines growing out of them, forming a beautiful contrast with the fiery red flowers.
This cactus grows in northern areas of Argentina, where it forms a group of specimens with various spine colors. Cactus growers are familiar with it, from collections, as a very variable taxon and some grow it under the generic name *Echinopsis*. Cultivation is relatively simple, provided you remember that this cactus requires adequate ventilation during summer. It responds very well to being grown outdoors in a sheltered location. The only effective method of propagation is by seed, but growing specimens on to flowering size can take many years.

Tephrocactus articulatus var. *inermis* 

SHRUBBY

The type species is an extremely variable cactus, but cacti of this varietas are unforgettable, because they have hardly any of the flat, paper-like spines on their sections, which are characteristic of the type. *Tephrocactus articulatus* var. *inermis* forms low bushes with individual sections about 2in in height and some 1 1/4in in diameter. There are extreme forms, however, with sections up to 8in long! White flowers with yellow anthers, up to 2in across, open during the daytime on the youngest sections during the summer and last for 2 or 3 days. This species is found in northern areas of Argentina down to Mendoza, and usually grows at higher altitudes. Growers propagate this cactus fairly simply by rooting individual detached sections. After about a week's drying under a table in the greenhouse or in some other shady, dry place, they can be planted in a sand and peat mix or in pure perlite, where they root within two months. They can then be potted up into pots filled with a suitable soil mix. It requires cold wintering and relatively early emergence from dormancy at the start of the growing season, but it is a real art to get this cactus to flower. The basic requirements for success here seem to be a large container and occasional applications of fertilizer when it is in active growth.

Trichocereus poco  ○

COLUMNAR

Most cactus growers are more familiar with this species under the name *Heliathocereus poco*, as it used to be recorded in older literature. It is a columnar plant, which usually grows to over 6ft in height. The stem diameter is between 10in and 14in. The spine covering looks threatening at first sight, with the individual spines reaching up to 1 1/2in in length and practically enveloping the stem. The red flowers open in the daytime and grow up to 4 3/4in long and about 4in across.
This cactus grows in many localities in Argentina and Bolivia, where it favors more gently sloping hillsides. In many places it is the dominant vegetation. Cactus growers are familiar with this cactus not only as a collection species but also as a rootstock, which has the same advantageous properties as the closely related *T. pasacana*, onto which cacti are grafted if slow growth is required. Cultivation is very simple and presents no major problems.

Soehrensia bruchii var. *nivalis*

Tephrocactus articulatus var. *inermis*

Trichocereus poco

Melocactus azureus

however, these plants need to be given max-imum light, and should be watered occasionally once or twice during the winter (depending on the temperature and light levels). The soil mix should be slightly acidic and free-draining. Cultivation is easier during the first years of life; older specimens are more sensitive to errors in cultivation.

Notocactus claviceps

Notocactus claviceps

 ■ ⊙

COLUMNAR

In earlier literature this species is usually listed as a member of *Eriocactus* and some taxonomists even classify it within Parodia. We feel that it is justified to classify it under *Novocactus*, but it appears under other names in many collections. When mature its stem grows to up to 3ft in height and 10in in diameter, though specimens of this size are rare in cultivation. There are usually up to 30 narrow ribs with yellow, bristle-like spines, up to 1 1/4in long, growing out of the relatively small areoles. The flower blooms on the crown of the plant. It is pale yellow and about 2 1/4in across when fully open.

This cactus grows on a series of rocky spurs, which run across the relatively flat countryside near the town of Julio de Castilhos in the Brazilian state of Rio Grande do Sul. Here it forms clumps. A slightly acidic soil mix with a pH of about 6 and a certain amount of shade is needed for cultivation of this species. Wintering should be at temperatures of about 50 °F. The vast majority of propagation is by seed, and seedlings reach flowering size after an average of 7 years.

Notocactus concinnus 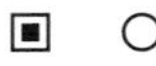

GLOBOSE

The globose stem of this species usually grows to a diameter of about 4in and is formed of 18–24 ribs. The areoles are 1/5in–1/4in apart and are covered in short, dense, grayish wool. There are usually 10–12 radial spines and 4 central spines, about 5/8in long. It has strikingly large flowers, which can reach up to 2 3/4in across. The inner petals are a characteristic yellow color and the outer petals can have a pinkish red edge.
This species is found across a relatively large area and its different forms are still being recorded even today. It grows in the state of Rio Grande do Sul in southern Brazil and in northern parts of Uruguay. It can be recommended to complete beginners. It does not require any special treatment and produces delightful, beautiful, large flowers every summer.

Notocactus horstii ▣ ○

COLUMNAR

This very neatly formed *Notocactus* boasts a striking habit and flower. Its columnar form, which can reach up to 3ftin height, can mainly be found in the wild. In collections it usually grows to 16in in height and 4in in diameter. It is difficult to distinguish between the radial and central spines both on plants in the wild and in collections. In both cases the spines are fairly tough and needle shaped. The flowers grow near the crown and have fascinating orange-red petals. They can reach about 1 1/3in across when fully open. The flowering period, which occurs in late summer as a rule, is also very interesting. The fruit is a berry, which distinctively opens at the base.
Leopoldo Horst, who discovered this species and after whom it was named, found it in the southern part of the Serra Geral mountains in the state of Rio Grande do Sul in Brazil. In 1965 L. Horst and F. Ritter came across a violet-flowered *N. horstii*, which F. Ritter recorded two years later as *N. horstii* var. *purpureiflorus*. This varietas is relatively rare in collections, however. The type species and its variants are fascinating *Novocactus*, and constitute a distinctive group within the genus together with *N. purpureus* and *N. muegelianus*. If you abide by the basic requirements for cultivation of most *Novocactus*, then growing this species is simple as well. It needs dappled shade, a free-draining, slightly acidic soil mix , and regular watering when in active growth. If the flowers bloom and you want to collect ripe seeds, place the cactus in a heated room and only allow the temperature to drop to about 50 °F once the fruits have ripened.

Notocactus concinnus

Notocactus leninghausii 

COLUMNAR

Frederico Guillermo Leninghaus, a cactus collector working in Brazil, sent the first specimen of this species to Europe in 1894. A year later it was classified as *Pilocereus leninghausii*. In the wild, the curved or slanting columnar stems can reach 3ft tall and a diameter of about 4in. Characteristically, the slanting crown is covered in a crest shaped quantity of fine spines. This species has about 30 ribs, the edges of which are thickly strewn with densely woolly areoles. 15–20 fine spines and 3 or 4 slightly stronger central spines grow out of these areoles. The yellow flowers bloom from the crown for 4-5 days, and measure 2 1/3 in across when open. The place of occurrence for the typical plant is

Notocactus horstii

Notocactus leninghausii

given very generally as the Brazilian state of Rio Grande do Sul. We know, however, that it grows on sandstone rock faces, such as the place where it was collected near Montenegro and also the place where F. Ritter discovered it to the north of Canela. This species can also be propagated from seed too, but the seedlings grow very slowly for the first season and growth only starts to accelerate the second year after sowing. They require a slightly acidic soil mix and respond best to dappled shade when young. A few of these cacti planted in a shallow pan can look very impressive. This also encourages them to develop a sizeable root system.

Notocactus magnificus

Notocactus magnificus   ○

GLOBOSE–COLUMNAR

This beautiful member of the genus initially has a globose stem, but becomes columnar when mature, its height measuring 3 times its width, which is not normally more than 6in in diameter. It usually does not grow to more than 6in in diameter. It has a beautiful, blue-green epidermis, which stands out because of the beautiful combination of the color of its spines and flowers. When mature, the 11–15 prominent ribs have areoles connected by densely woolly bridging, so the edges of the ribs are completely yellow. There are 12–15 soft, yellow spines growing from each areole, of which the longest can measure up to 3/4in. Flowers, measuring 1 1/2–2in across, bloom from the crown at the top of the plant. After fertilization these change into globose fruits, about 1/2in across, full of reddish brown seeds 1/25in long. *N. magnificus* was not discovered in the wild until 1964, found in the Serra Gerral mountains in the Brazilian state of Rio Grande do Sul by L. Horst and F. Ritter. It grows here in a warm subtropical climate in relatively high air humidity. It is a really beautiful cactus, which appeals to both laymen and experts. Cultivation is not parti cularly complicated, but the species must have a fairly acidic soil mix and responds best to partial shade.

Notocactus tephracanthus ▣ ○

FLATTENED-GLOBOSE

Many cactus growers may have this cactus listed as *Malacocarpus tephracantha*, because a similar group of plants used to be classified under that name. The dark green, flattened-globose stem is formed of 16–18 pointed ribs, with large areoles covered in fluffy white wool on the edges. 5 radial spines and 1 central spine, 3/4in–1 1/4in long, grow from these areoles. The flowers emerge from the woolly crown and are deep yellow with a red stigma. The fruit is a pink berry with gray-black seeds.

This species is relatively widespread and reportedly comes from three countries in South America: Brazil, Uruguay, and Argentina. It grows on rocky slopes, unshaded by associated vegetation. Like other members of the genus, it is easy to cultivate. It requires a slightly acidic, free-draining soil mix, abundant watering when in acive growth, and full sun. Propagation is by seed. The seed germinates well once ripe and the seedlings should be provided with partial shade during the early years.

Notocactus uebelmannianus ▣ ○

FLATTENED-GLOBOSE

The flattened-globose stem of this species is usually dark green and the largest specimens grow to a size of up to 7in. The spines are flattened against the stem and are of various lengths. The specimen in the photograph has very short spines, but selected smooth forms can be found in nurseries.

Notocactus tephracanthus

Notocactus uebelmannianus

The beautiful, violet flower blooms at the start of the summer and is one of the most attractive flowers among *Notocactus.*

As described below, the red-flowering form grows in Brazil in the same place as the yellow-flowering one. The former is a lot more widespread than the latter. Cultivation is relatively simple. The species can be grown either in full sun or light shade. It should be watered freely when in active growth and should be overwintered in a cold, dry, and light spot. It has the same soil requirements as the next taxon.

Notocactus uebelmannianus f. *flaviflorus*

GLOBOSE

This taxon is very variable. The main difference to the type species is its yellow flowers (the type species has purple flowers). The length, number of spines, and number of ribs vary considerably and selected plants now exist in nurseries which are almost smooth. With most plants the stem diameter does not usually exceed 6in and the plant is usually about 4 3/4in tall. The flower can grow to just over 2in across, and as with most *Novocactus* it has a dark red stigma surrounded by yellow stamens and anthers.

This Brazilian cactus comes from Rio Grande do Sul, where it grows near the town of Cacapava. It grows in association with the red-flowering form which is why this might be just a collector's selection. Germinating the seed and subsequent cultivation pose no problems. The soil mix should be kept a little damper than is usual with the Mexican species, for instance. It is best to add peat to the soil mix, to bring the pH to around 6.

Notocactus uebelmanniana f. flaviflorus

Quiabentia zehntneri

SHRUBBY

This is another very old cactus in terms of evolution, which has real leaves. These are up to 1 1/2in long, very succulent, and oval to *rhomboidal* (i.e. narrowest at the base and the tip and widest in the middle of the leaf). It forms a spreading bush, 6–10ft tall. Tiny, light-colored glochids sprout from the areoles. The pale pink flower is very elegant and up to 3in across. It has large seed and is interesting because of the aril, which is clearly an outgrowth of the funicle.

There is not too much information about where it occurs. Not many cactus growers have seen the species in the wild and literary sources are short on concrete information. All that is known is that it grows in the Brazilian state of Bahia. Few collections have this cactus on display. The seed availability is minimal as is its space requirement. For the plant to bloom it should ideally be planted directly in the greenhouse bed, where it forms a large bush capable of flowering within a few years. It is best to overwinter the species at a temperature of about 60 °F and it should be watered a little during the winter to prevent it losing its leaves, but only provided temperatures do not fall below the limit specified.

Quiabentia zehntneri

Pereskia aculeata

Pereskia grandifolia

Pereskia aculeata 

SCANDENT

In terms of evolution, this species belongs to the group of the oldest cacti, which have not completely lost their leaves. It already has the areoles, spines, and characteristic reproductive organ structure, however, typical of the whole *Cactaceae* family. The stems are trailing to climbing and can grow to tens of feet in length. The maximum length recorded is 33ft. It usually has 1–3 spines growing from the areoles, but no glochids. The flowers are fairly large and up to 2in across when fully open. They are creamy yellow with a tinge of pink inside.
The original area of distribution is given as Brazil, Uruguay, and Argentina, but it can now be found in the wild in the USA (Florida) and in India and other tropical countries as well. It needs partial shade to grow (but can withstand full sun as well) and adequate watering. If not given enough water it loses its leaves and growth slows down. It needs wintering at higher temperatures and should be watered occasionally so that it does not lose all the water from its storage tissue. *P. aculeata* does not suit a small greenhouse, because growth is too rampant and it is soon too large. Plants respond very well to renovative pruning.

Pereskia grandifolia 

SRUBBY

A very old cactus in terms of evolution, which has retained fairly large leaves (*grandifolia*). This species is shrubby and its straight stems grow to a height of as much as 16ft. The slightly succulent leaves are up to 8in long and 1 1/4in–1 1/2in across. It usually has 2 black spines growing from each areole, about 3/4in long. The flowers that appear in corymbs at the end of the stems are very beautiful. The petals are white at the base and become pink-violet toward the tip. The fruit is a unique, pear-like berry.
This species belongs to the *xerophytic* vegetation in the rare semi-deciduous forests of Brazil. It is usually only seen in exhibitions at botanical gardens, where it is a huge, eye-catching feature with its beautiful flowers. It is also a wonderful example of the early types of cactus in evolutionary terms. Cultivation is not complicated, but the species only flowers as a large shrub. That is why it is best to cultivate it in open ground in a greenhouse, where winter temperatures do not fall below 55 °F for long. Propagation is simple and involves taking cuttings of the new growth, which can then be rooted in a mix of sand and peat or in pure perlite.

Pilosocereus azureus 

COLUMNAR

This is a columnar species, which can grow to a height of 13ft in the wild. The stem is formed of 7–10 prominent ribs. The reason it is so beautiful is the blue-gray color of its epidermis, which combines wonderfully well with the yellow radial and central spines. The crown of the plant is covered in white, hair-like spines, which often disappear partly later. White flowers up to 2in long form toward the top of the cactus and open at night. After fertilization they turn into a fruit with scarlet pulp, full of tiny black seeds.
This cactus comes from hot areas of Brazil, where it grows among colonies of shrub vegetation. It grows on rocky outcrops where there is less vegetation and in clearings. It is very popular among

Pilosocereus azureus

cactus growers and is generally grown for the beautiful color of its epidermis. Mature specimens can be seen in collections where there is no problem with space. It requires a fairly large container, a nutrient-high, free-draining soil mix, and overwintering in fairly warm conditions in good light. Germinating seed is simple and seedlings are already very impressive when three years old.

Schlumbergera gaertneri ■ ◐

TRAILING

Up until only recently, this cactus was classified by certain growers under a separate genus, *Epiphyllopsis*, which consisted of this species and two other forms. We feel that it is justified and right to classify it within *Schlumbergera*. It forms a freely branching bush with the individual stems formed of oblong segments. There are a number of tiny brown bristles on the top sections. The flower is 1 1/2in–2in long, zygomorphic, and a luminous scarlet color.

The species grows epiphytically in treetops and the area of distribution is given very generally as Santa Catharina, Brazil. To find this species in the wild you have to be lucky enough to find a specimen low down or a recently fallen tree. In our experience, this is where these epiphytes can best be studied. The species is very easy to propagate from cuttings of stem sections. It is rarely raised from seed. Seed is very scarce and germinates poorly, and the seedlings are relatively delicate.

Schlumbergera orssichiana ■ ◐

TRAILING

This cactus was first discovered in the 1970s. It is not cultivated much in its straight form, but its colorful flowers have formed the basis for many new hybrids. The trailing stem spreads out and the individual flattened segments can be up to 3 1/2in long and 1 1/2in across. The edges are shaped into a number of points. New sections are reddish green in color. The beautiful, zygomorphic flowers are up to 3 1/2in long. They are a resplendent, pink-violet color, the centers of the inner petals being lighter, almost white . The flowers emerge from areoles located toward the top of the sections and bloom from the end of the summer to the later winter months. Mrs. Beatriz Orssich discovered the species in Brazil in the Serra de Mar mountains and introduced it into cultivation. It became the basis for a number of new, commercially produced cultivars. Cultivation of the type species is fairly delicate, because it grows at a time of year when other plants are in dormancy. This is a time when light levels are low and plants often fall victim to various fungal diseases. Cultivated hybrids are generally reliable growers, however, even in domestic conditions. They produce beautiful flowers and can be bought in many different color shades. Cultivation is as for the so-called “Christmas cactus.”

Schlumbergera gaertneri

Schlumbergera orssichiana

Schlumbergera truncata

Schlumbergera truncata ■ ◐

TRAILING

This species used to be listed under the name *Zygocactus truncatus*, although it is probably best known as the "Christmas cactus." It has become increasingly popular in recent years, with a number of cultivars and interspecific hybrids breaking onto the market. The stem of *S. truncata* is formed of individual offsets, composed of small, detachable segments with striking central veining. The individual sections have slightly jagged edges and there are tiny, delicate brown bristles growing from the top areoles. Zygomorphic flowers appear from early fall and continue throughout winter. The features and properties of the many hybrids are rather different from the type species. Usually they differ in terms of length of flowering period, flower longevity, and so on.

This is a typical epiphytic cactus, which originates from the forests around Rio de Janeiro in Brazil. Cultivation techniques and propagation have been refined almost to perfection for this group of cacti, because every year hundreds of thousands of plants are prepared in commercial nurseries for the winter and above all the pre-Christmas period. Nowadays by artificial daylight reduction, flowering "Christmas cacti" have become available on the market over the whole year. For amateur growers the "Christmas cactus" flourishes best over summer in a hanging basket suspended from a tree branch in the garden. To promote flower formation, a dry period at the end of the summer is required. Budding itself is triggered by shortening day-length. In early fall, place the plant in a room where the temperature must not be allowed to drop below 60 °F, but not exceeding normal room temperature (beware of overheated porches or glass-fronted balconies!). This treatment will ensure flowering during the winter months. When forming flowers and developing buds, these cacti are sensitive to over-handling and too much turning around, particularly cultivars with white or light-colored flowers. Bear this in mind if you move the plant into the house for an indoor flower display. They are usually propagated vegetatively: cuttings (with about five sections) should be rooted in a soil mix of perlite and

Stephanocereus leucostele

peat, at a ratio of 1:1. Seed should be used only to create new hybrids.

Stephanocereus leucostele ■ ○

COLUMNAR

This columnar cactus usually forms a single non-clustering offset, about 10ft tall. Generally it has 12–18 ribs which are densely covered in areoles with about 20 radial spines about 5/8in long growing from each one. There are fewer central spines, and these are up to 1 1/2in long. The flowers grow from a ring-shaped cephalium, made up of white hair and tough brown bristles. The flowers can grow to a length of about 2 3/4in and are white. The outer petals are green.
Because this plant comes from the tropics (the southern areas of the Brazilian state of Bahia to be precise), it has to have fairly warm wintering. It is found only very occasionally in collections and is more likely to be encountered as a rare specimen in the collection of some botanical garden.

Uebelmannia pectinifera  ○

COLUMNAR

The whole genus was named after the eminent Swiss cactus expert W. J. Uebelmann. This species was actually discovered only recently in 1967. Ever since its introduction it has always been a great rarity, unique because of its beautiful epidermis covered in white-gray scales. In the wild these plants can grow to a height of up to 3ftwith a stem diameter of about 6in. There are usually 15–18 ribs, which are very even and pointed. Protruding spines grow from the densely spaced areoles on the top of the rib and form a sort of crest along the whole length. This is the derivation of the epithet pectinifera, meaning crested. The tiny yellow flowers appear near the top and are about 1/2in across.
This species was discovered near the town of Diamantina in the Brazilian state of Minas Gerais. These cacti are found fairly high up in the mountains where the air humidity is quite high. They grow on rocky raised ground or in fissures. This cactus cannot be recommended to beginners. Even experienced cactus growers have real trouble with all the members of this genus and *U. pectinifera* is no exception. The germinated seedlings should be grafted at the earliest possible moment onto a good-quality *Pereskiopsis* stock; later, grafting onto a long-term stock can be considered. Cultivation is difficult – the plants have to be overwintered at fairly high temperatures. On hot days it is a good idea to damp down the greenhouse floor, but on the other hand it does not require high air humidity on cold days. Many other requirements could be listed, which is why it is advisable to first gain experience as a cactus grower with different species.

Uebelmannia pectinifera

Uebelmannia pectinifera var. *multicostata*

Uebelmannia pectinifera var. *multicostata*  ○

COLUMNAR

This varietas can grow up to 34in in height and can be distinguished from the type species primarily by the number of ribs. As reported by observers in the wild, this distinction has little value, because of the variability. Whereas the type species usually has 15–18 according to reports, this varietas has about 20 as a rule. The yellow-green flower is almost the same as the previous taxon.
These plants can be found in the Brazilian state of Minas Gerais east of the town of Diamantina, and the most specific information gives localities north of Rio Jequitinhonha, at altitudes of about 2,100ft. This varietas is also very difficult to cultivate. Like the type species it is best grafted immediately after germination onto *Pereskiopsis*; larger plants can later be grafted onto *Eriocereus jusbertii*. Seedlings on their own roots are available very rarely, though self-rooted plants have become more commonplace in nurseries. These are produced by micropropagation in laboratories.

7. Chile

This is without doubt one of the most interesting countries in South America and that applies from the cactus grower's point of view as well. Although it is medium-sized in South American terms, at 290,000 square miles, it holds the clear record in terms of length at 2,700 miles. (The average width of the country is less than 125 miles.) In the north, at the latitude 17 degrees south, it extends into the tropics, and the south of the country, somewhere around the 56th parallel, is in the cold zone. This region, also known as Patagonia or extremo sur (the extreme south), is now under the joint administration of Chile and Argentina. Cacti even grow here as well. So Chile is a unique strip of land, divided from the rest of the continent of South America by a ridge of mountains and cut off from the rest of the world by the Pacific. Some cacti in Chile grow in the driest places on the planet, because there are areas of the Atacama Desert where it practically never rains. The plants here have to get all their water from the substantial mists which form. There can be a fraction of an inch of precipitation over a single night because of these very regular mists. The unique climate of the coastal deserts, which regularly witness the formation of huge volumes of mist, is also known as garua, after the extensive mists.
The cacti here are very well adapted to these harsh conditions. One of the ways in which they are adapted is through their strong layer of crystallized wax, which prevents excessive evaporation of water. This wax gives the stems their distinctive gray or gray-green color. Root systems are also specialized, mostly shallow and spread out over a large area, in order to capture the largest possible quantity of precipitated mist. *Copiapoa* is a typical Chilean genus: it has a number of local and intermediate variants. The group of which the species *C. cinerea* is part has caused cactus experts some headaches, not only in terms of taxonomy but also in terms of cultivation. To be able to grow cacti which resemble the wild specimens requires enormous patience and care.
However, cacti in Chile also grow south of the driest regions in the north of the country. As you move from northern to central Chile the countryside becomes more prairie-like and plant communities are generally formed of all manner of grasses and other herbs. The commonest type of vegetation in the south of Chile is forest.

Left: *Trichocereus chilensis*

Copiapoa cinerea ▣ ○

COLUMNAR

All the plants in the group to which this *Copiapoa* belongs number among the most beautiful cacti in South America. They grow in unfavorable localities, where they dominate the plant community. *C. cinerea* is a columnar species which tends to cluster and forms huge mounds when mature. The individual stems grow to up to 3ft in height and 4–2in in diameter. The epidermis is covered in a crystalline waxy layer, which gives it its characteristic gray color. Younger plants or plants which grow in more favorable localities do not have such a pronounced wax layer and the epidermis is bronze. The number of ribs fluctuates between 14 and 30. There are usually 2 central spines and 2–4 radial spines growing out of the areoles. The longest central spines can grow to up to 1 1/2in in length. The yellow flower has reddish outer petals and is 1 1/4–1 1/2in across. The green, barrel-shaped fruit contains shiny black seeds, which are about 1/14in long.
The type species grows at altitudes of 300–1,300ft. It is found on both slopes of the Quebrada de Taltal near the Chilean town of Taltal, not far from the coast. It hardly ever rains there and the cacti have to get all the water they need from the regular mists that form, known as garua. Only a few dozen species of cacti have adapted to this unique desert climate (garua), and they constitute a special group of plants within the family as a whole. They are usually grafted for cultivation in collections, primarily because the seedlings grow very slowly initially. The only effective method of propagation is by seed. Although the seeds available in catalogs are very poor germinators, which is the main reason for the scarcity of plants, fresh seed almost always germinates. Every advanced cactus grower and specialist in South American cacti should have this species in their collection.

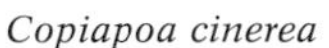
Copiapoa cinerea

Copiapoa cinerea ssp. dealbata

Copiapoa cinerea ssp. dealbata ▣ ○

COLUMNAR

There has been relatively little taxonomical transfer among the *C. cinerea* group of plants and, because of their similarity, every specialist has a slightly different opinion on the issue. This subspecies differs from the type species in having 1–3 central spines and either 1 central spine or none at all. The individual mounds can reach about 3ft across and 2ft 6in in height.

Copiapoa cinerea ssp. *dealbata* is the most southerly growing taxon in the whole *C. cinerea* group. It grows to the east of the settlement of Carrizal Bajo on ocean-facing hillsides. Those who have observed it report that it grows here in vast quantities, just in the belt from 650ft to 1,600ft. It is interesting that no other cacti occur in this sector. Like other related *Copiapoa*, it is usually grown as a graft on a slow-growing rootstock, but we have come across collections of beautiful specimens on their own roots among more experienced cactus growers. Although these cacti do not have strong, beet-like roots, they require a soil mix with a high mineral content (at least 50 %), or else their roots rot. The seedlings grow slowly and even though there is no shade at all in the wild, they respond best in dappled shade in cultivation in the northern hemisphere, because their waxy layer is not thick enough in the first few years of life. Protect them against scorch by the first rays of spring sunshine.

Copiapoa cinerea ssp. *gigantea*

COLUMNAR

C. Backeberg classified this cactus as a separate species back in 1936. It later underwent other taxonomic changes, but its status as a subspecies, which it was accorded by the Czech cactus expert Rudolf Slaba, is a very sensible compromise considering this group's complicated system. Although it is called *gigantea*, it is not actually the largest within this group. It usually grows to about 2ft 6in in height, with an individual stem diameter of 6–8in. There are usually 5–7 needle-shaped, radial spines (sometimes as many as 12) and usually 1 central spine, but 2 or 3 in exceptional cases. The flower is yellow and about 1 1/2in in height and width. This *Copiapoa* is found in an area which starts 12 miles north of the town of Taltal and extends to Paposo. It grows primarily on the coastal plains and on gently rising mountainsides at altitudes of about 160ft. Cultivation is the same as for other forms of *C. cinerea*.

Copiapoa cinerea ssp. *gigantea* var. *haseltoniana* ▣ ○

COLUMNAR

This is clearly the largest *Copiapoa* within this group. Its stems grow to 5 ft long and 10in in diameter, and large adult specimens are often spreading, forming mounds up to 6ft across. The spines are yellow and the flower is practically the same as the type species.

This varietas is found to the south of Paposo, but it disappears near the village and then occurs

Copiapoa cinerea ssp. gigantea

again to the north of the village. Its habitat has been destroyed near the human settlement by the influence of man, but further away from the village it is found in huge numbers. Its area of distribution stretches along the ocean to Caleta Colorada. It has the same cultivation requirements as other *Copiapoa* in this group. Its glassy yellow spines form a beautiful contrast with the gray of the epidermis, but it requires a huge amount of patience to wait for flowering specimens, as applies to all cacti from the *C. cinerea* group.

Copiapoa cinerea ssp. gigantea var. *tenebrosa* ▣ ○

COLUMNAR

It is very difficult to differentiate between this varietas and the previous, being almost the same plant. *Var. tenebrosa*, however, has black spins and grows in the mountains, whereas var. *haseltoniana* grows on the coast with light spines.

Copiapoa cinerea ssp. *gigantea* var. *haseltoniana*

Growing on windward-facing hillsides, northeast of Taltal at 1,300-1,600ft, it is cultivated as for other members of this group. Because of the marked similarity, it is best to have cacti in your collection from a verified source, so you know exactly where the seed came from.

Copiapoa cinerea ssp. *gigantea* var. *tenebrosa*

Copiapoa coquimbana ▣ ○

MOUND-FORMING

The columnar stems of this species form large, cushion-like mounds up to 3ft across and a maximum of 2ft tall. Individual stems are up to 4in in diameter and are formed of 10–17 ribs with fairly prominent tubercles. 8–10 radial spines grow from each areole, along with 1 or 2 central spines. These are firmer and about 1in long. The deep yellow, broadly funnel-shaped flowers emerge on the crown of the plant. They open on sunny days during the summer. The plant shown was photographed in Cerro Grande, the type locality, in the Chilean province of Coquimbo, where it grows at an altitude of 1,300ft. It was discovered there by K. Kníže, who gave it his first field collection number, KK 1. It is relatively simple to cultivate. The plant should be placed in full sun when in active growth and wintered at temperatures of about 50 °F, and the free-draining soil mix should be allowed to dry out completely between two waterings.

Copiapoa coquimbana var. *longispina* ▣ ○

GLOBOSE–COLUMNAR

This varietas has no valid description, which is why it is seldom mentioned. It is more a long-spined local form than a separate varietas or subspecies. It has distinctive brown-black or pitch black spines, up to 2in long.
It is found near La Serena, which is where K. Kníže collected it and listed it under field collection number KK 183. In collections it is best to ensure plants of this varietas are from a known source: these are of much greater botanical value than plants from an unknown source. Cultivation is the same as for the type species.

Copiapoa hypogea ▣ ○

GLOBOSE

This is one of the smallest *Copiapoa*. Its globose stem only grows to 1 1/2–2 1/4in in diameter and in the wild the bulk of the cactus is hidden in the ground. The dull, green-brown epidermis is a feature of this species, as are the spiraling ribs, for-

Copiapoa coquimbana var. *longispina*

med of tubercles ending in a densely woolly areole. 1–6 gray-black spines, just 1/10in–1/5in long, grow from each areole. The crown of the plant is covered in thick white wool. Broadly funnel-shaped, yellow flowers, about 3/4in long and 1 1/2in across emerge from the crown.
This species is found in fairly flat areas near the coast at altitudes of 1,000–1,300ft, near Chanaral in the Chilean province of Antofagasta. They produce a large, fleshy root and hence need to be watered very carefully. They can withstand full sun and high temperatures, but during the hottest part of the summer they become dormant and need hardly any water at all. Propagation is by seed. Grafting onto *Eriocereus jusbertii* or *Trichocereus pasacana* is recommended for beginners.

Copiapoa krainziana 

GLOBOSE

This cactus was discovered and classified as an independent species in 1963 by F. Ritter, who named it in honor of the director of the Zurich municipal cactus collection, Hans Krainz. A number of authorities have classified it as a subspecies of *C. cinerea*, because it has certain related features in terms of flower and fruit structure, and seed similarities. The columnar stem is usually 2 1/4in–4 3/4in in diameter, but it can be up to 3ft tall. The clusters are formed from some 10 separate stems. The epidermis is light greenish gray and is covered with a thin layer of crystallized wax. In this case, the thick white spines provide protection against the effect of too much sunshine. Radial and central spines are difficult to distinguish, and 22-30 hair-like spines usually grow out of each aerole. The yellow flowers measure 1in–1 1/3in across. This cactus grows north of the town Taltal, San Ramon valley. Damp ocean air flows down the valley, bringing practically the only moisture in the form of mist (garua). Many growers have this cactus in their collections and, as a rule, cultivate it grafted onto a slow-growing rootstock. It does well on its own roots, however, but needs to be planted in a mineral-high soil mix and provided with nutrients along a balanced fertilizer. Water sparingly but often: approximately once every two weeks in summer.

Copiapoa hypogea

Copiapoa krainziana

Copiapoa laui

Copiapoa laui 

GLOBOSE

This is clearly the smallest member of the whole genus. Its globose, clustering stem grows to only 1/2in–1 1/4in in diameter. The epidermis is a striking brown color and at first sight out of flower the plant looks like certain species from the *Blossfeldia* genus. The ribs are formed of flat, spiraling tubercles, on which there are areoles with dense white wool. The spines are very fine and almost invisible. Resplendent, deep yellow flowers, about 1 1/4in across, emerge from the woolly crown.
This miniature is found in flat areas in the Chilean province of Esmeralda, where it grows at altitudes of 300–1,000ft. In cultivation, grafted specimens cluster more freely than cacti in the wild, which is why they are generally propagated vegetatively by detaching and grafting offsets. Seed is relatively rarely available in catalogs. The actual germinating and, above all, growing on of small seedlings is by no means simple. Grafting is recommended, even to experienced growers. The species will then reach flowering size within two or three years.

Copiapoa serpentisulcata

Copiapoa taltalensis

Copiapoa serpentisulcata 

GLOBOSE

The stem of this species is initally globose and usually grows to a diameter of 4–6in. Later it generally grows into an almost columnar shape, which can reach about 20in in height. There are many ribs (20–38) and the epidermis turns reddish in those specimens exposed to full sun. There are 6–10 radial spines and usually 1–4 central spines, which are firm, woody, and about 1 1/4in long. The yellow flowers, which grow to about 1 1/4in in both height and width, have a faint scent. The fruit is a greenish red or red berry containing black seeds.
This species is found near Chanaral at altitudes of about 1,000ft. Specimens have been collected, however, from the areas between Paposo and Taltal, but also from certain points between Chanaral and Esmeralda. It grows in very inhospitable conditions with minimal screening provided by associated vegetation. K. Kníže collected this species on a few occasions and the field collection numbers recorded are KK 613, KK 623, and KK 1741. It is found relatively rarely in cultivation, but the principles are the same as for other members of the genus. These cacti grow slowly, but by grafting seedlings onto slow-growing rootstocks you can speed up flowering and also reduce problems with seedlings. The only effective method of propagation is by seed, despite the fact that large, adult specimens can cluster from the base.

Copiapoa taltalensis 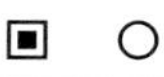

GLOBOSE

The solitary stem of this species clusters rarely. In the wild it is generally globose and in collections extends into an almost columnar form. It usually does not exceed 4in in diameter and about 6in in height. It has a gray-green epidermis. Only 6–8 spines grow out of the densely woolly areoles, of which the longest central spines can be up to 2in long in very spiny specimens. The flower emerges

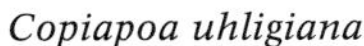
Copiapoa uhligiana

from the densely woolly growing point and is about 1 1/4in across.
This species is currently recorded as occurring in a relatively small area near Antofagasta in the Chilean department of Taltal, where it grows in the Sierra Esmeralda mountains. Cultivation is easier than for other *Copiapoa*, but it cannot be recommended to complete beginners. It requires full sun and very careful watering when dormant in summer. Propagation is by seed, but these are not often to be found in catalogs.

Copiapoa uhligiana ▣ ○

COLUMNAR

There is no valid classification of this species as yet and it is generally known as *Copiapoa* KK 1750 among cactus growers, which is how K. Kníže listed his original collection. We feel that it is probably a form of *C. cinerea* with a beautiful spine covering, which is of interest for its long, gray-black, erect spines.
As the author of the discovery stated, this species can be found near Esmeralda at altitudes of 300–650ft. The same principles of cultivation apply as for *C. cinerea*. In view of the peculiarities and distinctive features of these cacti, plants in collections should be from an authenticated source, because they are very difficult to distinguish as seedlings.

Eriosyce aurata ▣ ○

GLOBOSE–BARREL-SHAPED

E. aurata is now considered to be a synonym for the next species. It can be distinguished above all by its golden spines. This species is found in areas near Rio Molle in the Chilean province of Coquimbo. Huge variability means that it is just a form of the species *E. ceratistes* with extreme coloring and spines.

Eriosyce aurata

Eriosyce ceratistes ▣ ○

GLOBOSE-BARREL-SHAPED

This is a large, globose to barrel-shaped species, with a stem which can reach more than 20 in in height and diameter. It is formed of more than 30 prominent ribs, enveloped in thick spines. It is difficult to differentiate between the radial and central spines. All the spines are 1 1/4–1 1/2in long and are hugely variable in terms of color, ranging from reddish to brown and golden yellow. The red flowers are about 1 1/2in across and are carried near the top of the cactus.
This species occurs over a wide area, from lowlands (1,000ft) to high up in the mountains, where it can be found at altitudes of 9,000ft. There are collectors and growers who specialize in *Eriosyce,* some of whom are capable of producing flowering specimens, usually grafted onto large, strong rootstocks. It takes many years for these grafted cacti to flower. The seed are reluctant to germinate and the seedlings are delicate, so this is definitely not a species that is easy to cultivate or common in collections. It has encouraged many experiments in cultivation techniques because of its beautiful spines.

Eulychnia spinibarbis ▣ ○

COLUMNAR

This bushy, columnar species is eye-catching because of its striking spines toward the top of the stems, which is also the reason for the species epithet spinibarbis, meaning "with a spiny beard." Creamy white flowers appear toward the top of the stems, but struggle to force their way through the thick web of spines. This species has distinctive fruit, a feature of all species of *Eulychnia.* They swell up when ripe and have a pericarp covered thickly in spines and fine hairs.

Eriosyce ceratistes

Eulychnia spinibarbis

This species can be found in coastal deserts in the province of Coquimbo, where it grows in extreme conditions. Practically the only form of moisture available is in the form of mist (garua). In cultivation, *Eulychnia* is generally encountered only in collections belonging to specialists. This also applies to the species *E. spinibarbis.*

Eulychnia taltalensis 

COLUMNAR

This controversial but unknown species is classified as a synonym for *E. acida* or *E. longispina*. Its huge columns cluster just above ground level, and individual branches can grow to a height of 6ft.
It has white flowers, 3/4–1 1/2in across.
It is found in the Chilean province of Antofagasta in the department of Taltal, where it grows at altitudes of 1,000–1,600ft. IIt has been collected for example by F. Ritter as FR 214, or by K. Kníže as KK 1278, and is found rarely in collections.
Cultivation principles apply as for genus members, i.e. full light and cold wintering. Watering should be carefully when dormant in summer, or roots easily rot.

Eulychnia taltalensis

Horridocactus curvispinus ▣ ○

GLOBOSE

While experts doubt whether *Horridocactus* should be a separate genus, we prefer to use the old name because cactus growers know the species this way.

The greenish brown stem grows to a maximum diameter of 6in and is formed of 16 ribs. There are usually about 6 radial spines and 2 central spines, but qualitz and lenght vary. The flower is about 1 1/4in long and the same across. It has a reddish green tube and pinkish brown petals.

The most reliable literary sources indicate this cactus is found in the central areas of Chile, near Los Villos in the Santiago region at altitudes of 300–650ft. A number of cacti are grown in collections which barely correspond to the original description, and because of the variability of the species a number of different forms have been recorded, including *H. currispinus* var. *santiagensis, H. currispinus* var. *felipensis,* and *H. currispinus* var. *tilamensis*. Cultivation is as for the Neoporteria or Islaya.

Horridocactus curvispinus

Neochilenia imitans

Neochilenia paucicostata var. viridis

Neochilenia imitans 

GLOBOSE

The description of this species was published by C. Backeberg in volume III of his extensive monograph on *Cactaceae.* The squat, globose stem is usually 1 1/2–2in wide and there is a huge, beet-like root underground. The epidermis is greenish brown and the individual, indistinct ribs are formed of tubercles carrying areoles. Some 5–8 radial spines grow out of the areoles, but no central spine at all. The cactus in the photograph has slightly longer spines, which stand out more than is usual with this species, but there is considerable variety in these cacti, especially in terms of their spines. The yellow flower is almost the same size as the stem when open.

Neochilenia napina

The author of the description gives the type locality of this species, very succinctly, as Chile. More specific sources have pinpointed the locality as Tres Playitas, where it grows in a dry desert region with very sparse associated vegetation at an altitude of about 300 ft. The beet-like root makes the species very sensitive to indiscriminate watering, not only in the spring and fall but also when dormant in summer. Grafting onto *Eriocereus jusbertii* is recommended. This rootstock does not promote over-vigorous or distorted growth.

Neochilenia napina 

GLOBOSE–COLUMNAR

This is a flattened-globose species with a greenish brown epidermis and a large beet-like root. It is now classified within *Eriosyce,* but most cactus growers are still familiar with it under its old generic name. In the wild it can grow to about 2in in diameter, but in collections it extends into a column, particularly if grafted. It has about 14 ribs, consisting of tubercles carrying depressed, elongated areoles with dense wool toward the top. The very short, black spines, of which 3–9 grow from each areole, reach a maximum length of 1/8in. Yellowish white flowers with an orange-red stigma are produced near the top. They are very well disguised in the wild and most of the stem is beneath ground. This species is reported as occurring near Huasco (Chile), where it grows in sandy ground at altitudes of about 300ft. It used to be fairly common in cultivation, but there seems to have been a rapid fall in their numbers in collections for some reason. Because of their fleshy root they need to be planted in a very free-draining soil mix. They need full sun, cold wintering, and it is best not to water them at all when dormant in summer.

Neoporteria chilensis

Neochilenia paucicostata var. *viridis* ▣ ○

GLOBOSE

Few groups of cacti are as complicated in taxonomic terms as the genera *Neochilenia*, *Neoporteria*, and *Horridocactus*. Most are now classified as *Eriosyce*, but we do not feel that this is an ideal solution. When adult, the stems are slightly columnar and most are non-clustering. They form 8–12 ribs, consisting of tubercles. The areoles are set in a slight depression, and 5–8 radial spines and usually 1–4 central spines up to 1 1/2in long, grow out of each one. The funnel-shaped flowers are pink or pinkish white and about 1 1/3in aross.
There is very little information about where these cacti are found and all that is known for certain is that they grow in Paposo, on the coast of Chile, at altitudes ranging from 33ft to 1,000ft. This was where K. Kníže collected the species and the cactus in the photograph was grown from seed listed under field collection number KK 67. Cultivation is the same as for other South American cacti from this group. It requires full sun, a free-draining soil mix, and careful watering in the summer: frequently but always in small doses.

Neoporteria chilensis ▣ ○

COLUMNAR

Even current specialists have trouble with the correct classification of this cactus. It has already been classified under *Neochilenia* and *Chilenia*, but it looks as though it is correct to include it within *Neoporteria*. The individual stems can grow to 1ft in height and are not usually more than 4in in diameter. They have a green-brown epidermis and a fairly large quantity of spines growing from their large, woolly areoles. There are usually about 20 radial spines and 6–8 central spines. They are all white or whitish gray. The flower grows from the top of the cactus and is a pink-violet color.
Although the area of distribution of this species remained unknown for a long period of time, it is now known to be found at points near the settlement of Algarrobito in Chile, at altitudes of 1,000–1,600 ft. This *Neoporteria* has frequently been replaced in collections and it is not easy to get hold of correctly designated plant material. Unfortunately there is a lack of seeds available from plants from an authenticated source, so we will probably long continue to cultivate plants without being certain whether they match the species description. Cultivation requirements are the same as for other *Neoporteria*. For grafting, a slow-growing rootstock, such as *Trichocereus pasacana*, is recommended. It does not grow so vigorously on this rootstock and does not distort.

Neoporteria gerocephala ▣ ○

GLOBOSE-COLUMNAR

This cactus has beautiful spines and a globose or slightly columnar stem, which is limited to 4 in tall and 2 in wide, and is covered by intertwined radial spines.
Most of these spines are white and some (2–4) are blackish. At the end of the summer, long, pinkish red, tubular flowers appear on the cactus and add to its beauty.
This species has been collected in the wild on several occasions and and its origin is the Elqui valley southwest to Vicuta and Illapel in Chile. This cactus must have sufficient sun and ventilation, which is why some growers prefer to place it outdoors in summer, with some shelter against persistent rain. It is best to grow this cactus on its own roots, because it has beautiful spines, although it does grow relatively slowly.

Neoporteria gerocephala

Neoporteria microsperma var. *serenana*

Neoporteria microsperma var. *serenana*

GLOBOSE

The stem of this species measures about 6in in diameter and slightly more in height. It has a grass green epidermis and about 20 ribs. The spines range in color from light yellowish to gray. The crimson flowers bloom near the top and grow to about 1 1/4in in length and about 3/4in across.

This varietas occurs near the Chilean town of Coquimbo on the Cerro Grande mountain, at altitudes of about 1,300ft. It was here that K. Kníže collected it under field collection number KK 1460. Cultivation is the same as for other members of the genus.

Neoporteria sociabilis 

GLOBOSE–COLUMNAR

This species is now classified within *Eriosyce*, but many cactus growers are familiar with it among the *Neoporteria*. The stem is globose initially and then becomes slightly columnar. It is usually 3–4in in diameter and about half that in height. The thick spine covering is formed of 16–20 straight radial spines, about 3/4in in length, and 7–14 central spines, up to 1 1/4in long. Both types of spines are grayish or black in color. The pinkish red flower, which often has a lighter edge to its petals, appears near the crown of the plant and is about 1 1/4in across.

In the wild this *Neoporteria* can be found over a relatively small area in northern Chile, where it grows on hillsides near Totoral Bajo. In addition to the type species, *N. sociabilis* var. *napina* is sometimes cultivated in collections. Both taxa are relatively undemanding, but the first flowers take about 10 years to appear.

Neoporteria tuberisulcata 

GLOBOSE–COLUMNAR

Like many related plants, this cactus has been classified under many genera within the family, so many cactus growers know it as *Horridocactus* or *Pyrrhocactus tuberisulcatus*. The stem is globose when young and later becomes almost columnar. The largest specimens can measure up to 8in in diameter. It has up to 20 firm ribs covered in a dark green epidermis. The elongated, woolly areoles have a maximum of 10 radial spines and 4 central spines (but usually fewer), which all point away from the stem. The flower is a fascinating reddish brown color and grows near the crown.

The coastal areas of Chile, near Valparaiso, are thought to be the best-known place where this cactus occurs. It grows here on hillocks near the ocean. It is not particularly common among cactus growers, most probably because of controversy surrounding nomenclature. It is therefore important to acquire seedlings from

Neoporteria sociabilis

verified sources. Germinating seed and cultivation are not demanding: what these cacti most need is adequate sun and ventilation during the summer, when it is best to place them outdoors with shelter against persistent rain.

Neoporteria villosa 

GLOBOSE–COLUMNAR

As the species epithet suggests (*villosa* means hairy), this cactus has fine hairs. Its columnar stem grows to a height of 6–8in and a diameter of about 3in. Adult plants usually have a reddish green epidermis. The 13–15 ribs are formed of round tubercles. The central and radial spines are difficult to differentiate and form a thick web. This web is composed of white hairs, which are soft or fine, and stiffer, black or brown spines, which are possibly central spines. According to the description, the flowers are only 3/4in long, but in collections and in the wild specimens occur with longer flowers. They are variable in color, but are usually pinkish red with a tinge of orange.

This species is found over a relatively wide area, extending north to south for dozens of miles from Rio Huasco in Chile. Today cacti on their own roots can be found in collections, but in the past they were usually only grown grafted on rootstocks such as *Eriocereus jusbertii*. The species requires full sun, good ventilation, and early coaxing from dormancy, because it flowers very early in the spring.

Neoporteria tuberisulcata

Neoporteria villosa

Opuntia miquelii

Opuntia miquelii ▣ ○

SHRUBBY

This species used to be classified as *Austrocylindropuntia*, because of the cylindric sections that make up the plant's entire stem. It grows to a height of about 3ft, and the individual sections, with their bluish epidermis, are about 2in across and up to 6in long. Spines up to 4in long grow from the oval areoles, along with a huge number of microscopic, brown glochids. The pinkish white flowers are 1 1/2in–2in across and open in the daytime in summer.

This species grows in the driest places in Chile's Atacama desert, where it often falls victim to the parasite *Phrygilanthus aphyllus* (the red stems in the photograph). This parasite has a chlorophyll-free stem, which is nourished from the stem of the cactus. It is found relatively seldom in collections, because plant material is rare and also these cacti are not considered attractive. Otherwise the same principles apply as for other members of the genus.

Trichocereus chilensis 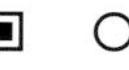

COLUMNAR

This is a relatively variable species and all manner of discussion has arisen as to its height. In the wild it forms shrubs, clustering from the base, which usually do not grow to more than 8ft in height. They are covered in spines and it was from this feature that the varietas *T. chilensis* var. *eburneus*, which has an even more striking spine covering, derived its name. The species has white flowers, with a greenish edge to their petals. These

Trichocereus chilensis

Trichocereus skottsbergii

open at night from near the top of the plant.
This species occurs in the Chilean province of Coquimbo near Las Cardas and Socos, at altitudes of 650–1,300ft. It was there that K. Kníže observed it and gave it field collection numbers KK 1423 and 1424. It is found only rarely in collections. It requires full sun and, in the summer, relatively abundant watering with occasional applications of a balanced fertilizer.

Trichocereus skottsbergii ▣ ○

SHRUBBY

This species has also been classified within *Echinopsis* in the past, with which it is possibly just distantly related. The stem clusters from the base and forms a large shrub up to 6 ft in height. The individual stems have a diameter of 5 1/2in and are covered in a gray-green epidermis. A fairly large quantity of radial spines (22–26), up to 2 1/4in long, grow from the elliptical areoles, usually with 3 central spines up to 4 3/4in long. The current season's spines are yellow-brown, later turning gray. The flower tube is covered in grayish hairs. The petals are white and the flower is up to 4 3/4in long.
This species is reported as occurring in inhospitable areas of the Chilean province of Coquimbo, where it grows near the coast between Talinay and Fray Jorge. It was there that K. Kníže collected it under field collection number KK 101. Because of the limited supply of seeds, this cactus is relatively rare in collections, despite being simple to cultivate. It is important to choose a fairly large container, or to plant the cacti directly into the greenhouse bed. After a few years these cacti are then ready to display their beautiful spines and produce their first flowers after about 15 years.

8. Minor areas

This chapter deals with the minor areas, i.e. those areas where cacti constitute only a minor element of the flora and where the number of cactus species is virtually negligible. By this, it is not meant that cacti from such countries as Paraguay, Uruguay, or Cuba are less interesting. Quite the opposite! The Galapagos Islands, for instance, are home to the extremely rare *Brachycereus nesioticus* and a number of endemic Opuntia, such as *Opuntia echios* var. *gigantea*. The minor areas are, therefore, really only those places where cacti are not found in such abundance as in the central areas of distribution. These areas are of interest because the cacti found there often constitute endemic species, such as in Cuba for instance.
The minor areas can be divided into two basic categories: firstly the tropical regions, such as Cuba, and secondly regions with very inhospitable climatic conditions, such as Patagonia or Canada. In this book Uruguay and Paraguay are included among the minor areas because there is not enough diversity in cactus species in those two countries to warrant a separate chapter.
Cacti in areas with less favorable climatic conditions are adapted to very harsh conditions and can withstand the toughest winters in cultivation. The important point is to provide them with excellent drainage. It is also advisable to provide a roof to collect and drain away most of the rain. Rain is most harmful during the very cold and damp weather at the start and, above all, at the end of winter. *Opuntia compressa*, originally the northernmost species, has been recorded on about the 57th parallel north latitude, whereas the southernmost cacti, such as *Tephrocactus darwinii* or *Maihuenia patagonica*, have been found on about the 49th parallel south latitude, at San Julian in Patagonia.
Tropical cacti in dry areas are usually adapted to extremes of heat and are very demanding to cultivate. This applies in particular to the island species of the genus *Melocactus*. Cultivation is relatively difficult, even where they can be provided with hot, dry conditions over winter. However, they have great potential as houseplants, since they are adapted to thrive in centrally heated living rooms.
"Minor areas" could, in principle, include places where cacti now occur having been introduced there by man. Cacti can now be found, as non-indigenous species on every continent on the planet (excepting Antarctica), but this book focuses primarily on cacti in their indigenous locations.

Left: *Hylocereus undatus, detail*

Cleistocactus flavispinus 

COLUMNAR

The thin, erect stems of this cactus grow to a height of 32in. In shade, they can also be arching. The spines are not striking, but this cactus does produce beautiful, zygomorphic flowers. These are crimson at the base and gradually change to orange and yellow.
The exact original location is not known. This species is found today in many places in Paraguay. It is unusual to find it in collections, but it is occasionally encountered in a few specialized botanical garden collections, often listed as *C. baumannii* var. *flavispinus*, however.

Cleistocactus flavispinus

Dendrocereus nudiflorus

Escobaria cubensis

Dendrocereus nudiflorus ■ ○

COLUMNAR

This is an unusual, and almost unique, tree-like cactus, which can grow up to 33ft tall. Shoots about 4 3/4in in diameter, formed of 3–5 prominent ribs, emerge from the trunk from 3ft above the ground. These have tiny white areoles on the edges, with 2–15 spines of various lengths growing out of them. The longest of these can reach up to 1 1/2in in length. The elegant white flowers bloom at night, opening wide to about 4 3/4in across.
This species is endemic to Cuba. Originally it grew in Cuba's southwest, from where it was introduced as a specimen plant to parks all over the island and also to other countries in the tropics. It requires hot wintering, with temperatures not below 60 °F, and a large container with a nutrient-high soil mix. Older plants take up a relatively large amount of space, and so are usually only encountered as feature plants in certain botanical gardens.

Escobaria cubensis ■ ○

GLOBOSE

This species, like most members of the genus, comes under miniature cacti. The individual stems usually grow to a maximum diameter of 1 1/4in, cluster slightly, and form small clumps. The stem consists of cylindrical mammillae. Each of these has an areole with about 10 radial spines growing out of it. It has pale yellow flowers, which bloom in the summer and are about 3/4in long.
This is a very rare endemic cactus, which only grows in the southwest regions of Cuba. It is only rarely found in collections. It is not particularly demanding to cultivate, but it requires winter temperatures above 60 °F.

Frailea asteroides

GLOBOSE

This rare species is a real midget among cacti and is always in high demand. The stem does not usually grow more than 1 1/4in in diameter and is made up of 10–15 indistinct ribs. There are a number of areoles in the middle of the ribs, with about 8 short, brown-black spines growing out of each one. The greenish brown epidermis, which changes color significantly in direct sunlight, is also of interest. The flower only opens on sunny days, and is often wider than the stem. The flowers can often change into fruit without opening: they pollinate and fertilize themselves with their own pollen at the bud stage (cleistogamy). *F. asteroides* is found in Uruguay and also in Brazil, where it extends to the state of Rio Grande do Sul. It is definitely not a species to be recommended to beginners and is probably one of the most problematic within the genus. Some growers recommend grafting it onto *Selenicereus* or *Eriocereus*, on which it grows and flowers well, but grafted plants grow larger than they would on their own roots. It requires full sun, good ventilation, and watering only once the soil mix has completely dried out. It is best to overwinter this species at the fairly high temperatures of 54–60 °F.

Gymnocalycium megalothelos ▣ ⊙

GLOBOSE

The species epithet *megalothelos* is somewhat misleading, because it translates as "with large mammillae." In the case of *Gymnocalycium*, however, the stem is formed of ribs, which can look a little like mammillae. This species grows to about 6 1/2in in diameter and usually a maximum of 5 1/2in tall. The radial spines are arranged in the form of rays, mostly flattened against the stem or sticking out a little. Usually there is no central spine. The flower blooms in late spring and the inner petals are white or pinkish. The yellow fruit, which splits lengthwise, is also of interest.
The type loction of this species is given very generally as Paraguay. In collections, however, this is a relatively well-known and widespread cactus, above all among specialists in this genus. Cultivation is not difficult: these cacti respond best in partial shade and tolerate low light levels in winter (with low temperatures of about 50 °F).

Frailea asteroides

Gymnocalycium megalothelos

Gymnocalycium mihanovichii ▣ ⊙

GLOBOSE

This is one of the most interesting *Gymnocalycium* and it has become extremely popular among amateurs and specialists. Its globose stem can grow up to 2 1/4in in diameter and has a delightfully colored epidermis, which can be green-red to green-brown. Lighter colored bands usually stretch across the areoles. There are generally 8 ribs with areoles on the edges. 4–6 radial spines grow from the areoles. The yellow-green flowers reach 1 2/3in in length and the buds are shielded by pinkish green scales.
This species was rediscovered in Paraguay, not far from Bahia Negra, where it grows in colonies of grasses and other xerophytes. As already mentioned, it spread among collectors because of its great variability and diversity in coloring. Cultivation is also extremely simple: all that is needed for abundant flowering every year is to provide the plant with a location in the shade, a slightly acidic soil mix with added peat, and cold wintering. Propagation is by seed and the seedlings usually flower after three years.

Gymnocalycium mihanovichii var. *stenogonum* ▣ ○

GLOBOSE-COLUMNAR

This varietas is very similar to the type species and there are some experts who doubt whether it should be distinguished. The plants are more robust, however, the ribs have sharp-edged tubercles, and the horizontal bands are narrower in comparison with the type. The flower is white or greenish white and also larger than is the case for the type. Mature specimens can have flowers up to 3in long. This varietas also originates from Paraguay, where it grows at Toro Alarachi. Cultivation is the same as for other undemanding *Gymnocalycium*. It is essential that this cactus has a degree of shade, because it responds badly to full sun. This applies in particular to young seedlings, which can easily overheat and rot as a result of the neck being scalded.

Gymnocalycium mihanovichii var. *stenogonum*

Gymnocalycium mihanovichii

Gymnocalycium netrelianum ▣ ⊙

FLATTENED-GLOBOSE

The stem is depressed, but becomes more globose as it ages. It usually does not grow to more than 3in in diameter and forms quite a few clusters later on. The dark green stem is made up of 14 ribs with prominent tubercles. 5–7 radial spines grow out of the areoles, only 1/4–5/8in long. The beautiful, large yellow flower can be up to 2in across when fully open.
The author of the original description of this plant did not publish the location, but from recent observations by travelers, it grows in many localities across Uruguay. Cultivation is not difficult. Both seed and offsets, which root on the parent plant, can be used for propagation. This species requires a soil mix with added peat and a certain amount of shade. It prefers lower summer temperatures to an overheated greenhouse. It should be overwintered in cool conditions and tolerates low light levels.

Gymnocalycium netrelianum

Mammillaria columbiana

Gymnocalycium uruguayense var. *roseiflorum* ▣ ⊙

FLATTENED-GLOBOSE

The barrel-shaped stem of this cactus reaches 3– 4in across and is formed of 12 flat ribs. 3–7 flattened radial spines grow out of the oval areoles. This varietas differs from the type species because, as its name suggests, it has a pink flower.
Specimens with pure white flowers are encountered in places where this pink-flowering form grows, and so doubt exist as to whether this really is a bona fide varietas. It grows in a different locality, however, to the type. Paso de los Toros in Uruguay, Paso Rial or 25 miles to the south of the town of Artigas. This *Gymnocalycium* also prefers partial shade to full sunlight. Germinating seed is not difficult and the plants mature after 5–7 years. A combination of soil, peat, and sand is a suitable soil mix.

Gymnocalycium uruguayense var. *roseiflorum*

Mammillaria columbiana ■ ○

COLUMNAR

This columnar species, which forms solitary stems about 6in tall and 2–2 1/4in diameter, belongs to the *Mammillaria* genus. This columnar species forms solitary stems about 6 in tall and 2-2 in in diameter. A large quantity of white wool forms in the axils with crimson flowers, and 18-20 radial spines, glossy white and 1/5-1/3 in long, grow from the densely woolly areoles on the tips of the mammillae. 4-5 yellow central spines point away from the stem, growing from the areoles to a maximum length of 1/3 in The orange-red fruit contains brown seed.
This is one of the few *Mammillaria* which comes from the northern regions of Southern America but is not found in Mexico or the USA. It grows not only in Columbia, as the species epithet suggests, but also in Venezuela. It has been collected here in the past by a number of cactus experts and can be found today in collections under field collection number Rep 2227 or Rep 2230. In cultivation this *Mammillaria* requires warm wintering and should be placed in full sun. These cacti stop growing in the summer and watering should be limited then to avoid rotting. Propagation is by seed, which germinate freely when fresh.

Mammillaria nivosa

Mammillaria nivosa ■ ○

COLUMNAR

This cactus clearly derives its species epithet *nivosa* (meaning snow white in Latin) from the white hair that forms in the axils and areoles on the crown of the plant. It is usually solitary initially and only clusters from the base on maturity. The cylindrical stem, which can be up to 4in tall, has a dark green epidermis and consists of tubercles about 5/8in long. Straw yellow or brownish central and radial spines grow out of the areoles. The yellowish flowers, which are 3/4in long, have trouble pushing through the thick wool. The main feature of this cactus, however, is its club-shaped, scarlet fruit, which it produces from the axils about a year after pollination and fertilization.

This is one of the few species to have settled in the very dry places on the tropical belt in the Bahamas and the Little Antilles. It grows primarily on rocky outcrops near the ocean and, despite the temperatures in its original habitat, which never fall below 68 °F for long, does not have specific requirements in cultivation. The winter temperature should be somewhere between 54 °F and 60 °F, but it is not too adversely affected if temperatures fall below 50 °F for a short time. It flourishes well on its own roots, but the soil mix should be slightly alkaline. These cacti should not be misted or watered from overhead, because they then lose their most beautiful feature: the white wool in the axils.

Melocactus acunai ■ ○

GLOBOSE

As it gets older, this cactus starts to become columnar (up to 1ft tall and about 4in in diameter). It produces striking, beautiful spines. The longest of these, which can reach up to 2in long, are woody and very firm. The cephalium takes many years to grow. The dark red flowers are minute and only grow to about 5/8in across. The fruit is a red, club-shaped berry.

Melocactus acunai

Melocactus caesius

Melocactus communis

This species is a typical island endemic cactus. It originates from Cuba, where it grows in the coastal regions. From the point of view of cultivation, all coastal *Melocactus* are very demanding plants. They clearly dislike a long winter period at low light levels. Be sure to overwinter them in the sunniest spot possible and do not allow the temperature to fall below 60 °F. The soil mix should be free-draining with added minerals.

Melocactus caesius ■ ○

GLOBOSE

The solitary stem of this cactus grows to about 8in in height and almost the same in diameter. It is eye-catching because of its bluish epidermis. There are usually 10–15 prominent ribs with depressed areoles on the edges, from which 6 radial spines and 1 central spine grow. All of these are about the same length (3/4–1 1/4in). The terminal cephalium is covered in wool and bristle-like spines. During the summer violet-red flowers, up to 3/4in across, emerge from this cephalium. The fruit is a red berry containing a relatively small quantity of seed.

This is one of the few species of cactus to come from Venezuela, but it also grows on the island of Trinidad in the Caribbean, not far from the coast of Venezuela. Like all *Melocactus* it needs very warm wintering, ideally in good light. The temperature should not be allowed to fall below 61 °F for long. Seedlings grow relatively well on their own roots, but older plants can be problematic. They tend to lose their roots easily and it takes a number of months or even years for these to regenerate. If you choose to graft this species, the best rootstock is *Myrtillocactus geometrizans*.

Melocactus communis ■ ○

COLUMNAR

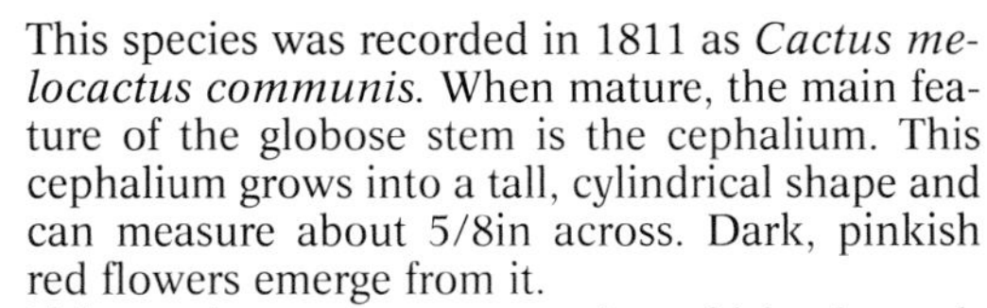

This species was recorded in 1811 as *Cactus melocactus communis*. When mature, the main feature of the globose stem is the cephalium. This cephalium grows into a tall, cylindrical shape and can measure about 5/8in across. Dark, pinkish red flowers emerge from it.

This species grows on a number of islands, such as Jamaica, the small islands off Guadeloupe, and the Southern Bahamas generally. It is relatively abundant in collections and has the same requirements as the most demanding members of the genus.

Melocactus guitarti ■ ○

GLOBOSE

This species has a solitary, globose stem which can grow to up to 6in in diameter. The radial spines are firm and woody. It has 2 central spines which stick out from the cactus and point upward. The cephalium is 1 1/2in high and up to 2 3/4in across. The flowers are the largest in the genus and can be up to 1 1/2in long.

Today this species is a very rare endemic cactus in central regions of Cuba. Its area of distribution is limited to just a few hills in the Sierra de Jatibonico. Experts are of the opinion that this is the most endangered cactus in the world. Because seed from imported cacti have been available for a few decades, there is enough plant material available. Cultivation of this species is problematic, however, and so it is a good idea to graft the seedlings onto a slow-growing rootstock.

Melocactus guitarti

Melocactus harlowii ■ ○

COLUMNAR

The stem of this species grows into a virtually columnar form and up to 10in tall. When adult it usually measures 6in in diameter. It is generally formed of 12 prominent ribs, a great proportion of which are hidden beneath spines, however. Pinkish red flowers about 3/4in across grow from the gray-brown cephalium.

This species is also endemic to Cuba, where it grows in the province of Oriente in the east of the island, near the ocean. It is a rare *Melocactus* in collections because of the demands it poses. Warmth and good light in winter are the basic requirements for success. Propagation is exclusively by seed. Although the plant illustrated appears to have produced an offset at the crown of the plant (at the base of the cephalium), which could be used for propagation, this is very unusual for *Melocactus*.

Melocactus maxonii ■ ○

GLOBOSE

The barrel-shaped stem of this cactus grows to a maximum diameter of about 6in and is made up of 11–15 prominent ribs. The upper 2 of the 7–10 radial spines, which grow out of the densely woolly areoles, are usually very small and thin. There is 1 central spine as a rule, occasionally 2. Bright

Melocactus maxonii

red flowers with a whitish sparkle grow from the cephalium, which is short and wide and formed of white hairs, wool, and short bristles. The red fruit is bluntly cylindrical and bears the remains of the dried out perianth.

This cactus hails from Central America, where it can be found in the extensive woods of Guatemala, not far from El Rancho and Salama. This species is relatively rare in collections, primarily because older specimens tend to die for some unknown reason. Seedlings grow strongly and quickly, but tend to lose their roots easily and succumb to rot after about 10 years, once they have become fairly large. Cultivation is as for all other *Melocactus.*

Notocactus apricus ▣ ○

GLOBOSE

As it ages this species starts to cluster. The individual stems are about 2in in diameter. There are up to 20 ribs, formed of small tubercles. The spine covering is fairly variable, but the spines are relatively fine and flexible. The flowers are large in comparison with the stem and can be up to 3in

Notocactus apricus

Notocactus bezrucii

long and 2in across. Like most members of the genus, *N. apricus* also has a yellow flower with a blood red stigma.

This Uruguayan cactus grows at fairly low altitudes of about 1,600ft. It has been collected in the wild by a number of cactus experts, including K. Kníže, who gave its type location as near Treinta Tres and allocated his specimens field collection number KK 159. Like a number of *Notocactus*, cactus growers with little experience can cope with this species, because it can put up with a number of errors in cultivation without any problem. The flowers produce quantities of viable seed; seedlings are easy to germinate and grow on, and flower after just 3–4 years. Low light levels at temperatures of about 50 °F are tolerated in winter.

Notocactus bezrucii ▣ ○ ⊙

FLATTENEDGLOBOSE

This was originally classified by A. V. Frič as *Malacocarpus bezrucii,* but today it is included within *Notocactus*. Some experts doubt whether it should be a separate species. The barrel-shaped stem features firm spines, which are assembled in 3s horizontally or pointing downward. Occasionally 2 more small, delicate spines emerge from each areole, pointing upward. Usually these are thin and hardly noticeable. This cactus produces a yellow flower, about 1 1/2in across, with a characteristic red stigma.

As A. V. Frič said in his description, these cacti can grow to huge sizes in the wild, up to 2ft across, but tend to be flattened. The species grows among grass and under scrub vegetation. It has been reported to be found in both Uruguay and southern Brazil. Cultivation is relatively simple and these cacti can be propagated easily by seed, which germinates freely. Larger specimens can withstand full sun, but smaller ones are best in partial shade. Overwinter in cool conditions in good light.

Notocactus corynodes 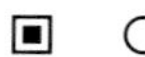

FLATTENED-GLOBOSE

The barrel-shaped stem of this cactus, which can be up to 6in across, is formed of about 16 prominent ribs. There are huge differences in the number of spines: young plants can have up to 10 growing out of each areole, whereas on older specimens the number falls to 4 or 5. Sulfur yellow flowers with a red stigma sprout from the crown, which is covered in white wool. These flowers have 10 lobes, 1 1/2–2in wide.
In the original description, the type location was given as Montevideo in Mexico. Other authorities perpetrated this error, but the species actually occurs in the grasslands of Uruguay. It has been cultivated relatively little in collections, despite the fact that it is a beautiful and undemanding cactus. Its flowers bloom over the whole summer and into early fall, when other cacti do not usually flower.

Notocactus floricomus 

GLOBOSE

This is an extremely variable species in terms of spination. A huge number of forms have been recorded, which have lost a little of their value under the present system of botanical classification. This species boasts about 20 ribs, formed of conical tubercles. The radial spines are hard and needle-shaped. There are usually up to 5 central spines, 1 of which can reach a length of 1in. It produces a large, yellow flower with a red stigma in the summer.
This cactus originates from Uruguay, where it grows in grass colonies in meadows near the towns of Rivera and Tacuarembo. This is another species that is suitable for beginners, because it can withstand minor errors in cultivation. It needs cold wintering in goodlight for abundant flowering. It is best to use a free-draining soil mix with added peat for successful cultivation.

Notocactus corynodes

Notocactus floricomus

Notocactus grossei  

COLUMNAR

The columnar stem of this species can reach a height of almost 6ft and a diameter of 1ft in the wild. It does not usually grow as big as this in collections. It is made up of 16–25 ribs and the crown is covered in white wool. There are usually 4 or 5 yellowish brown spines, which are soft and stick out a little. The finest of these spines can be as translucent as glass. When fully open, the bright golden yellow flower can be about 1 1/3in long and up to 1 1/2in across.
Emil Kuntz, who discovered this cactus, gave the type location as the province of Misiones in Paraguay. Unfortunately it appears that these plants cannot be found there any longer. The last field research gave the location for this species as between Carepegua and Acahay. It is a great ornament to collections, but it is not easy to distinguish from its close relation *N. schumannianus.* Only with older plants is a reliable distinction possible, because *N. schumannianus* has more ribs, its spines are finer, and there are usually more of them. Cultivation is easy: once germinated, seedlings are slow to put on growth, because they are absolutely minute, but after about a year they grow more strongly. Beware of allowing the sun to scorch the seedlings. This species requires a slightly acid, free-draining soil mix, and it prefers dappled shade to full sun.

Notocactus grossei

Notocactus macambarensis

Notocactus macambarensis  ○

GLOBOSE

At first sight this species is very similar to *N. mammulosus*. In fact the only difference is that all its spines are very firm, needle-shaped, and prickly. This is particularly marked on the crown of the plant. Another distinguishing feature is that it has cylindrical fruit. The flowers, seed, and whole structure of the stem are really very similar to *N. mammulosus.* According to the author of the description, K. H. Prestlé, *N. macambarensis* is found in the Uruguayan province of Salto, near Cuchilla del Salto, on raised, granite ground and in pastures of about 1,000 square yards in area. Cultivation is simple and even beginners can grow them from seed. Cultivation is as for other members of the genus.

Notocactus mammulosus  ○

GLOBOSE-COLUMNAR

This species is usually globose, and only when older does it extend into a columnar shape, about 4in high and 2 1/4in in diameter. The areoles formed in the ribs are egg-shaped and slightly woolly. They have 10–13 radial spines growing out of them and 3 central spines, which are stronger and longer than the radials. The flowers can be up to 2 1/4in across when fully open. When ripe, the fruit is elongated and partly concave. The seeds are brownish black and bell-shaped.
There is a certain amount of divergence as to where the species grows. One thing that is certain, however, is that it grows in Uruguay. Lemaire, the author of the description, said that the plants on which he based it (known as *Echinocactus mammulosus)* came from near the capital city, Montevideo. However, later reports about its place of occurrence state that it grows on the southern coast of Uruguay, near Piriápolis and Maldonado. F. Ritter even claims that he found this taxon in southern Brazil. It favors grass colonies on hills in the pampas and Kníže found it near Valentin (Uruguay) at an altitude of 2,000–2,600ft (KK 121). The species is very popular among cactus growers and it is a cactus that even beginners can cultivate successfully. An abundance of beautiful flowers is guaranteed as long as you make sure to provide the cactus with sufficient water, a slightly acidic soil mix, and cool winter temperatures.

Notocactus mammulosus

Notocactus roseoluteus

Notocactus roseoluteus 

GLOBOSE

This cactus is solitary and its stem can reach up to 7 1/4in in in diameter. It usually has 15–18 ribs, formed of prominent tubercles. The areoles are positioned below the tubercles and have about 8 radial spines and a maximum of 4 central spines growing out of them. The longest central spines can reach a length of 1 1/4in. The pink and yellow flower, which opens up to 3in across, gives this cactus its species epithet – *roseoluteus*. The plant in the photograph has slightly darker flowers than normal, but variation in color is common on the whole.
The type locality of the species is given as Tanqueras in the Uruguayan province of Rivera, where it grows on hilly terrain at an altitude of about 1,000ft. Its area of distribution extends, however, to the southern regions of the neighboring Brazilian state of Rio Grande do Sul. Propagation, which is not particularly difficult, is by sowing the helmet-shaped seeds, which germinate very well when fresh. The species is self-pollinating, so there are no problems with availability of seed. It is not particularly demanding in terms of soil mix and favors a fairly nutrient-high medium. Wintering should be in cool conditions and when in active growth it needs to be placed in full sun and watered freely. It takes 8–10 years to reach flowering size.

Notocactus schumannianus

Notocactus schumannianus 

COLUMNAR

The columnar stem of this cactus can grow to a height of about 6ft in the wild and a diameter of about 1ft. In collections, however, it does not usually grow as big as this. It consists of about 45 ribs and the crown is covered in white wool. There are usually 6–8 yellowish brown spines which are soft and protruding. The finest of these spines are as translucent as glass. The bright golden yellow flower is about 1 1/3in long when fully open and up to 2 1/4in across.
Emil Kuntz, who discovered this cactus, gave the type location as the province of Misiones in Paraguay. Unfortunately it appears that these plants cannot be found there any longer. It is a very attractive feature in collections, but it is not particularly easy to differentiate between this cactus and its close relative *N. grossei*. Only on older plants is it possible to make a reliable distinction, because *N. grossei* has fewer ribs, its spines are firmer, and there are usually fewer of them. Cultivation is easy: once germinated, seedlings make slow progress initially, because they are absolutely

Notocactus scopa

minute, but after about a year growth is more vigorous. Beware of allowing the sun to scorch the seedlings. This species requires a slightly acid, free-draining soil mix, and it prefers dappled shade to full sun.

Notocactus scopa 

COLUMNAR

This diverse and variable taxon covers a vast area. There have been disputes not only among experts in the *Notocactus* genus but among taxonomists in general about the validity of the variants that have been recorded for this cactus. The almost columnar stem of this species usually grows to about 12in tall, but it is also possible to come across plants that are nearly 20in tall and have a stem diameter of about 4in. There are usually about 40 radial spines and 3 or 4 central spines. The flowers grow from the youngest areoles on the crown and are a unique lemon yellow color with a scarlet stigma.
The center of distribution for this species is Uruguay, where it grows from the southern coast right the way to the Brazilian state of Rio Grande do Sul. It can be found on rocky outcrops and among clumps of grass at fairly low altitudes. The various conditions in which this cactus grows in the wild predetermine its cultivation requirements in collections, which is why it is best to know the source of the seeds or the seedlings for this species as well. Few cactus growers know where their plants come from, however. A number of collectors brought a large quantity of seed, or plants, into cultivation a long time ago, and these are still in circulation (FR 1393a, KK 591, HU 291, and many more). Cultivation of this species is not particularly demanding.

Notocactus sellowii 

FLATTENED-GLOBOSE

The barrel-shaped to globose stem of this species grows to a diameter of up to 7 1/4in and is formed of 10–18 prominent ribs. There are large areoles on

Notocactus sellowii

Opuntia dillenii

the edges of these ribs, which are covered in dense, white wool. The spines usually grow in bundles of 10 or so. The upper radial spines are short and barely protrude from the wool around the areoles. The 3 lower ones are up to 1in long and flattened against the stem. The lemon yellow flower, which usually measures up to 2in across, blooms in the summer.
This cactus grows practically throughout Uruguay and even spreads into the south of the Brazilian state of Rio Grande do Sul. Two important requirements for successful growth and development of this plant are a position in light shade and a slightly acid soil mix. Stocks can be increased by sowing the bell-shaped seed. Old specimens become corky at the base, a phenomenon which also occurs in the wild.

Opuntia dillenii 

SHRUBBY

This short, freely clustering cactus grows up to 10 ft, and can form a large, stout trunk. The individual segments are oval, up to 16in long and 4in across, and a bright luminous green. The number of spines growing from each areole is variable, but there are no more than 10 as a rule. The glochids are very fine and hook backward. These unique cacti have lemon yellow or reddish flowers, and the ripe fruits are red with many tiny glochids.
Today it is fairly difficult to plot where this Opuntia originates, because it grows on the east coast of the USA, in Bermuda, and in Cuba as well. It can also be found growing in the wild in southern India and even in Australia, where it was introduced. It is not found too often in collections because of its size, but it is unusually easy to cultivate. Detached segments will root reliably and this species is tolerant of a certain amount of neglect in cultivation. Unfortunately it takes many years for these cacti to flower in cool climates.

Opuntia rubescens

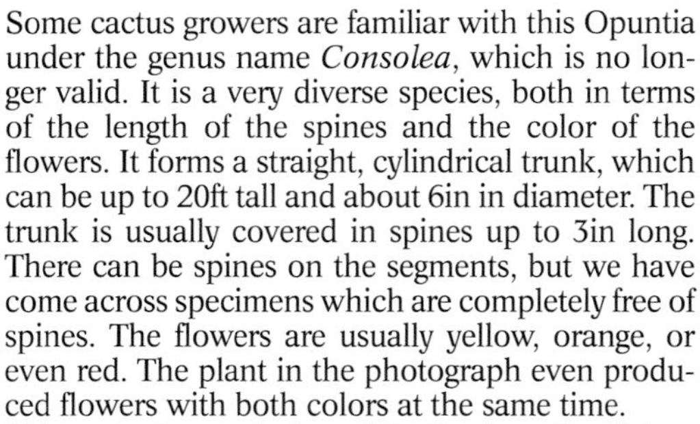

Opuntia rubescens ■ ○

SHRUBBY

Some cactus growers are familiar with this Opuntia under the genus name *Consolea*, which is no longer valid. It is a very diverse species, both in terms of the length of the spines and the color of the flowers. It forms a straight, cylindrical trunk, which can be up to 20ft tall and about 6in in diameter. The trunk is usually covered in spines up to 3in long. There can be spines on the segments, but we have come across specimens which are completely free of spines. The flowers are usually yellow, orange, or even red. The plant in the photograph even produced flowers with both colors at the same time.

This cactus is recorded as originating from Brazil, but, as some authorities have noticed, this is actually a mistake. *O. rubescens* comes from the dry southwestern regions of the island of Puerto Rico, the Virgin Islands, and parts of the Little Antilles, from Martinique to Guadeloupe. Today, however, it is cultivated in many parks and gardens in the tropics as a beautiful specimen. This particular Opuntia is found in collections and it can also be encountered in certain botanical gardens. It requires fairly warm wintering, with temperatures not allowed to fall below 60 °F for long.

Selenicereus grandiflorus

Selenicereus urbanianus

Selenicereus grandiflorus ▣ ○

SCANDENT

This is a kind of climber, the stems of which scramble up tree trunks or any other form of support toward the sun. They are usually only about 1 1/4in across and several feet long. The needle-shaped spines are 1/5–1/2in long and not particularly prominent. While waiting for the wonderful flowers produced by this species, notice how the bud starts to emerge from an areole, covered in fine hairs. It later develops into a fruit, about 8in in diameter. The flower opens at night, the reason for the common name "queen of the night." The exact type locality of the species is not known, but it is safe to say that it originates from Jamaica and Cuba and perhaps also from the lowlands in eastern Mexico. It has now become naturalized in many tropical and subtropical countries, where it is grown in gardens and parks for the beauty of its flowers. Some cactus growers propagate it in quantity from stem cuttings. It is rare that *S. grandiflorus* achieves its full potential in cultivation, since it requires plenty of room but is normally grown in small pots.

Selenicereus urbanianus

SCANDENT

The stem of this scandent climber has evolved to scramble up tree trunks, can be several feet long and 1 1/2 - 2 in wide, with aerial roots. The spine covering is not at all striking, but the flowers are fascinating, reaching 12 in in width and length. The yellow outer petals spread out radially around the flower when it opens, while the creamy white inner petals form a sort of narrow tube. *S. urbanianus* originally only grew on Cuba and Haiti, but was exported to many countries, bringing beaty to parks and gardens. In cool climates, it is most often seen in collections. Because plants belonging to this genus are so vigorous, they present problems to growers with limited space available in their greenhouses.Propagation by stem cuttings is extremely simple, because the aerial roots start to function as normal ground roots immediately after planting and provide the plant with water and nutrients.

9. Cultivated hybrids and specialist varieties

The contents of this chapter include both those cacti produced through the efforts of cactus growers and gardeners and mutations that occur spontaneously in the wild and in collections and are then propagated by cactus growers.
Hybrids have recently become the focus of interest and certain genera in particular have attracted considerable interest from commercial growers. *Schlumbergera* in particular has produced a series of interesting cultivars ("cultivated varieties") that brighten up the market with their flowers. The interspecific x *Epicactus* hybrids are equally popular.
With regard to intentional hybrids, cacti are something of a unique group since most growers try to have the "purest" species in their collections. The hybrids within *Astrophytum, Echinopsis, Lobivia,* and *Chamaecereus* are perhaps exceptions to this rule. Collections specializing in the most diverse hybrids do exist, although the number of these is negligible in comparison with other collections.
Sometimes a few, unique, spontaneous mutations emerge in a collection which are then used as the basis for further cultivation and find their way into commerce, as was the case with *Gymnocalycium denudatum* 'Jan Šuba' for instance.
The selectively bred *Astrophytum* mutations, primarily created by Japanese growers, and colorful mutations without the green chlorophyll pigment constitute a fairly unique group. The latter are mostly forms of *Gymnocalycium mihanovichii* which come in red, dark violet, orange, or various combinations of colors. Chlorophyll-free mutations of *Mammillaria* and *Lobivia* species also exist. If a plant loses the ability to create chlorophyll through the effect of mutation, it cannot survive. In collections such a plant has to be maintained grafted onto a rootstock that provides it with its sustenance.
Cristate cacti constitute a completely unique and separate group. These sometimes occur spontaneously in the wild, and there is actually nothing you can do to prevent the dividing tissue (meristem) from starting to create a cristate formation (from the Latin *cristatus* meaning crested) instead of a normally structured stem. It is actually quite rare to find a cristate cactus in the wild, but in cultivation such mutations are often propagated in their thousands. Recently commercial nurseries have started cultivation of the cristate form of *Mammillaria elongata*, which is very easy to propagate by cuttings or removal of the offets. Rarer cristate cacti are usually propagated by grafting sections cut from the parent.

Left: *Chamaecereus* hybrid

Ariocarpus retusus 'Cristata' ▣ ○

CRISTATE

There is no point providing any recommendations for the cultivation or propagation of this mutation, because there is probably only one cristate form of this species and size in the world. This is, without a doubt, a remarkable freak of nature.
We found this cristate form near the town of Matehuala, a good hunting ground for cactus lovers. It is impossible to hazard the age of this extraordinary cactus and its discovery caused a real sensation among cactus enthusiasts. Growers are familiar with a number of naturally occurring cristate forms of *Ariocarpus* and their whereabouts have become places of pilgrimage for various expeditions. Everyone wants to have their photograph taken next to one, or leave messages and greetings there. This specimen warrants a

Ariocarpus retusus 'Cristata'

Astrophytum „Marakuro – Kabuto“

place in the Guinness Book of Records, because the crest is about 4ft long.

Astrophytum Marakuro-Kabuto' ▣ ○

FLATTENED-GLOBOSE

Japanese cactus growers specialize in mutations and Astrophytum is a genus they have focused on. This hybrid was selectively bred from the original species *Astrophytum asterias*.

Cereus peruvianus 'Monstrosus'

Cereus peruvianus 'Monstrosus' ▣ ○

COLUMNAR

This is a unique mutation which appeared in cultivation showing malformation of the stems. The individual ribs split and form irregular tubercles. The species can be easily propagated from cuttings or by detaching offsets, which take root easily, from mature plants. Obviously this monstrous form does not produce flowers.

Cereus peruvianus 'Spiralis' ▣ ○

COLUMNAR

This is a unique mutation. What should be straight ribs spiral up the stem. The mutation appeared in cutivation and stocks were increased by vegetative propagation. Ample room in the greenhouse and a large container are needed if this form is to display its unconventional beauty to the full.

Cereus peruvianus 'Spiralis'

Echinocactus grusonii 'Monstrosus'

Echinocactus grusonii 'Monstrosus' ▣ ○

GLOBOSE

At first sight this cactus does not appear to have anything in common with the golden-spined barrel that is seen so often in collections and botanical gardens. This monstrous form does not grow as large and forms woolly, almost smooth areoles. Tiny offsets grow from these, which are relatively easy to detach and graft. Because this form produces chlorophyll normally, the offsets can be rooted and grown on on their own roots. This relatively recent mutation will surely soon spread into all collections belonging to growers with a taste for the unusual.

Echinopsis arachnacantha var. *torrecillasensis* ▣ ○

GLOBOSE

This cactus is closely related to the type species, the only differences being its slightly larger stem and, primarily, its large crimson flower, which can be up to 2 1/4in long and about 2in across.
There is no exact knowledge of where this cactus occurs in the wild and it looks as though it first appeared in cultivation, although some authorities give its place of occurrence as near the town of Torrecilla in Bolivia. It had some currency under the name *Pseudolobivia torrecillasensis*, and later as *Lobivia arachnacantha* var. *torrecillasensis*, but clearly the classification preferred here is the correct one. Most cactus growers are probably familiar with the species and the varietas under this name. Propagation and cultivation are as simple as for the type species. Because it has such beautiful flowers, this cactus can be recommended to all budding cactus growers who want to start off their collection successfully.

Echinopsis arachnacantha var. *torrecillasensis*

x *Epicactus 'Little Star'* ▣ 

TRAILING

The whole of this group of "leafy" cacti boast unique colors and diverse flower sizes. This hybrid was first produced by crossbreeding in the USA in the 1950s. It has a violet-red flower, which can measure up to 6in across when fully open, a greenish throat, and white reproductive organs. The flowers appear in spring and the plant carries on blooming throughout the summer. Like other members of this genus, it requires a little shade and can be placed outdoors over summer. Wintering should be at temperatures of around 54 °F.

x Epicactus 'Little Star'

x *Epicactus 'Phosper'* ▣ ⊙ ◐

TRAILING

This hybrid was created in 1936 in the USA. It is distinctive in having about 15 wide flowers, consisting of golden yellow outer petals and pure white inner petals. These appear on the flattened stems from spring and bloom throughout the summer.
For successful cultivation this cactus needs a slightly shaded spot, a sufficiently large container, and a nutrient-high soil mix. Like other "leafy" cacti, around three applications of a balanced fertilizer should be given at regular intervals during the growing season. Alternatively, when repotting add a slow-release fertilizer to the soil mix, which will provide the cactus with nutrients over the whole season.

Epithelantha micromeris 'Cristata' ▣ ○

CRISTATE

Cristate forms of this species occur relatively often. These mutations are also found in collections and are particularly widespread because of the ease with which they can be propagated.
Divide a fairly large crest into sections and then graft these onto a suitable rootstock, such as *Myrtillocactus geometrizans* or *Trichocereus pasacana*, in late spring or early summer. These have a dwarfing effect and the cactus stays more compact.

x Epicactus 'Phosper'

Espostoa mirabilis 'Cristata' ▣ ○

CRISTATE

The appearance of this giant cristate form in the wild clearly shows that cacti can also exhibit abnormalities in their natural environment. There are a limited number of these specimens, however, because the mutation is not transmitted genetically. Some cristate forms do not even flower, because the cristate growth does not form a flower-bearing cephalium.

Gymnocalycium denudatum 'Jan Šuba' ▣ ⊙

GLOBOSE–COLUMNAR

This is one of the few hybrids (apart from the "leafy" cacti) which have been cultivated in collections for many years. It first appeared in 1942 in a collection belonging to Mr. F. Pažout as a hybrid of *G. denudatum* and *G. baldianum*. It was later named in honor of the Czech cactus expert Jan Šuba. The barrel-shaped stem grows to a diameter of up to 4 3/4in and, in terms of spines and shape, it is closer to *G. denudatum*. However, the flower is large, funnel-shaped, and opens up to 2 3/4in across, while the petals can vary from pink to red in color.
This cactus has proved popular in collections because it is completely undemanding. The situation has changed slightly recently and, for some reason, this established cultivar is starting to disappear from collections. Because of its ability to self-pollinate, however, it is unlikely to drop out of cultivation altogether. Make sure, however, that it does not hybridize with other members of the genus or back-cross with one of its parents.

Epithelantha micromeris 'Cristata'

Espostoa mirabilis f. *cristata*

Gymnocalycium denudatum 'Jan Šuba'

Gymnocalycium mihanovichii *'Hibotan'*

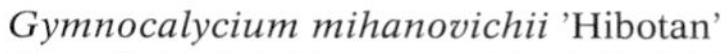

GLOBOSE

This special mutation does not produce the green chlorophyll common to all plants, which is why it cannot be grown on its own roots, but only as a graft on a suitable rootstock. Red specimens are the most popular, but yellow-orange and dark red forms also occur. Recently patchwork mutations have appeared as well.

This cactus is produced in huge numbers in nurseries, above all in South Korea, from where it is exported. In view of the fact that these plants are usually grafted onto xerophytic rootstocks of *Hylocereus*, experienced cactus growers would be advised to regraft onto *Myrtillocactus geometrizans*. The reason is because *Hylocereus* is adapted to hot, dry conditions and does not respond well to cold wintering. The best way to propagate is by grafting offsets about 1/2in long, which it produces in abundance. Because these plants are short-lived, it is best always to have young replacement plants at the ready.

Gymnocalycium mihanovichii 'Hibotan'

Gymnocalycium ragonesei f. *roseiflorum*

Gymnocalycium ragonesi f. *roseiflorum* ▣ ○

FLATTENED-GLOBOSE

This colorful mutation appeared spontaneously among seedlings of the white-flowered *G. ragonesi* in the collection belonging to the Czech grower M. Zubra. Its progeny then spread into collections. It is interesting because the flower tube and petals (the outer petals above all) are a striking pink color. Cultivation is as for the type species. The name is as yet provisional, because no classification has yet been agreed for this pink-flowering variant.

Hildewintera aureispina 'Cristata'

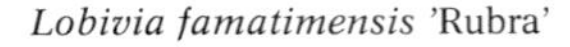

Lobivia famatimensis 'Rubra'

Hildewintera aureispina 'Cristata' ▣ ○

CRISTATE

Here the trailing stem of the type species has mutated into a cristate formation, which creates fairly large and elegant crests with golden spines. It is usually increased commercially by cuttings, butto emphasize its beauty it can also be grafted onto a strong, tall rootstock. Unfortunately, cristate cacti do not usually flower.

Lobivia famatimensis 'Rubra' ■ ⊙

COLUMNAR

The photograph shows an artificially cultivated mutant which has no chlorophyll. Like other plants with no chlorophyll, this can only be maintained on a rootstock to provide essential nutrients. Any durable rootstock is suitable for this, but experience has shown that it probably grows best on *Eriocereus jusbertii* and *Myrtillocactus geometrizans*. Offsets of about 1/2in in size can be grafted.

Lobivia pectinata

Lophocereus schottii 'Monstrosus'

Lobivia pectinata ▣ ○

COLUMNAR

Classification and identification of the plant in the photograph is relatively complicated. This specimen originates from the collection of F. Pažout. The parent plant of the cactus illustrated came from the collection belonging to A. V. Frič. It is perfectly possible that this is a hybrid of unknown origin, but Pažout and Frič considered it to be an extreme form of *L. pectinata*. This cactus is almost spineless, however, and produces pinkish red flowers. Cultivation is very simple, and because this species forms offsets, it can be propagated vegetatively. This is the only certain way of maintaining all the features and properties of the parent.

Lophocereus schottii 'Monstrosus' ▣ ○

COLUMNAR

This cactus reportedly resulted from a mutation in a collection, and spread from there into the large greenhouses in botanical gardens as a curiosity and also as a specimen in parks in tropical and subtropical areas. Vegetative propagation is achieved through cuttings and offsets, which fully retain the properties of the parent plant. This monstrous form grows fairly vigorously, but to the best of our knowledge it has never as yet flowered.

Lophophora williamsii 'Cristata' ▣ ○

CRISTATE

It is wonderful to discover a cristate form of *Lophophora* in the wild. The plant illustrated is not a first-rate specimen, but the simple discovery of this small cristate form was an incredible experience for a cactus lover. The crest was about 6in long and it was found near where *Gymnocactus mandragora* grows, in the Mexican state of Coahuila.

Lophophora williamsii 'Cristata'

Mammillaria bocasana var. *multilanata*

Mammillaria bocasana var. *multilanata* ■ ○

GLOBOSE

This variant arose in cultivation and differs from the type species in having much thicker and longer hair-like spines, which form a sort of wool on the areoles. Cultivation and propagation are as for the type.

Mammillaria herrerae 'Cristata'

Mammillaria herrerae 'Cristata' ▣ ○

CRISTATE

The plant in the photograph is a remarkable specimen. A chance mutation occurred and the grower managed to preserve it by timely grafting. Propagation is only possible by splitting the crest into a number of smaller sections and repeatedly grafting them onto a suitable rootstock. It is important when grafting cristate forms to be sure to choose a strong, well-developed rootstock, which will enable the graft to form a beautiful crest early on. In its cristate form *M. herrerae* produces flowers only very seldom.

Mammillaria prolifera 'Cristata' ▣ ○

CRISTATE

This *Mammillaria* is one of the cacti that you are most likely to spot in the windows of houses, offices, and schools. It has become so common because it is simple to cultivate and easy to propagate from offsets, which root on the parent plant. Constant vegetative propagation is clearly the cause of the relatively frequent variation shown in the formation of the crests. These can spontaneously arise on plants that hitherto had been growing normally. Even on these it is possible to propagate the cristate form by detaching and grafting it. You can even cultivate this mutation on its own roots by detaching a cristate section from the parent plant.

Mammillaria spinosissima *'Unopico'* ▣ ○

COLUMNAR

This is one of the few cultivars among *Mammillaria* species. It has not been around for long, but has become an attractive commercial plant because of its unusual spines. It has been increased by micropropagation and there are now thousands in commerce. This cultivar is best increased vegetatively, the only way of maintaining the exact features and properties of the parent plant. Seeds are viable but result in considerable variation. Some seedlings will have the characteristics of this named form, but most will revert to type. Cristate forms of this cultivar are also available.

Mammillaria prolifera 'Cristata'

Mammillaria spinosissima 'Unopico'

Mammillaria vetula f. *monstroza*

Mammillaria vetula *'Monstroza'* ▣ ○

GLOBOSE

This cactus, which was propagated from a mutation, first appeared in cultivation and appears in collections under all sorts of names. Although it is a frequently cultivated monstrous form, and its flowers betray its true allegiance, it is sometimes listed under the generic name *Turbinicarpus*, and sometimes as *Neolloydia*.
Cultivation is as for *M. vetula* ssp. *gracilis*, but this variant grows a shade more slowly and is also more delicate. At any rate this is an interesting and very elegant plant.

Notocactus ottonis var. *vencluanus*

Notocactus uebelmannianus f. *brevispinus*

Notocactus ottonis var. *vencluanus* ▣ ○

GLOBOSE

The globose, solitary stem of this cactus can also produce a few offsets when older. The plant measures 2–2 3/4in in diameter and the stem is divided into 11–13 rounded ribs. On the edge of the ribs, there are areoles with 3 or 4 central spines and about 10 radial spines. This varietas has a distinctive red flower, but the color can change to orange-red.
This cactus has never yet been found in the wild and the description was recorded from plants cultivated from imported seed by the gardener F. Venclů from Liberec. The seed reportedly came from a catalog published in 1936 by R. Blossfeld from Brazil. It is possible that *Notocactus ottonis* var. *vecluanus* is a hybrid or cultivated form. At any rate, it is a rewarding and undemanding cactus that can be recommended for beginners' collections. It boasts beautiful flowers which make it an impressive addition to the *Notocactus* genus. Most members of this genus are yellow-flowering.

Notocactus uebelmannianus var. *brevispinus*

FLATTENED-GLOBOSE

This unique, short-spined form appeared spontaneously in collections. Its taxonomic classification is provisional and it has yet to be proved whether it is a mutation or an extreme form with short spines.
It is starting to make its way into collections as an oddity and a larger number of cacti with these shortened spines can now be found in commercial nurseries. It seems that this feature is inherited and so it is very probable that this Notocactus will become increasingly common in the future, because it is very simple to cultivate.

Opuntia inamoena var. *flaviflora* ▣ ○

SHRUBBY

This is a short, freely clustering shrub, which forms clumps up to 3ft across and about 2ft tall. Woolly, completely spineless areoles grow on the dark green segments. Flowers appear on the edges of the segments and these are orange-yellow or reddish in the case of the type species and bright yellow in the case of var. *flaviflora*. This taxon was described from one specimen, grown in the Les Cedres garden in France, and it has spread among growers under this name. We feel, however, that in view of the variability of the type species this distinction should be rejected, mainly because no one yet knows whether this form occurs in the wild. In cultivation it is very tolerant. For good flowering it needs adequate space, a nutrient-high soil mix, and cold wintering, preferably in good light.

Opuntia inamoena var. *flaviflora*

Opuntia microdasys 'Cristata'

CRISTATE

In light of the experience of those who have grown this cactus, it is clearly the easiest cristate form to cultivate. It takes root very easily and does not need grafting. It generally grows well and it is possible to create a beautiful collection from the cristate forms of *O. microdasys* alone, considering the color range of its spines. Beware, however, of the unpleasant glochids, which lodge themselves in the skin on the slightest contact with the plant and are difficult to remove.

Pragochamaecereus hybr. Nr. 31

COLUMNAR

These cacti with their beautiful flowers were deliberately crossbred and cultivated before the Second World War by the Czech cactus expert and explorer A. V. Frič. He named this group of hybrids in honor of the city of Prague, where they were produced. These are actually hybrids of various species of *Lobivia* and the trailing or slightly columnar *Chamaecereus silvestrii.*
The hybrids created are very tough, produce

Pragochamaecereus hybr. Nr. 31

beautiful flowers, and are easy to propagate, because most are clustering. To ensure that the offspring have the same features and properties as the parent, propagate vegetatively. This guarantees that the flower color, size of plant, and growth habits, etc. will be the same. If you use pollen from a different plant then further variation will occur in the following generation.

Rebutia marsoneri 'Cristata' 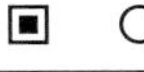

CRISTATE

This cactus forms beautiful, distinctive, crested formations, which spiral as the cactus gets older. It is interesting that it usually only flowers from one side, or from half of the crest. This cristate form of the species is best propagated by grafting onto a suitable rootstock. Otherwise the same cultivation principles apply as for other *Rebutia.*

Rhipsalis goebeliana 

TRAILING

You would almost think that this is not a cactus at all. It is a bushy, trailing plant with flattened stems, only about 1/3in in cross-section through the middle. The individual stems can be up to 8–10in long and 1–1 1/4in across. Yellow flowers grow from the areoles on the edge of the flattened shoots and are only about 1/2in across.

It is assumed that this species originates in cultivation, because it has never been recorded in the wild. It responds best to being grown in partial shade in fairly high humidity. Do not place it in direct scorching sunshine or conditions that are too dry. During the summer you should

Rebutia marsoneri 'Cristata'

water more frequently than for globose or columnar cacti. The simplest form of propagation is by rooting stem cuttings, which should be allowed to dry for a few days and then planted in pure perlite or a mixture of one part sand to one of peat. Wintering should be at fairly high temperatures, and if the cactus is kept at room temperature it should be watered sparingly during the winter.

Rhipsalis goebeliana

Schlumbergera x 'Gold Charm'

Schlumbergera x 'Gold Charm'

TRAILING

This is a beautiful hybrid, but it is not easy to pinpoint its parent plants. It is probably an interspecific hybrid involving selections of *S. truncata* and *S. orssichiana*. The light, creamy color of its flowers, which can even be yellow in the case of freshly developed buds, make it unique. It has the same cultivation demands as other members of the genus, but the plants are very sensitive to overhandling when setting their flowers, as discussed for the species *S. truncata* in the chapter on Brazil.

Schlumbergera x 'Westland'

Turbinicarpus pseudopectinatus 'Cristata'

Schlumbergera x 'Westland' ■ ◐

TRAILING

Cactus breeders are aiming to create a cultivar of the Christmas cactus with very dark flowers. This hybrid already comes close to what they are aiming for, because it has a dark red flower with yellow anthers and a beautiful violet stigma. The flowers start to appear early in fall and carry on blooming until long after Christmas.

Turbinicarpus valdezianus 'Cristata'

Turbinicarpus pseudopectinatus 'Cristata' ▣ ○

CRISTATE

The cristate form of this species is created through the meristem cells splitting lengthwise as opposed to developing normally. It is very evident in the photograph that flowers are formed along the whole length of what should be the crown of the plant. This species produces cristate forms only fairly rarelyand only vegetative propagation is possible. Any seed produced yields plants that grow normally, which proves that cristate forms are chance mutations of a given specimen, and that these mutations are not transferred genetically.

Turbinicarpus valdezianus 'Cristata' ▣ ○

CRISTATE

The plant in the picture is an example of a beautiful cristate form, but it also shows that a mutation of this kind can change the nature of the spines. In this case the spines on the side of the crest are more similar to *T. pseudopectinatus*, but on the top section they correspond more to the spines of the type species *T. valdezianus*. The only method of propagation is by grafting sections of the crest. The best time for this is during the late spring and early summer.

Bibliography

Anderson F. E., Arias M. S., Taylor P. N., 1994: Threatened Cacti of Mexico, Royal Botanic Gardens, Kew.

Backeberg C., 1961: Die Cactaceae, 1–6, Gustav Fischer Verlag, Jena.

Benson L., 1982: The Cacti of the United States and Canada, Stanford University Press, Stanford, California.

Bravo H. H., Mejorada H. S., 1991: Las Cactáceas de México, 2–3, UNAM, Mexico.

Blum W., Lange M., Rischer W., Rutow J., 2000: Echinocereus, PROOST, N.V., Belgium.

Briton N. L., 1919–1923: The Cactaceae, 1–4, Pasadena.

Buining A. F. H., 1976: The Genus Discocactus, Venlo.

Grym R., 1997: Rod Lophophora, VID, Bratislava.

Haage W., 1981: Kakteen von A bis Z, Neumann Verlag, Leipzig.

Haustein E., 1983: Der Kosmos-Kakteenführer, W. Keller and Co., Stuttgart.

Innes C., Glass Ch., 1992: Kaktusy – illustrovaná encyklopedie, INA, Prague

Lux A., Staník R., 1992: Všechno o kaktusech, Slovart, Bratislava.

Pavlíček P., Kunte L., 2000: Nová kniha o kaktusech, Dona, Czech Republic.

Pilbeam J., 1999: Mammillaria, Nuffield Press, Oxford.

Ritter F., 1980: Kakteen in Südamerika, 1–4, Spangenberg.

Říha J., Šubík R., 1989: Kaktusy v přírodě, Academia, Prague.

Říha J., Šubík R., 1992: Encyklopedie kaktusů, Brázda, Prague.

Schumann K., 1899: Gesamtbeschreibung der Kakteen, Neudamm.

Stuchlík S., 1993: Rod Notocactus, Moravské nakladatelství Květen, Brno.

Šída O., 1997: Rod Rebutia, Moravské nakladatelství Květen, Brno.

Zachar M., Staník R., Lux A., Dráb I., 1996: Rod Turbinicarpus, Vyd. Roman Staník, Bratislava.

Aztekia – zpravodaj pro členy sekce Aztekia (bulletin for members of the Aztekia section) – Klub kaktusářů, Prague.

Cactus and Succulent Journal, The Cactus and Succulent Society of America.

Kakteen und andere Sukkulenten – journal of the Deutsche Kakteen Gesellschaft.

Kaktusy – journal of the Společnosti českých a slovenských pěstitelů kaktusů a sukulentů.

Kolektiv autorů, 1986–2001: Atlas kaktusů, 1–16, Chrudimský kaktusů, Chrudim.

Left: *Ariocarpus kotschoubeyanus*

Index

A

Acanthocalycium klimpelianum 199
Acanthocalycium violaceum 139
Akersia roseiflora 140
Ancistrocactus crassihamatus 125
Ancistrocactus megarhizus 15
Ancistrocactus scheeri 125
Ancistrocactus tobuschii 125, 126
Ancistrocactus uncinatus 16
Ancistrocactus uncinatus var. *wrightii* 16
Arequipa erectrocylindrica 140
Ariocarpus agavoides 16
Ariocarpus bravoanus 16
Ariocarpus confusus 17
Ariocarpus fissuratus 16, 18
Ariocarpus fissuratus var. *hintonii* 16, 18
Ariocarpus fissuratus var. *lloydii* 18
Ariocarpus kotschoubeyanus 19, 283
Ariocarpus kotschoubeyanus var. albiflorus 19
Ariocarpus retusus 17, 20, 21
Ariocarpus retusus 'Cristata' 267
Ariocarpus scapharostrus 20
Ariocarpus trigonus 17, 21
Armatocereus cartwrightianus 140
Armatocereus laetus 141, 142
Armatocereus matucanensis 141
Armatocereus oligogonus 142
Arrojadoa eriocaulis 219
Astrophytum 'Marakuro-Kabuto' 268
Astrophytum asterias 15, 22, 268
Astrophytum capricorne 22
Astrophytum capricorne var. *crassispinum* 23
Astrophytum myriostigma 23
Astrophytum myriostigma f. *nudum.* 23
Astrophytum myriostigma f. *quadricostatum* 24
Astrophytum myriostigma var. *strongylogonum* 24
Astrophytum ornatum 24
Austrocephalocereus dybowskii 220
Austrocephalocereus estevesii 220
Aylostera muscula 186
Aztekium hintonii 25
Aztekium ritteri 25, 26

B

Backebergia militaris 26
Blossfeldia liliputana 200
Brachycereus nesioticus 251
Brasilicactus graessneri 220
Brasilicactus haselbergii 220, 221
Brasilicereus markgrafii 222
Browningia candelaris 142

C

Cactus melocactus communis 256
Carnegiea gigantea 13, 125, 126
Cephalocereus hoppenstedtii 27
Cephalocereus senilis 27
Cereus forbesii 201
Cereus peruvianus 142
Cereus peruvianus 'Monstrosus' 268
Cereus peruvianus 'Spiralis' 268
Chamaecereus silvestrii 201, 278
Cintia knizei 175
Cleistocactus baumannii var. *flavispinus* 251
Cleistocactus flavispinus 251
Cleistocactus jujuyensis 201
Cleistocactus smaragdiflorus 202
Cleistocactus strausii 201, 202
Cleistocactus strausii var. *jujuyensis* 201
Copiapoa cinerea 235, 241
Copiapoa cinerea ssp. *dealbata* 236
Copiapoa cinerea ssp. *gigantea* 236
Copiapoa cinerea ssp. *gigantea* var. *haseltoniana* 236
Copiapoa cinerea ssp. *gigantea var. tenebrosa* 237
Copiapoa coquimbana 238
Copiapoa coquimbana var. *longispina* 238
Copiapoa hypogea 238
Copiapoa krainziana 239
Copiapoa laui 240
Copiapoa serpentisulcata 240
Copiapoa taltalensis 240
Copiapoa uhligiana 241
Corryocactus apiciflorus 143
Corryocactus ayacuchoensis 144
Corryocactus brevistylus 144
Corryocactus puquiensis 145
Coryphantha borwigii 28
Coryphantha bumamma 28, 32
Coryphantha difficilis 28
Coryphantha elephantidens 28, 29
Coryphantha erecta 29
Coryphantha georgii 29
Coryphantha longicornis 30
Coryphantha neglecta 30
Coryphantha pallida 30
Coryphantha palmeri 31
Coryphantha pseudoechinus 31
Coryphantha retusa 32
Coryphantha retusa var. *melleospina* 32
Coryphantha vivipara 125, 127

D

Dactylopius coccus 13
Dendrocereus nudiflorus 252
Denmoza rhodacantha 202
Discocactus horstii 8, 221
Discocactus nigrisaetosus 222
Discocactus pugionacanthus 222
Discocactus silicicola 223

E

Echinocactus grusonii 32
Echinocactus grusonii f. *albispinus* 32
Echinocactus grusonii 'Monstrosus' 269
Echinocactus horizonthalonius 33
Echinocactus loricatus 208
Echinocactus mammulosus 261
Echinocactus platyacanthus 13, 34
Echinocactus texensis 34
Echinocereus chloranthus 128
Echinocereus coccineus 129
Echinocereus dasyacanthus 129
Echinocereus davisii 128
Echinocereus engelmannii 129
Echinocereus fendleri 128
Echinocereus ferreirianus ssp. *lindsayi* 35
Echinocereus grandis 35
Echinocereus knippelianus ssp. *reyesii* 36
Echinocereus leucanthus 36
Echinocereus morricalii 36
Echinocereus nichollii 129
Echinocereus pectinatus 37
Echinocereus pectinatus f. *castaneus* 38
Echinocereus pentalophus 38
Echinocereus pentalophus ssp. *procumbens* 38
Echinocereus poselgeri 39
Echinocereus poselgeri ssp. *kroenleinii* 40
Echinocereus procumbens 38

Echinocereus pulchellus 40
Echinocereus pulchellus var. *amoenus* 41
Echinocereus pulchellus ssp. *sharpii* 41
Echinocereus pulchellus ssp. *weinbergii* 41
Echinocereus reichenbachii 38
Echinocereus reichenbachii ssp. *baileyi* 130
Echinocereus rigidissimus 42
Echinocereus rigidissimus ssp. *rubispinus* 42
Echinocereus scheeri ssp. *gentryi* 43
Echinocereus schereri 43
Echinocereus stramineus 43
Echinocereus subinermis 44
Echinocereus subinermis var. *aculeatus* 44
Echinocereus subinermis ssp. *ochoterenae* 45
Echinocereus triglochidiatus 130
Echinocereus viereckii ssp. *morricalii* 36
Echinocereus viridiflorus 128, 130
Echinocereus x *lloydii* 129
Echinofossulocactus phyllacanthus 48
Echinofossulocactus arrigens 45
Echinofossulocactus coptonogonus 46, 47
Echinofossulocactus erectrocentrus 46
Echinofossulocactus lloydii 46
Echinofossulocactus multicostatus 47
Echinofossulocactus sulphureus 48
Echinomastus intertextus 131
Echinomastus johnstonii var. *lutescens* 131
Echinomastus mariposensis 132
Echinopsis arachnacantha 176
Echinopsis arachnacantha var. *torrecillasensis* 269
Echinopsis cv. 16
Echinopsis eyriesii 10
Echinopsis mamillosa var. *kermesina* 203
Echinopsis sp. 18
Echinopsis subdenudata 176
x *Epicactus* 'Little Star' 269
x *Epicactus* 'Phosper' 270
Epiphyllum chrysocardium 223
Epithelantha micromeris 49
Epithelantha micromeris 'Cristata' 270
Epithelantha micromeris var. *greggii* 49
Epithelantha unguispina 49
Epithelantha aff. *unguispina* 49
Eriocereus jusbertii 61, 136, 151, 221, 233, 239, 247, 272
Eriosyce aurata 241
Eriosyce ceratistes 242
Eriosyce villosa 9
Escobaria asperispina 50
Escobaria cubensis 253
Escobaria grata 50
Escobaria chaffeyi f. *viridiflora* 50
Escobaria minima 132
Escobaria nelliae 132
Escobaria sneedii var. *leei* 133
Escobaria zilziana 51
Espostoa lanata 139, 145
Espostoa lanata var. *sericata* 146
Espostoa melanostele 146
Espostoa melanostele var. *nana* 147
Espostoa mirabilis 147
Espostoa mirabilis 'Cristata' 270
Eulychnia acida 242
Eulychnia longispina 242
Eulychnia ritteri 148
Eulychnia spinibarbis 242
Eulychnia taltalensis 242

F

x *Ferobergia* 'Gil Tegelberg' 65
Ferocactus chrysacanthus 51
Ferocactus cylindraceus 133
Ferocactus cylindraceus var. *eastwoodiae* 133
Ferocactus echidne var. *victoriensis* 52
Ferocactus flavovirens 52
Ferocactus glaucescens 53
Ferocactus gracilis 53
Ferocactus gracilis var. *coloratus* 54
Ferocactus haematacanthus 54
Ferocactus hamatacanthus 55
Ferocactus histrix 55
Ferocactus latispinus 55
Ferocactus peninsulae 54, 56
Ferocactus pilosus 56
Ferocactus recurvus 57
Ferocactus reppenhagenii 57
Ferocactus robustus 57
Ferocactus setispinus 58
Ferocactus viridescens 134
Ferocactus wislizenii 134
Ferocactus wislizenii var. *herrerae* 58
Frailea asteroides 253
Frailea chiquitana 176

G

Geohintonia mexicana 25
Gymnocactus beguinii 58
Gymnocactus beguinii var. *senilis* 59
Gymnocactus horripilus 59
Gymnocactus knuthianus 60
Gymnocactus mandragora 273
Gymnocactus mandragora 60
Gymnocactus subterraneus 9, 60
Gymnocactus subterraneus ssp. *zaragosae* 61
Gymnocactus viereckei 62
Gymnocactus ysabelae 62
Gymnocalycium andreae 203
Gymnocalycium baldianum 270
Gymnocalycium bruchii 204
Gymnocalycium calochlorum 204
Gymnocalycium cardenasianum 177
Gymnocalycium carminanthum 205
Gymnocalycium denudatum 270
Gymnocalycium denudatum 'Jan Šuba' 267, 270
Gymnocalycium horridispinum 205
Gymnocalycium horstii 224
Gymnocalycium kurtzianum 206
Gymnocalycium lafandense 204
Gymnocalycium megalothelos 253
Gymnocalycium mihanovichii 254
Gymnocalycium mihanovichii 'Hibotan' 271
Gymnocalycium mihanovichii var. *stenogonum* 254
Gymnocalycium mostii 206
Gymnocalycium netrelianum 254
Gymnocalycium oenanthemum 206
Gymnocalycium ochoterenai 206
Gymnocalycium pflanzii 178
Gymnocalycium ragonesei 207
Gymnocalycium ragonesei f. *roseiflorum* 272
Gymnocalycium saglionis 208
Gymnocalycium saglionis var. *roseiflorum* 208
Gymnocalycium schuetzianum 208
Gymnocalycium spegazzinii 208
Gymnocalycium uruguayense var. *roseiflorum* 255
Gymnocalycium valnicekianum var. *polycentralis* 209
Gymnocalycium vatteri 209

H

Haageocereus acranthus 148
Haageocereus aureispinus 148
Haageocereus chosicensis 148
Haageocereus chrysacanthus 149
Haageocereus repens 150

Hatiora salicornioides 224
Helianthocereus grandiflorus 210
Helianthocereus tarijensis 178
Heliathocereus poco 216
Hertrichocereus beneckei 63
Hildewintera aureispina 178
Hildewintera aureispina 'Cristata' 272
Horridocactus curvispinus 243
Horridocactus curvispinus var. *felipensis* 243
Horridocactus curvispinus var. *santiagensis* 243
Horridocactus curvispinus var. *tilamensis* 243
Hylocereus undatus 251

I

Ibervillea sonorae 112
Islaya grandiflorens 150, 151
Islaya grandiflorens var. *spinosior* 150
Islaya grandiflorens var. *tenuispina* 150
Islaya islayensis 151
Islaya maritima 151
Isolatocereus dumortieri 63

L

Lemaireocereus chende 64
Leuchtenbergia principis 10, 64
Lobivia arachnacantha var. *torrecillasensis* 269
Lobivia aurea 152
Lobivia aurea var. *albiflora* 152
Lobivia aurea var. *callochrysea* 152
Lobivia aurea var. *fallax* 152
Lobivia backebergii 179
Lobivia chrysantha 210
Lobivia ducis-pauli 179
Lobivia famatimensis 'Rubra' 272
Lobivia ferox 179
Lobivia ferox var. longispina 210
Lobivia jajoana 152
Lobivia jajoana var. *fleischeriana* 152
Lobivia jajoana var. *nigrostoma* 152
Lobivia pampana 152
Lobivia pectinata 273
Lobivia tiegeliana 180
Lobivia wrightiana 153
Lophocereus schottii 'Monstrosus' 273
Lophophora diffusa 65
Lophophora fricii 66
Lophophora williamsii 13, 66
Lophophora williamsii 'Cristata' 273
Lophophora williamsii var. *koehresii* 66
Loxanthocereus clavispinus 154
Loxanthocereus eriotrichus 154
Loxanthocereus lanatus 154
Loxanthocereus seniloides 155
Loxanthocereus sulcifer 155

M

Machaerocereus eruca 67
Machaerocereus gummosus 13, 67
Maihuenia patagonica 251
Malacocarpus bezrucii 259
Malacocarpus tephracantha 228
Mammillaria glassii var. *ascensionis* 76
Mammillaria alamensis 90
Mammillaria albiarmata 70
Mammillaria albilanata 68
Mammillaria baumii 68
Mammillaria bocasana 68
Mammillaria bocasana var. *multilanata* 274
Mammillaria bombycina 69, 86
Mammillaria candida 69
Mammillaria capensis 70
Mammillaria carmenae 70, 90
Mammillaria coahuilensis ssp. *albiarmata* 70
Mammillaria coahuilensis var. *albiflora* 70
Mammillaria collina 78
Mammillaria columbiana 255
Mammillaria compresa 71
Mammillaria crucigera 71
Mammillaria deherdtiana 72
Mammillaria deherdtiana var. *dodsonii* 72
Mammillaria densispina 73
Mammillaria dixanthocentron 73
Mammillaria dixanthocentron var. *rubrispina* 73
Mammillaria duwei 74
Mammillaria elongata 267
Mammillaria elongata 74
Mammillaria elongata var. *echinaria* 74
Mammillaria fittkaui 74
Mammillaria formosa 75
Mammillaria geminispina 76
Mammillaria grusonii 77
Mammillaria guelzowiana 77
Mammillaria haageana 77
Mammillaria haageana ssp. *conspicua* 77
Mammillaria haageana ssp. *elegans* 78
Mammillaria hahniana 78
Mammillaria hernandezii 78
Mammillaria herrerae 79, 274
Mammillaria herrerae var. *albiflora* 80
Mammillaria herrerae 'Cristata' 274
Mammillaria huitzilopochtli 80
Mammillaria laui 90
Mammillaria laui f. subducta 80
Mammillaria leptacantha 87
Mammillaria longiflora 81
Mammillaria longimamma 82
Mammillaria marksiana 82
Mammillaria melanocentra 82
Mammillaria melanocentra ssp. *rubrograndis* 82
Mammillaria mercadensis 83
Mammillaria microhelia 84
Mammillaria mystax 84
Mammillaria nivosa 85
Mammillaria orcutii 85
Mammillaria pectinifera 86, 90
Mammillaria perezdelarosae 86
Mammillaria pottsii 86
Mammillaria prolifera 'Cristata' 274
Mammillaria rekoi ssp. *leptacantha* 87
Mammillaria saboae f. *haudeana* 88
Mammillaria sempervivi 89
Mammillaria sheldonii 90
Mammillaria schiedeana 88
Mammillaria schwarzii 88
Mammillaria solisioides 90
Mammillaria sp. 90
Mammillaria sphaerica 91
Mammillaria spinosissima 91
Mammillaria spinosissima 'Unopico' 275
Mammillaria supertexta 68
Mammillaria surculosa 92
Mammillaria theresae 92
Mammillaria theresae f. *albiflora* 93
Mammillaria vetula ssp. *gracilis* 93, 276
Mammillaria vetula 'Monstroza' 276
Mammillaria wilcoxii 124
Mammillaria winterae 94
Mammillaria wrightii 134
Mammillaria zephyranthoides 94
Matucana aurantiaca 156
Matucana aureiflora 156
Matucana formosa 156, 157
Matucana formosa var. *longispina* 156
Matucana haynei var. *erectipetala* 157
Matucana herzogiana 158
Matucana intertexta 158
Matucana krahnii 158

Matucana madisoniorum 157, 159
Matucana myriacantha 159
Matucana paucicostata 160
Matucana variabilis 160
Melocactus acunai 256
Melocactus azureus 224
Melocactus bellavistensis 160
Melocactus caesius 256
Melocactus communis 256
Melocactus dawsonii 94
Melocactus delessertianus 95
Melocactus guitarti 257
Melocactus harlowii 258
Melocactus maxonii 258
Melocactus peruvianus 161
Melocactus peruvianus var. *lurinensis* 161
Micranthocereus violaciflorus 222
Mila caespitosa 162
Mitrocereus fulviceps 95
Mitrocereus ruficeps 96
Morawetzia doelziana 162
Myrtillocactus geometrizans 10, 12, 16, 61, 90, 96,106, 126, 221, 256, 270, 271, 272

N

Neobinghamia climaxantha 162
Neobuxbaumia euphorbioides 97
Neobuxbaumia macrocephala 96
Neobuxbaumia mezcalensis 98
Neobuxbaumia polylopha 98
Neocardenasia herzogiana 175, 180
Neochilenia imitans 244
Neochilenia napina 244
Neochilenia paucicostata var. *viridis* 245
Neolloydia conoidea 99
Neolloydia grandiflora 99
Neolloydia smithii 58
Neoporteria gerocephala 245
Neoporteria chilensis 245
Neoporteria microsperma var. *serenana* 246
Neoporteria sociabilis 246
Neoporteria tuberisulcata 246
Neoporteria villosa 247
Neoraimondia roseiflora 163
Neowerdermannia vorwerkii 181
Nopalea nuda 100
Nopalxochia phyllanthoides 100
Notocactus apricus 259
Notocactus bezrucii 259
Notocactus claviceps 225
Notocactus concinnus 226
Notocactus corynodes 260
Notocactus floricomus 260
Notocactus grossei 260, 262
Notocactus horstii 226
Notocactus horstii var. *purpureiflorus* 226
Notocactus leninghausii 226
Notocactus macambarensis 261
Notocactus magnificus 227
Notocactus mammulosus 261
Notocactus muegelianus 226
Notocactus ottonis var. *vencluanus* 276
Notocactus purpureus 226
Notocactus roseoluteus 262
Notocactus scopa 263
Notocactus sellowii 263
Notocactus schumannianus 260, 262
Notocactus tephracanthus 228
Notocactus uebelmannianus 228
Notocactus uebelmannianus f. *brevispinus* 276
Notocactus uebelmannianus f. *flaviflorus* 228

O

Obregonia denegrii 100
Opuntia auberi 101
Opuntia azurea 101
Opuntia basilaris 283
Opuntia clavaroides 211
Opuntia compressa 251
Opuntia dillenii 263
Opuntia durangensis 102
Opuntia echios var. *gigantea* 251
Opuntia ficus-indica 7, 10, 13
Opuntia imbricata 102
Opuntia inamoena var. *flaviflora* 277
Opuntia kleiniae 103
Opuntia leptocaulis 103
Opuntia leucotricha 104
Opuntia microdasys 104, 278
Opuntia microdasys var. *albispina* 104
Opuntia microdasys 'Cristata' 278
Opuntia microdasys var. *pallida* 104
Opuntia microdasys var. *rufispina* 104
Opuntia miquelii 248
Opuntia pachypus 164
Opuntia phaeacantha 135
Opuntia rosea 106
Opuntia rubescens 264
Opuntia spinulifera 102
Opuntia stanlyi 104
Opuntia stenopetala 105
Opuntia subulata 212
Opuntia tomentosa 211
Opuntia tomentosa 13, 211
Opuntia tunicata 8, 106
Oreocereus celsianus 181
Oreocereus neocelsianus 182
Oreocereus trollii 181
Oroya borchersii 164
Oroya laxiareolata 164
Oroya neoperuviana 165
Oroya peruviana 165, 166
Ortegocactus macdougalii 106

P

Pachycereus pecten-aboriginum 107
Pachycereus pringlei 107
Pachycereus weberi 108
Parodia gracilis 182
Parodia maassii 182
Parodia nivosa 212
Parodia occulta 183
Parodia sanguiniflora 213
Parodia schuetziana 213
Parodia schwebsiana 183
Parodia slabaiana 183
Pediocactus bradyi 135
Pediocactus paradinei 136
Pediocactus peeblesianus 136
Pediocactus peeblesianus var. *fickeiseniae* 136
Pediocactus simpsonii 136
Pediocactus winkleri 125
Pelecyphora aselliformis 108
Pelecyphora strobiliformis 108
Pelecyphora valdeziana var. *albiflora* 123
Peniocereus greggii 9
Peniocereus viperianus 109
Pereskia aculeata 230
Pereskia grandifolia 230
Pereskiopsis sp. 10
Phrygilanthus aphyllus 248
Pilocereus leninghausii 226
Pilosocereus azureus 230
Pilosocereus tehuacanus 109
Pinus ponderosa 125
Porfiria schwarzii var. *albiflora* 70
Pragochamaecereus hybr. Nr. 31 278
Pseudococcus sp. 12
Pseudolobivia torrecillasensis 269
Pterocactus australis 214
Pterocactus tuberosus 214
Pygmaeocereus rowleyanus 166
Pyrrhocactus bulbocalyx 214
Pyrrhocactus tuberisulcatus 246
Pyrrhocactus villicumensis 215

Q

Quiabentia pflanzii 184
Quiabentia zehntneri 229

R

Rebutia albiareolata 184
Rebutia aureiflora 215
Rebutia aureiflora var. *kesselringiana* 215
Rebutia aureiflora var. *sarothroides* 215
Rebutia costata 188
Rebutia eucaliptana 188
Rebutia heliosa 184
Rebutia heliosa var. *cajasensis* 184
Rebutia heliosa var. *condorensis* 184, 185
Rebutia huariensis 216
Rebutia huasiensis 216
Rebutia marsoneri 216
Rebutia marsoneri 'Cristata' 279
Rebutia mixticolor 185
Rebutia muscula 186
Rebutia perplexa 186
Rebutia pygmea 187
Rebutia pygmea 'Elegantula' 187
Rebutia pygmea 'Eos' 187
Rebutia pygmea 'Haagei' 187
Rebutia steinmannii 188
Rebutia steinmannii f. *costata* 188
Rebutia torquata 188
Rhipsalis goebeliana 279
Rhizoecus falciferi 12
Ritterocereus pruinosus 110

S

Sclerocactus wrightiae 125
Selaginella lepidophylla 61, 118
Selenicereus grandiflorus 265
Selenicereus urbanianus 265
Schlumbergera gaertneri 231
Schlumbergera orssichiana 231, 280
Schlumbergera truncata 232, 280
Schlumbergera x 'Gold Charm' 280
Schlumbergera x 'Westland' 281
Soehrensia bruchii 216
Soehrensia bruchii var. *nivalis* 216
Stenocereus marginatus 13, 110
Stenocereus treleasii 110
Stephanocereus leucostele 233
Stetsonia coryne 188
Strombocactus disciformis 111
Strombocactus disciformis ssp. *esperanzae* 111, 117
Sulcorebutia alba 190
Sulcorebutia breviflora 190
Sulcorebutia candidae 191
Sulcorebutia gerosenilis 191
Sulcorebutia krahnii 192
Sulcorebutia rauschii 192
Sulcorebutia steinbachii 192, 193
Sulcorebutia steinbachii f. *violaciflora* 192
Sulcorebutia swobodae 193
Sulcorebutia tuberculata-chrysantha 193
Sulcorebutia verticillacantha 194

T

Trichocereus chilensis var. *eburneus* 248
Tephrocactus articulatus var. *inermis* 216
Tephrocactus bolivianus 194
Tephrocactus crispicrinitus 167
Tephrocactus crispicrinitus subv. *flavicomus* 167
Tephrocactus darwinii 251
Tephrocactus dimorphus 167
Tephrocactus floccosus 168
Tephrocactus ignescens 168
Tephrocactus kuehnrichianus 169
Tephrocactus pentlandii 194
Tephrocactus sphaericus 169
Tephrocactus sphaericus var. *rauppianus* 169
Tephrocactus sphaericus var. *unguispinus* 169
Tetranychus urticae 12
Thelocactus beguinii 58
Thelocactus bicolor 12, 112, 116
Thelocactus bicolor var. *bolansis* 112
Thelocactus bueckii 112, 118
Thelocactus conothelos 113, 114
Thelocactus conothelos var. *aurantiacus* 113
Thelocactus conothelos var. *macdowellii* 114
Thelocactus flavus 114
Thelocactus heterochromus 115
Thelocactus hexaedrophorus 115
Thelocactus lausseri 116
Thelocactus leucacanthus var. *schmollii* 116
Thelocactus rinconensis 116
Thelocactus sanchezmejoradai 116
Thelocactus schwarzii 116
Thelocactus tulensis 114
Thelocacus hastifer 114
Thrixanthocereus senilis 170
Toumeya papyracantha 137
Trichocereus chilensis 235, 248
Trichocereus pachanoi 13, 63, 126, 136, 200, 245, 270, 239
Trichocereus poco 217
Trichocereus skottsbergii 249
Trichocereus tacaquirensis 194
Trixanthocereus blossfeldiorum 170
Turbinicarpus alonsoi 117
Turbinicarpus flaviflorus 118
Turbinicarpus hoferi 118
Turbinicarpus krainzianus ssp. *minimus* 119
Turbinicarpus pseudomacrochele 119
Turbinicarpus pseudopectinatus 120
Turbinicarpus pseudopectinatus 'Cristata' 281
Turbinicarpus pseudopectinatus var. *rubriflorus* 120
Turbinicarpus schmiedickeanus 120
Turbinicarpus schmiedickeanus var. *dickisoniae* 121
Turbinicarpus schmiedickeanus var. *klinkerianus* 121
Turbinicarpus schmiedickeanus var. *macrochele 122*
Turbinicarpus schmiedickeanus var. *panarottoi 122*
Turbinicarpus schwarzii var. *rubriflorus* 123
Turbinicarpus valdezianus 123
Turbinicarpus valdezianus 'Cristata' 281

U

Uebelmannia pectinifera 233
Uebelmannia pectinifera var. *multicostata* 233

V

Vatricania guentheri 195

W

Weberbauerocereus albus 170
Weberbauerocereus horridispinus 170
Weberbauerocereus rauhii 171
Weberbauerocereus rauhii var. *laticornus* 171
Weberbauerocereus seyboldianus 172
Weberbauerocereus weberbaueri 173
Weingartia fidaiana 183
Weingartia knizei 196
Weingartia mairanana 196
Weingartia neocumingii 196
Weingartia neumanniana ssp. *kargliana* 197
Weingartia pulquinensis 196
Weingartia riograndensis 197
Wittia amazonica 173

Z

Zygocactus truncatus 232